A
SCOTTISH
ELECTRICAL ENLIGHTENMENT

Celebrating 100 years of the

Institution of Electrical Engineers

in Scotland

1899 - 1999

Edited by **David Dick OBE**

Foreword by **Prof. HW Whittington**

IEE Scotland

Published by
The Institution of Electrical Engineers, Scotland,
Scottish Engineering Centre,
St Enoch Square,
Glasgow

ISBN 0 9537790 09

Printed by:

    Mackenzie & Storrie Ltd,
    Colour Printers,
    28-32 Coburg Street,
    Leith
    Edinburgh EH6 6HA

Typeset by David Dick
Cover Design: Muriel Dick
Cover Photographs:

    Lord Kelvin, *courtesy of IEE Archives*
    James Clerk-Maxwell, *courtesy of Clerk-Maxwell Foundation*
    Alexander Graham Bell, *courtesy of British Telecom*
    John Logie Baird, *courtesy of Strathclyde University*
    Transmission line to Cockenzie Power Station, *courtesy of D.Dick*
    IEE Scotland crest

Acknowledgements

Ronald Anderson (the great-great grandson of the founder of Wm Teacher & Son Ltd (whose former head office, built in 1876, is now the IEE Scottish office) for the photograph of his house which was built by Professor S Parker-Smith in 1923.

The late **JS Baillie,** editor of the *Bruce Peebles News* for useful material used in the history of the company (Chapter 9, section iv)

Ms Sarah Barnard, IEE Archives, for dealing with a series of requests and providing the photographs of Sir Archibald Page and DS Munro.

J. Berry for his assistance in the preparation of Chapter 9(i) *100 Years of Cable Manufacture in Scotland.*

BICC Brand Rex, Glenrothes for allowing the choice of company photographs for the section on Cable Manufacturing.

BT Corporate Picture Library for permission to use the photographs in Chapter 6

Mrs Marie Casey for providing the photograph of Professor Magnus Maclean.

Dr AJU Cruikshank for his help to Professor WEJ (Ewart) Farvis with Chapter 2(i)

Professor CW Davidson for his help to Professor WEJ (Ewart) Farvis with Chapter 2(i)

PG Davies, British Energy, for his assistance in the preparation of Chapter 4(i) Electricity Generation in Scotland.

WAS Doig, British Energy, for his assistance in the preparation of Chapter 4(i) Electricity Generation in Scotland.

Dr JC Earls for his help to Professor WEJ (Ewart) Farvis with Chapter 2(i).

Professor WEJ (Ewart) Farvis for additional information for Chapter 2(iii) *The Scottish Electrical Training Scheme (SETS).*

Glasgow University Archives and Business Records centre for providing the photograph of Professor GWO Howe.

Dr Douglas S Gordon, the author of Chapter 1, for his help to Professor WEJ (Ewart) Farvis with Chapter 2(i).

JT Henderson for his help to Professor WEJ (Ewart) Farvis with Chapter 2(i).

The Herald **(Glasgow)** for permission to use the picture of ANGUS 001 in Chapter 3(ii).

Clive Hotham, previously Director Qualifications of the Institution of Electrical Engineers at Savoy Place, London for his help to Professor WEJ (Ewart) Farvis with Chapter 2(i).

WAS Howatson for his assistance in the preparation of Chapter 9(i), *100 Years of Cable Manufacture in Scotland.*

M Jewkes of Glasgow University Hanterian Museum, For advice and for the provision of photographs of Lord Kelvin and apparatus

S MacDonald, Scottish and Southern Energy, for his assistance in the preparation of Chapter 4(i) *Electricity Generation in Scotland.*

Dr J McKeown, UKEA, for his assistance in the preparation of Chapter 4(i) *Electricity Generation in Scotland*

Ron McMurtrie for encouraging and obtaining the agreement of the contributors to this volume. Without his intimate knowledge of the Scottish membership of the IEE this book could never have been contemplated. His advice and his unfailing interest in this project have been of immeasurable help.

Dr Ken MacTaggart, Head of Knowledge, Information & Telecommunications, HIE for his help with Chapter 6, *The History of Telecommunications*.

Robin Melrose for his helpful suggestions and proof reading of Chapter 4(ii), *The*

Development of the Electricity Grid Transmission System in Scotland.

I Mitchell, BNFL/Magnox, for his assistance in the preparation of Chapter 4(i) *Electricity Generation in Scotland.*

GD Morrison BSc for his assistance in the preparation of Chapter 9(i), *100 Years of Cable Manufacture in Scotland.*

National Archives of Scotland for allowing access to old records of Parsons Peebles (formerly Bruce Peebles) which were deposited there under reference GD349.

A Ness CEng, MIEE, for his help with Chapter 6, *The History of Telecommunications.*

David B Nisbet, for providing the photographs for Chapter 9(v) *The Ferranti Contribution to Electronics in Scotland.*

IHD O'Donnell, Scottish and Southern Energy, for his assistance in the preparation of Chapter 4 (i) *Electricity Generation in Scotland*

L Oswald for his assistance in the preparation of Chapter 9(i), *100 Years of Cable Manufacture in Scotland.*

VA Tech Elin Peebles Power Transformers and to **Peebles Electrical Machines Ltd** for permission to use illustrations and material and for approval of the final text of Chapter 9(iv).

Mitchell Reid, Media Relations Manager, BT Scotland for his help with Chapter 6 *The History of Telecommunications.*

Dr WS Robertson for his help to Professor WEJ (Ewart) Farvis with Chapter 2(i) *Electrical Engineering Education before 1960.*

Mrs RM Rose, the Regional Officer of IEE Scotland, for her help with Chapter 1 in providing Committee minutes and other archival material.

VJ Ross BSc, CEng, FIEE for his assistance in the preparation of *100 Years of Cable Manufacture in Scotland.*

David Say for the photograph of his father Professor MG (Dick) Say.

Iain Shepherd for his help to Professor WEJ (Ewart) Farvis with Chapter 2 section (i).

JI Smith, Scottish and Southern Energy, for his assistance in the preparation of Chapter 4(i) *Electricity Generation in Scotland.*

MRA Smith, BNFL/Magnox, for his assistance in the preparation of Chapter 4(i) *Electricity Generation in Scotland.*

J Stuart, ScottishPower, for his assistance in the preparation of Chapter 4(i) *Electricity Generation in Scotland.*

Lenore Symons, Senior Archivist of the Institution of Electrical Engineers at Savoy Place, London for her help to Professor WEJ (Ewart) Farvis with Chapter 2(i).

Professor David Tedford for his invaluable assistance in compiling and editing the section on Research in Electrical Engineering in Scottish Universities (Chapter ..) and for his help to Professor WEJ (Ewart) Farvis with Chapter 2(i).

Alan Thomson for his assistance in proof reading Chapter 8 *The Scottish Coal Industry.*

KB Watson, Honorary Secretary IEE Scotland for documents and helpful information for Chapter 1 *The First 100 Years of the IEE in Scotland.*

H Williamson, Scottish and Southern Energy, for his assistance in the preparation of Chapter 4(i) *Electricity Generation in Scotland.*

The Library Archivists at Dundee, Heriot-Watt, Paisley, Robert Gordon's and Strathclyde Universities for their help to Professor WEJ (Ewart) Farvis with Chapter 2(i).

Foreword

Imagine a world without television, without telephones, without an electricity supply, without air transport and all the other benefits we enjoy from the technical advances of the past 100 years. That's how things were in 1899 when the Institution of Electrical Engineers first established a presence in Scotland.

The Millennium is a popular time for retrospection. With the Centenary of IEE Scotland falling in December 1999, the case for marking the occasion was overwhelming. The IEE Scotland Committee is to run a series of events throughout the Centenary year and has complemented these with this book, which should act as a permanent reminder, a century of contribution by Electrical Engineers to Scottish life and development.

We have taken both retrospective and prospective views on Electrical Engineering in Scotland, as it appears in 1999. In 1949, to commemorate the 50th anniversary of the IEE Scottish Centre (as it was then), the Centre Committee compiled a short book which, among other things, listed all those members and associate members of the IEE who lived in Scotland at that time. In this book we have not attempted such a list, since membership has risen in the last 50 years to around 8,000. Instead, we have concentrated on describing a century of progress, of achievement and, importantly, of personalities in various fields of Electrical Engineering endeavour in Scotland. The coverage is as wide as the editorial panel could manage and, although there may be some omissions, these were not deliberate but were rather caused by the inability to locate suitable authors.

It is most important that we also allow ourselves the time to look forward to an increasingly challenging future. We are confident that the next century will see Electrical Engineers continuing to have an important influence on the industrial, commercial and political development of Scotland. Scotland now has its own Parliament, established in Edinburgh, which is still finding its way both structurally and operationally. Already the IEE Scotland has held meetings with senior civil servants in the Scottish Executive to attempt to identify ways in which we can assist the Scottish Parliament in a professional sense. The hope is that we can mirror the close links existing between IEE headquarters in Savoy Place and Westminster. IEE Scotland believes that it is in a position to offer Professional advice and guidance, initially, in the fields of power and energy, of electronics and microelectronics, of education and of information technology.

I hope that you enjoy this book, I hope that you learn from it, I hope it brings back memories of colleagues and of achievements, and I trust that it encourages you to take a pride in the major contribution made by our predecessors to the development of Scotland in the last 100 years. I should also like to record my personal thanks to the editor and the team of authors who have produced this excellent volume at very short notice.

Professor HW Whittington,
Chairman, IEE Scotland 1999-2000

Introduction

This centenary publication is a celebration of the achievements of Chartered Electrical Engineers past and present - members of the **Institution of Electrical Engineers in Scotland**.

The word *Enlightenment* in the title is used in the sense of the Enlightenment of the 18th and 19th centuries when Scotland could boast of many geniuses who brought clarity, order and reason to our thinking. Scottish electrical engineers in their discoveries through experiments, research, design, manufacture and teaching have enlightened us in a multiplicity of ways, as shall be seen in this volume.

Emile Zola (1840-1902) in his *Travail* (1902) predicted:

> *The day must come when electricity will be for everyone, as the waters of the rivers and the wind of heaven. It should not merely be supplied, but lavished, that men may use it at their will, as the air they breathe. In towns it will flow as the very blood of society. Every home will tap abundant power, heat and light like drawing water from a spring. And at night another sun in the dark sky, putting out the stars. There will be no more winter, summer will be eternal, warmth will return to the old world, melting even the highest snow.*

The generation and supply of electrical energy has indeed brightened our homes, given warmth and ease in a variety of chores and enabled progress in learning and research. The ingenuity and growth of the electronics industry led to the 'Scottish Silicon Glen' and many electrical industries have grown and flourished and, while some have disappeared, others have merged with bigger companies.

As you will read in this centenary publication we have been *Enlightened* from intellectual darkness to brightness through the ingenuity and brilliance of electrical engineers who have transformed our lives and expanded the horizons of our world at an ever quickening pace.

This volume was produced by those eminent in their specialist fields in a such a short time span that inevitably there are omissions and apologies are tendered to any who have been unintentionally neglected.

David Dick, Editor

Contents

Chapter 1

The First 100 Years of the IEE in Scotland

by Douglas Gordon BSc, PhD, CEng, FIEE

Introduction

For centuries men with similar interests have formed clubs and societies where they could socialise and discuss matters of common concern. In 1771 the *Society of Civil Engineers* (as opposed to military engineers) had a 'fraternity of friendship that remains a pattern of excellence and as a reminder of the need for the cultivation of good companionship as an antidote to the degeneracy that awaits detached specialists' (1). Attendances at their meetings were probably very good as a member had to pay a forfeit of one shilling for being absent unless he was out of town. The notion of continuing professional development is therefore not new.

Clearly, the tremendous significance of the world wide network of overland and undersea telegraph systems with its state of the art digital technology (Morse code) encouraged the engineers concerned to set up a Society of Telegraph Engineers in 1871. This would give them a forum for reporting new developments and exchanging opinions on professional matters.

The generation, distribution and utilisation of electrical energy were rapidly expanding fields towards the end of the 19th century. To bring the benefits of electricity to the wider public required new and improved materials such as conductors of low resistance and low cost, insulation having good performance with a long life and steels of consistent magnetic performance. Domestic lighting was a particular challenge and the production of an acceptable filament lamp involved the development of many new technologies. The end product was a commercial compromise between cost, life and efficiency. Thus, as occurred on many occasions since, the members had to discuss proposals to alter the rules of their Society to take account of the changing and broadening fields of interest.

In 1881 the Society changed its name to *The Society of Telegraph Engineers and of Electricians*. However, by 1883 this title had been further modified to *The Society of Telegraph-Engineers and Electricians*. By 1888, following even more discussions and a referendum of members, the current title ***The Institution of Electrical Engineers*** was adopted.

The change in title was deemed desirable 'as the existing title did not adequately represent the present body of electrical engineers in England and this feeling may lead to the formation of a new and rival society' (2). Thus, even so long ago we can sense the dichotomy of argument between being all-embracing or catering for a specialist group.

In the same year the President had stated that 'Telegraph Engineers are still the most numerous units in our body, but from force of circumstances they can no longer be said to be the special representatives of its character. The Institution of Electrical Engineers is a title comprehensive enough to include all devotees of the science.' (3) This was indeed a very prescient observation. With a total membership of about 1500, the Institution elected **Sir William Thomson (1824-1907)** to be its first President and he gave his inaugural address on 10th June 1889.

William Thomson, 1st Baron Kelvin 1899

The first Wiring Rules had been published in 1882 as it was appreciated that electrical engineers, hitherto electricians, should take professional responsibility for their installations. For example, it was recommended that:

> .....the value of frequent testing of the wires cannot be too strongly urged. It is an operation, skill in which is easily acquired and applied. The escape of electricity cannot be detected by the sense of smell as can gas, but it can be detected by apparatus far more certain and delicate. Leakage not only means waste, but in the presence of moisture it means destruction of the conductor and its insulating covering, by electric action. (4)

By 1898 the Institution considered the proposal to hold meetings in the 'provinces' and to create Branch Societies or Local Sections. An unique event took place the following year when the first lady, Mrs Ayrton, was elected a member. Initially, the President admitted that it was unclear whether there was a legal disability against such an election. The United Kingdom membership was now about 3500.

By the end of 1899 in response to petitions it was agreed that local sections should be formed in Dublin, Glasgow, Newcastle-upon-Tyne and Cape Town. The last was probably influenced by the war in South

Africa. Manchester District Local Section was formed in the following year. The 'Initiatory Meeting' of the Glasgow Section was held at the Institution of Engineers and Shipbuilders in Scotland on 18th January 1900 with an attendance of 120 'gentlemen'.

Institution of Electrical Engineers (Glasgow Section)

Minutes of the Initiatory Meeting held in the Institution of Engineers and Shipbuilders on the evening of Thursday the 18th January. 1900

A meeting of the Electrical Engineers resident in & Glasgow and the West of Scotland was held as above to initiate the Glasgow Section of the Institution of Electrical Engineers. The sanction of the Council of the Institution for the formation of this section was obtained on the 14th Dec. 1899 in response to a petition signed by gentlemen connected with the Electrical Industry in this district.

Professor Perry, the Senior Vice-President of the Institution, occupied the chair and was supported by Mr McMillan, the Secretary of the Institution, and by Professor Maclean. About 120 gentlemen were present and Prof. Perry gave a very interesting and entertaining address on the objects and work of the Institution.

A local committee was elected as follows :-

President - Lord Kelvin - proposed by Prof. Watkinson and seconded by Prof. Maclean Prof. Jamieson.

Vice-President - Prof. Maclean - proposed by Mrs E.G. Tidd and seconded by Mrs J. M. M. Munro

Hon. Secy. Prof Watkinson - proposed by Mr H. A. Mavor and seconded by Mr Chas. L. Ross.

As the result of a ballot the following were elected members of the Committee - W.A. Chamen; A.C. Mavor ; W. W. Lackie ; W.B. Sayers; Thos Young; J. M. M. Munro; Prof. Andrew Jamieson, Francis Teague

After the election Mr McMillan gave some explanations regarding the working of local sections of the Institution

The Formative Years

By the end of the 19th century Scotland had an extensive telegraph network, a growing telephone system and considerable investment in the generation and utilisation of electrical energy. Furthermore, there were many firms involved in the manufacture of generators, rotary converters, switchgear, cables and motors. Students were being taught the theory and practice of this burgeoning branch of engineering by eminent academics at Glasgow University, the Heriot Watt College, Edinburgh, the Glasgow and West of Scotland College and elsewhere. Thus, as stated earlier, the time was ripe for the formation of a society where the engineers involved could exchange ideas, report on their work and learn from others in 'North Britain' and elsewhere. With no precedent on which to base their relationships there was necessarily a period when rules were instituted and the interactions between parent and offspring were refined. In this respect the first two decades are of particular interest.

The newly formed Glasgow Section of the Institution of Electrical Engineers elected **Professor Sir William Thomson**, who by now was **Baron Kelvin of Largs** (although born in Ireland) as their first 'president' with **Professor Magnus Maclean** as vice-president. By session 1902-03 these titles had become chairman and vice-chairman. It was stated that 'Glasgow was flourishing with fresh ideas and that Lord Kelvin was its greatest personality, improving, practical, persistent and visionary' (5). Despite his age, 76 years, and many commitments, he chaired meetings and took an active part in the Section.

Kelvin's moving-iron volt   magneto-static tangent   multicellular electrostatic
balance 1884   galvanometer 1887   voltmeter by Kelvin 1888

By the end of 1900 there were 119 members in Glasgow and Edinburgh was seeking its place in the action. There was the question of funding and it was considered that the capitation grant should be 10/- (50p) in the first year and 7/6 (38p) in subsequent years. It is not always easy to compare the present value of the pound with that at the beginning of the century. A ticket for the annual dinner cost 7/6 and apparently there was a loss of 12/6 (63p) on the 1902 event. This was dealt with by transferring 10/6 (53p) to the general account and disposing of a photograph of Lord Kelvin for 2/- (10p). Attendances at Council and

London committees were a charge on the local section and efforts to obtain reduced fares to London or Edinburgh were refused unanimously by the railway companies. The Section was also expected to pay the travelling expenses of authors and this was a burden it could not afford from the grant. Initially, most papers were generated and assessed locally with preprints being available before presentation. Later, about 1907, the Papers Committee in London became responsible for approving the standard of papers and this was often a source of friction as delay in assessment might mean a paper was not available on the evening it was to have been presented. London could also insist that a paper be presented there before being released to the Section. The Section was also unhappy about accepting a paper that had been read elsewhere on the grounds that it was 'second-hand'.

From the start the Section had a programme of about seven lecture meetings each session with social functions such as an annual dinner, a smoking concert and a summer outing in the form of a steamer excursion. Attendances at meetings were regularly over 70 which was remarkable considering the number of members. In Glasgow these meetings started at 8 p.m. and frequently there is a comment in the minutes "due to the lateness of the hour the meeting was adjourned". The discussion would be continued at the next meeting which was generally a month later. The lectures covered a very wide range with generation, distribution and utilisation being the most popular topics, but radioactivity, high-frequency waveforms and radio-telegraphy also found their place and were well supported. On one occasion the minutes note a complaint that the refreshments after the meetings were 'somewhat rough and coarse'. At a cost of sixpence (2.5p) they might have expected something better.

As early as 1903 it was reported that while Council was likely to consent to a change in name to "Scottish Section" it would veto anything in the nature of a sub-section. The first meeting in Edinburgh seems to have been held in February 1904 with a lecture on *Electric Hauling Machines* coupled with a visit to the works of Bruce Peebles Ltd but no further meetings in the capital city are recorded until 1911.

Then, as now, any proposed change in rules led to lengthy and, on occasion, acrimonious discussions. National prestige was at stake as the existing name was considered by some to reduce Scotland, of which Glasgow was only a part, to the equivalent of an English city. However, the committee in Glasgow was prepared to support a proposal to include Edinburgh within the Glasgow area as it was only an hour's journey away and to hold some of the meetings there.

At the beginning of 1911 the committee of the Glasgow Section proposed that the whole of the Scottish membership be incorporated in the section and its name changed to **"The Scottish Section of the Institution of Electrical Engineers"**. This was approved by Council and the second ordinary meeting of the 1911-12 Session was held in the Heriot-Watt College, Edinburgh, in December 1911 with **Professor Francis Baily** of the College reading his paper on *The Electrical Engineering Laboratory*. The minutes of the section record, without comment, a change of title to **The Scottish Centre** from Session 1918-19 and so it remained until 1990 when the current title of **IEE Scotland** was approved.

The section had a representative on Council but in October 1911 there was the first annual meeting in London of the honorary secretaries of sections to discuss matters relevant to the conduct of the sections. In November of the same year there was a significant meeting to revise the Articles of Association. Appleyard (6) in his *History* reports that Council had resolved to raise the annual subscription of all members from 1912. It was taking advantage of the elation arising from the move to the new and recently refurbished headquarters in Savoy Place in London. The pronouncement was well received in London and after the first year of the increased subscriptions the Honorary Treasurer of the Institution announced that 'there was an intense desire on the part of the members to pay up with promptitude'. The reaction in Scotland, as reported in the minutes, was rather different. There was a strong feeling that members living more than 50 minutes from Charing Cross should not pay the increase as distance would prevent them from benefiting from the library and other facilities of the new building. The subscription of 4 guineas (£4.20) does seem rather large for that date but Council was probably wise to safeguard the financial future of the Institution.

Glasgow was the venue for a three-day Summer Visit in 1912 which attracted an attendance of several hundred. An ambitious programme of functions, visits and receptions was arranged with special events for the ladies. The highlight, on the final day, was an excursion on the steamer *Duchess of Hamilton* with the Glasgow Tramways Pipe Band providing on-board musical entertainment. The Caledonian Railway Company quoted a charge of about ten shillings (50p) per head to cover

First Class rail travel to Gourock, luncheon and tea for a minimum of 300 passengers. The cost of the pipe band was £2.00.

The 1914-18 war appeared to have little effect on the learned society activities and the Kelvin Lectures held in 1916, 1917 and 1918 attracted audiences of up to 200. However, social events were curtailed or suspended and the annual dinner was not resumed until 1923. Nevertheless, the committee continued to meet for dinner after dealing with the formal business.

Council made a significant change in 1917 when proxy voting was introduced so that the wider membership could have the opportunity of expressing their views. This development was strongly supported by the Scottish Section.

The Period 1918 to 1950

The 1914-18 conflict had resulted in significant innovations in electrical engineering with regard to materials, manufacturing techniques, instrumentation and wireless. A wireless section was inaugurated in London in 1919 but the Scottish Centre resisted any such specialisation. It was argued that as papers on wireless were regularly before the committee and were being presented at meetings, a wireless section would not serve any useful purpose.

The first Faraday Lecture was given in Edinburgh by **Professor GWO Howe** of Glasgow University in February 1925 on *World-Wide Radio Telegraphy*. The telephone trunk network was used in October 1929 to link the Presidential Address at Savoy Place with nine centres in the U.K. **Professor Magnus Maclean** in Glasgow seconded the vote of thanks to the President, a Scot, **Colonel Sir Thomas Purves** who was educated at the Heriot-Watt College and Edinburgh University. There was also a proposal to "broadcast" one of the named lectures but apparently this idea was abandoned.

Other aspects of radio-frequency technology were discussed in lectures on medical applications such as diathermy and the effect of the upper atmosphere on world-wide communications from the Empire Service Broadcasting Station at Daventry. The early work of **John Logie Baird** on television does not seem to have been reported to the members, but the 1936 Faraday Lecture in Glasgow attracted a capacity audience of 1300 to hear **Dr Mallet** on *Television - an Outline with Experiments*.

"Electronics", as we understand the term now, hardly existed but there were lectures on the use of thermionic valves in applications such as cardiography, repeaters for trunk and multi-channel telephone links and measuring instruments. The cathode-ray oscillograph was a novelty and the subject of lecture demonstrations. At one such meeting there was an audience of 120, but the minute does not explain how so many were able to view a screen that was probably about 10 cm in diameter. However, the majority of meetings were still concerned with power topics. **Professor Stanley Parker Smith**, Professor of Electrical Engineering of the Royal Technical College, Glasgow (his *Problems in Electrical Engineering* teased several generations of students) who was Chairman of the Scottish Centre in sessions 1939 to 1941 built an all-electric house in 1923  which was the subject of a paper to the Institution (7). Coincidentally, this house is now owned by one of the great-great-grandsons of the founder of Wm Teacher & Sons Ltd, the whisky distillers, whose former Head Office built in 1876 is now the Scottish Engineering Centre in St Enoch Square.

The inauguration of the 132-kV National Grid in April 1930 spawned many papers on a wide range of related subjects with high-voltage transmission, protection, rural electrification and earthing being examples. A talk in 1934 on d.c. transmission at very high voltages was perhaps somewhat premature with regard to the U.K. The hydro-electric developments in the Grampian and Galloway power schemes were of considerable interest and gave rise to joint meetings with other institutions. The shadow of things to come was hinted at by a paper in 1935 on *Electrical Control of Traffic by Vehicle Activation.*

It is clear from the records that the learned society activities were well supported and that a good proportion of the membership was taking the opportunity of keeping in touch with developments. Curiously, although joint meetings with other professional bodies were not uncommon, a non-member attending a technical meeting was charged a fee which was increased to £1 in October 1947. As a dinner-dance ticket at that time was only slightly more expensive, a non-member would have to be very keen to attend a lecture.

Social activities were not neglected. Lecture meetings in Dundee were held on Friday evenings, often preceded by lunch in Carnoustie and followed by an overnight stay there or perhaps in Dunkeld with a coach tour and golf match. In 1927 the Chairman,, **WL Winning,** and a committee member, **A Hutcheson,** presented a golf challenge cup to be named *The Scottish Centre Benevolent Cup.* The proceeds from the matches have always been a welcome contribution to the Benevolent Fund. The Faraday Lecture was an annual event in Dundee for many years with the Lord Provost and other dignitaries participating in the social events. However, in 1937 the Centre Committee decided that henceforth the lecture would be held successively in Edinburgh, Dundee and Glasgow. Not unnaturally the Dundee Sub-committee was unhappy and so probably were those from elsewhere who could afford the time and cost of an enjoyable weekend.

The *Annual Dinner and At Home* was held in Glasgow at the Grosvenor Restaurant in Gordon Street which was its venue until the disastrous fire in 1970. The 'at home', sometimes delayed by overlong after-dinner speeches, consisted of dancing or cards depending on inclination. Cost was of concern and there was a body of opinion that the price of the ticket, about 90p, should be reduced either by excluding wines or supplying cheaper varieties. The minute does not mention the quantity provided. The smoking concert had its following and was a cheaper event held in the Grand Hotel , Charing Cross. Alas, it too has disappeared with motorway developments.

Scotland was a popular and regular destination for the Institution Summer Meetings which attracted over 500 participants on some occasions, mainly from England. They lasted several days with an intensive programme of technical visits, sightseeing, civic receptions and social events. The organisation had to be meticulous to arrange accommodation, transport and feeding for so many participants, particularly when visiting the more remote locations. Generous hospitality was always shown by public and private concerns while rail strikes, petrol rationing and weather did not deter our enthusiastic guests.

The Centre organised a Spring Meeting for members and ladies at Gleneagles in May 1950 with a three-day stay at less than £2 per person per day with golf and fishing extra. This became an established event but with Pitlochry, the favoured venue, offering visits to hydro stations and the theatre. It was also an opportunity to compete for the Winning-Hutcheson Trophy.

The organisation of the Centre had not changed greatly since its foundation although its development made increasing demands on the office bearers who were seeking ways of sharing the load by having assistants and secretarial help. Professional auditors were appointed in 1928. However, in 1963 it was decided that, as a cost cutting measure, they would be replaced by honorary ones elected from the membership.

The minutes give some insight into various matters that were exercising the minds of the Committee. In 1927 it was proposed that there should be a gold badge of office for the chairman. The notion was considered again in 1953, but only in 1998 did it come to fruition. However, by then solid gold was considered an unnecessary luxury, but even so the medallion is an emblem worthy of the status of the office. There was also a proposal in 1933 that records, including uniform size photographic portraits of chairmen, should be kept. Unfortunately nothing seems to have come of this although a sum of money up to £40 was allocated for the purpose.

In the 1930s the recommendations of the Membership Committee in London with regard to the election and transfer of corporate members were discussed by the Centre Committee who signified their approval or otherwise. This procedure appears to have continued until the 1950s when the Membership Committee instituted a strictly confidential procedure and this was enforced by **JHP de Villiers** when he was appointed Scottish Interview Convener.

The outbreak of war in September 1939 resulted in a brief cancellation of meetings until January 1940 when a programme of joint meetings with the students was started. The notices convening the meetings emphasised that "a substantial tea would be provided". Surprisingly, the minutes indicate remarkable normality during the war years except for the cancellation of social functions. By 1942 the students, with their section renamed "Junior Section", resumed their separate meetings.

In the late 1930s there had been rumblings about the possibility of having separate eastern and western centres and **JS Pickles** even proposed a Solway sub-centre with headquarters in Carlisle. The formation of an Edinburgh Centre continued to exercise some minds but it was pointed out that there were inadequate numbers for this status. Nevertheless, the discussions continued with a petition to Council for a South-East Sub-Centre. Not to be left out, Members in Aberdeen were seeking the formation of a North-East Sub-Centre.

JHP de Villiers and **S Winstanley** suggested in 1943 that a wireless group should be instituted. The support was assessed by a questionnaire and from this it appeared that "Radio and HF Engineering Section" would be a more representative title. Finally, in 1946 there was a meeting with the President and Secretary when it was decided that the travel by car, complaints about lecture rooms and their facilities and the arrangements for the 1949 Institution Summer Visit were being hampered by travel restrictions. All appeared to have been dealt with satisfactorily.

Two thousand copies of the Jubilee Booklet, edited by **DS Munro**, were produced for the 1949-50 Session and issued free to members. In this publication were recorded personalities and achievements in the first fifty years and as its editor stated, the Centre had more than fulfilled the high hopes of its worthy founders. The membership had grown to nearly 1500 and among them were some of the most famous names in the electrical engineering profession. The Centre was now preparing itself for the reforms necessary to face the challenges of the next half century.

The Introduction of a Federal Structure

It had become apparent that some reform of the committee structure was necessary to take account of the geographical spread of the Centre and the interests of its members outwith the central belt. Although membership numbers were increasing they did not justify additional centres. However, in October 1950 it was proposed that a federal scheme should be adopted with three sub-centres, North-East, South-East and South-West, each having representation on the Centre Committee. **John Henderson** chaired a small committee entrusted with formulating a new constitution. This was presented in draft by January 1951, in agreed form in May of the same year and approved by Council to be implemented in Session 1952-53. This was achieved with remarkable smoothness considering the many details to be resolved such as finance and the roles of the several committees. Not all aspirations had been satisfied as the formation of specialist sections had been postponed in the meantime, and Edinburgh still hankered after centre status although the membership in the South-East was only about 480 compared with 800 in the South-West and 270 in the North-East. There was some concern about student numbers as there was a general lack of interest perhaps due to more pressing demands on their time in this post-war period. A recruiting film entitled *The Enquiring Mind* was made available from 'Savoy Place' but unfortunately did not seem to arouse much interest in Scotland although it received glowing reports from elsewhere.

The new scheme gave considerable autonomy to the three sub-centres and this engendered enthusiasm for innovative programmes including the organisation of district meetings in several towns such as Thurso, Inverness, Dumfries and Dunfermline. These meetings, often arranged in conjunction with a local electrical society could attract good attendances, disseminated much useful technical information, were often a social occasion and gave valuable publicity for the Institution.

The rules of the Centre were amended in the light of experience after three sessions. Initially it had been decreed that the Centre chairman should be a British subject but this restriction was quickly deleted. The relationships between Centre and sub-centres with regard to programmes, finance and the like required more consideration and co-ordination, but it was the general opinion that a satisfactory scheme was now in being , and moreover, 'Savoy Place' recognised its merits.

London did not always agree with Scotland. For example, 'Savoy Place' has on occasion found the differences in the educational systems difficult to reconcile with its rules. About this time the Institution Examination had a paper to assess competence in English, but was quite adamant that a pass in Lower English in the Scottish Leaving Certificate examination was unacceptable for exemption although it was accepted by universities in Scotland and England. Some strong words were expressed in committee on the matter and it was agreed that a firm stand should be taken against the apparent assumption that the education system in England applied to Scotland. The minute states "it is both inaccurate and rude; in fact it is just a piece of ill-mannered bullying". In a similar vein a senior member of the IEE Secretariat is on record as saying that it was absolutely fatal to mention what the English Joint Committee for HNCs and Diplomas would do because the corresponding Scottish committee would then do the exact opposite! He was not being entirely serious, but it has been necessary from time to time to argue for Scotland to be treated as a special case.

At last, in March 1957 it was decided in view of the continued popularity of 'light current' papers, there could be a case for setting up a specialised group attached to the Scottish Centre. As an experiment a programme of eight meetings in Edinburgh and Glasgow was arranged for the l957-58 session. It was emphasised that these lectures were not intended to be of general interest but would cater for members engaged in the fields of **Radio and Measurements (R&M)**. The sub-centres would continue to include in their programmes 'light current' papers of a more general nature. By the end of 1958 there were nearly 150 members registered with the R & M Section and there was pressure to have it organised on a permanent basis. However, meagre attendance at some meetings raised doubts but nevertheless the section survived. By 1964 it was suggested that "measurement" should be replaced by "control" as being a better description of interests. In the same year a **Microminiaturisation Symposium** organised in conjunction with the **British Institution of Radio Engineers (BritIRE)** attracted 250 delegates and produced a surplus of several hundred pounds. The section was now firmly established and even split off a sub-group on **Medical Electronics**, but this appears to have been short lived.

By the end of 1963 there was some pressure to form a **Power Section**. This also had an ulterior motive as it would give an *ex officio* representative on the Power Division Committee in London. The matter was discussed several times in 1964 and in later years, but it was not until 1970 that the section was formed and approved by Council with **W L Kidd** being nominated as its first chairman. The delay had been occasioned to a large extent by a feeling that support for the section would weaken the sub-centres. There were now three sections and a proposal for the formation of yet more specialist groups. The latter only came about in 1970 with the setting up of the Industrial Utilisation of Electric Power and the Project Planning and Control groups.

It was a decade of change and innovation. In September 1968 **FH Fielder** took on the task of recording and preserving early electrical apparatus. In October of the same year, Student Counsellors were appointed in the five universities and Paisley College of Technology with responsibility for bringing the IEE to the attention of students, advertising its activities and encouraging students and staff to join. Industrial representatives were also to be appointed with a similar mandate. Membership advisors had already been appointed in each of the sub-centres about three years earlier.

The effect of inflation on social functions was causing concern. It was decided that formal evening wear was neither necessary or desirable, so no longer would guests at the top table require evening dress and a white tie. In 1967 Louis Freeman whose band regularly played for the dinner dance reduced his fee from 38 to 35 guineas and suggested cutting out the meal normally given to his men before playing. It was pointed out that the entertainments sub-committee was really unnecessary as the work was largely carried out by the Centre honorary secretary who was bearing an ever increasing burden.

There were also increasing problems with finances, the preparation of budgets and keeping to their limits. A range of economies was suggested, such as printing the chairman's report on the back of the AGM notice and issuing the programme for the entire session in September. The success of the latter would require the co-ordination and co-operation of about ten committees to have programmes finalised in time. Clearly, the overall organisation of the Centre with its increasingly complex committee structure needed revision. There was also a request from London that the Scottish Centre should consider the feasibility of a joint programme with the Institution of Electronic and Radio Engineers (IERE previously Brit IRE). There had already been co-operation between the two Institutions for some time, particularly with regard to symposia and exhibitions.

IEE Scottish Centre Power Section - visit to Tullis Russell Paper Mill, Markinch, Fife March 1979. *Courtesy of Jack Davidson*

The Institution itself was entering into major discussions about the machinery of its government and had passed a sheaf of documents to centre committees for their consideration. There was a strong feeling in Scotland that the draft proposals did not address the problem of integrating the centres with headquarters. As early as the beginning of 1966 there had been thoughts about revising the Centre constitution and a committee of five under the chairmanship of **John Stewart** was given the task. Later that year it was instructed by the Centre Committee not to follow the London Local Centres Committee proposals but to put forward its own ideas to suit the conditions peculiar to Scotland. It would be nearly a decade before a new constitution would be implemented.

The New Constitution of 1974

The review of the Constitution was difficult and protracted as members held widely differing and apparently inflexible views with regard to the size of the Centre Committee and its relationship with other committees. The formulation of a policy for the future role of the Institution in Scotland was fraught with problems and there were prolonged arguments about the proliferation of committees, the paramount importance of the sub-centres and the need to cater for specialist interests without fragmentation. There was also the need to take account of a budget that was not unlimited. By August 1970 it was clear that no agreement could be reached and a new sub-committee was set up, but in April 1972 it submitted its collective resignation. In November of the same year, **GI Thomas** submitted proposals on behalf of another new sub-committee. These had been discussed and generally approved in principle by the sub-centres and sections. By mishap the report landed up with the Secretary and Deputy Secretary in London who found the thinking in the report "perverse". Two new drafts were produced, the one satisfying Dr Laverick's objections and the other Dr Gainsborough's. With commendable speed an acceptable version was ratified by the Local Centres Committee and Council to come into effect in Session 1974-75 but it took until September 1976 before the final wording was agreed.

Other matters on the agenda of the Centre at this time included, the possibility of amalgamation with the Institution of Mechanical Engineers (IMechE), the formation of an 'Institution of Engineers' and the withdrawal of the IEE from the Council of Engineering Institutions (CEI). The Education and Training (E & T) Circle was wound up in 1974 and replaced by the **Science Education and Management Section**.

In the midst of these organisational changes there were the **IEE 1971 Centenary celebrations**, with the principal events in Scotland being held in Glasgow. These included a full civic reception with nearly 700 guests at the City Chambers, a talk on *Microelectronics* for schoolchildren and the Centenary Lecture by **Dr Eastwood** on *Radar, Birds and Aircraft*. In the following year, 1972, we joined the BBC in celebrating fifty years of broadcasting.

The *Merriman Report* was presented to Council in May 1978 and not unreasonably the Centre considered that it had failed to take into account the Scottish four-year degree course. Representations were made and undergraduates in Scotland were given an extra year before the requirement for a 2nd class honours degree was implemented. Another consequence of the report would be the need to interview all candidates for election and transfer to corporate membership. The *Finniston Report* called for the accreditation of degree courses, so these two reports led to a general tightening up of the requirements for both education and responsibility for corporate membership of the IEE. Although the new procedures were the responsibility of the Membership Committee and Qualifications Board, they required assistance from members in Scotland.

In the 1980s there was plenty to engage the attention of committees in Scotland including topics such as reduced representation in London on the proposed Local Centres Board, the Engineering Assembly and Regional Structure, the merger with the IERE which was effected in 1987 and, as a sign of the times, the Electronics and Control Section became the **Electronics, Computing and Control Section** in Session 1984-85.

A study of the Centre activities shows a range of lecture subjects that covers most interests with more general review papers on divers topics such as large generators, the future of world communications, North Sea gas developments, computer graphics, etc. With social events such as the dinner-dance, spring and summer meetings, ladies' nights and visits, there were full programmes around the country that should have offered something for everyone. However, as always, there was concern about the small percentage of the membership who took advantage of the opportunities for updating and broadening their professional knowledge. The venues and timing of meetings as well as their form were discussed and were the subject of questionnaires. Half-day symposia were suggested as one method of attracting larger audiences and some of the specialised sections had been leaders in this form of presentation. Nevertheless, the Centre Committee dismissed a suggestion from Savoy Place that centres might run short courses. However, in 1983 the South West Sub-Centre organised a very successful series of lectures on the BBC Microcomputer which was the start of their annual sponsored lectures that have continued to attract capacity audiences to a wide range of technical and associated topics such as *Finance for Engineers* and *The Engineer in Business.*

The Faraday Lectures and the Schools Liaison Service, the latter co-ordinated by **R McMurtrie**, had been giving publicity to the Scottish

Centre for many years. It was now decided to improve the public profile by inaugurating a children's Christmas lecture to be presented in Glasgow and Edinburgh and a prestige lecture delivered by a speaker of "eminence". These events have continued with considerable success. The expanding activities with fewer members able to devote adequate time to their organisation and to office-bearing duties stimulated headquarters to appoint a Regional Officer to assist with secretarial and administrative tasks in Scotland. The first incumbent was **Mrs LM Watson**.

Thus, the changes and developments in the organisation and activities of the Centre mirrored the ever increasing rate of change in the profession at large.

The Last Decade

The Institition, when considering its structure, had put forward ideas about 'regionalisation'. Scotland took umbrage at the possibility of being designated a region and, under the chairmanship of **JA Errett**, a modified constitution was introduced in September 1990 with little opposition and the approval of the Council. The significant modifications were change of title from Scottish Centre to IEE Scotland with the sub-centres becoming IEE Scotland North, etc. and a more flexible scheme for the election of office bearers.

The merger with the **Institution of Electronic and Radio Engineers (IERE)** had been accomplished locally with negligible difficulty as the two institutions covered overlapping fields of interest so that the Scottish Branch of the IERE fitted neatly into the Electronics, Computing and Control Section and greatly enhanced its standing. After a ballot the IEE decided to merge with **The Institution of Manufacturing Engineers** in October 1991. Although the IEE had members whose principal professional interest was manufacturing, it now had to accommodate new members from another discipline. In Scotland this was achieved by the formation of a **Manufacturing Section**.

In March 1991 a Presidential Working Party was set up to consider the future strategy for the Institution. It was argued that at a time of increasingly rapid change with regard to technology and the growth of computer-orientated multinational industries some reform was necessary to further the future interests of the 130,000 members and to stimulate the inactive majority into supporting their Institution.

In Scotland there were wide-ranging discussions about a more autonomous IEE Scotland with some form of devolution or empowerment within its structure. These led to a business plan and annual action plans with a range of proposals which were promulgated in September 1992. Some have come to pass, with the most significant being the establishment of the **Scottish Engineering Centre** and the appointment of **JC Crowe** as its manager. The Centre was opened officially by HRH The Princess Royal in March 1997. Having a central location in Glasgow with good accommodation and state-of-the-art facilities it has proved attractive to sister institutions and other users.

The **South West Retired Members Section** was formed in 1991 with a programme of afternoon lectures and daytime visits. It was immediately successful with good attendances and active discussions at the lecture sessions. The South East followed a year or two later and occasional joint meetings have been held.

Another outcome of Action Planning has been the publication of the six-monthly *IEE Scotnews* giving information about Scottish personalities and affairs as well as short articles of general interest. **R McMurtrie** has been responsible for its design and editing since its inception in 1994.

Engineers can rapidly become out of touch with current practice without in-service education and training and this has particular relevance to some branches of electrical engineering where a new technology can be superseded almost before it is introduced. The **Continuing Professional Development Scheme** was started in 1995 to encourage members to keep up to date. After a trial period it has been modified in 1999 to take account of the Engineering Council's Code of Practice which recognised a wide range of ways that an individual could achieve the broadening and updating necessary for a progressive career.

In 1998 the EC & C Section once again changed its name. It became the **Electronics, Control and Informatics Section** to take account of the changing scope of "computing" and the revised divisional structure in London. The Section, concerned about the small percentage of its members who attended its meetings, produced, in successive years, two audio tapes each giving an account by experts of some half dozen topics in fields of interest to the members. This was an innovation that had value for those who welcomed some updating and who did not attend meetings. However, it lacked the advantages of participation in meetings with the interactive exchange of views in discussion.

Conclusion

The report from the President's Strategy Working Party of 1991 contained a Mission Statement for the Millennium Strategy which defined the function of the Institution as follows:

To promote the advancement of electrical and manufacturing engineering, and to facilitate the exchange of information and ideas. To provide a broad range of services to members to assist them to develop their careers by improving their abilities as engineers, and to play their full part in contributing to society. To raise the standing and visibility of the Profession and to maintain a high standard of professional conduct.

This brief history has shown how well IEE Scotland has played its part in promoting these objectives over the past century. From a beginning of just over 100 members and a dozen or so meetings in the session, there are now nearly 8000 members and the *1999-2000 Guide to IEE Scotland* lists 13 committees and some 113 meetings and sponsored lectures. Members act as advisers, industrial representatives and student counsellors as well as serving on Council, Boards, committees and specialist group meetings in London. Although we now have an Engineering Centre with staff and a Regional Officer, IEE Scotland like the rest of the Institution depends on its members devoting time and effort for its continuing development and success. It is therefore fitting to quote from the foreword by the late **Professor MG (Dick) Say** to the 1950 Jubilee Booklet:

I hope that the younger members, on whom will fall the burden of the days to come, will be inspired to advance the honour, prestige and usefulness of the Institution and its Scottish Centre.

The younger members of 1950 did not fail the Institution nor will those of 2000. IEE Scotland can look forward with confidence to a future of continuing development and success.

Eminent Scottish Centre Chairmen

Lord Kelvin (1900-01)

Sir Archibald Page
(1917-18)

Prof. Magnus Maclean
(1925-26)

DS Munro (1928-29)

Prof. GWO Howe (1931-32)

Prof. S Parker-Smit
(1939-40; 1940-41)

Prof. MG Say (1949-50)

JHP de Villiers (1963-64)

Prof. CW Davidson
(1976-77)

Scottish Centre - Roll of Chairmen

1900-01 Lord Kelvin
1901-02 Prof. Magnus Maclean
1902-03 HA Mavor
1903-04 WA Chamen
1904-05 R Robertson
1905-06 JMM Munro
1906-07 Lord Kelvin
1907-08 Prof. FG Baily
1908-09 WW Lackie
1909-10 E George Tidd
1910-11 S Mavor
1911-12 FA Newington
1912-13 W McWhirter
1913-14 JA Robertson
1914-15 J Lowson
1915-16 DA Starr
1916-17 JK Stothert
1917-18 Sir Archibald Page
1918-19 JF Neilson
1919-20 WB Hird
1920-21 JE Sayers
1921-22 ET Goslin
1922-23 AS Hampton
1923-24 RB Mitchell
1924-25 A Lindsay
1925-26 Prof. Magnus Maclean
1926-27 WL Winning
1927-28 DM Mcleod
1928-29 DS Munro
1929-30 G Morgan
1930-31 E Seddon
1931-32 Prof. GWO Howe
1932-33 DH Bishop
1933-34 NC Bridge
1934-35 Prof. FG Baily
1935-36 JB Mavor
1936-37 HC Babb
1937-38 Major H Bell
1938-39 WJ Cooper
1939-40 Prof. S Parker Smith
1940-41 Prof. S Parker Smith
1941-42 Sir Edward MacColl
1942-43 W Sutcliffe

1943-44 D W Low
1944-45 Col. H Carter
1945-46 RI Kinnear
1946-47 P Philip
1947-48 HM Spiers
1948-49 J Gogan
1949-50 Prof. MG Say
1950-51 J Henderson
1951-52 P Butler
1952-53 JSA Primrose
1953-54 CHA Collyns
1954-55 JS Hastie
1955-56 Dr E Wilkinson
1956-57 Prof. FM Bruce
1957-58 Prof. EO Taylor
1958-59 RJ Rennie
1959-60 JA Aked
1960-61 RB Anderson
1961-62 Prof. EG Cullwick
1962-63 Prof. EG Cullwick
1963-64 JHP de Villiers
1964-65 J Mendelson
1965-66 WL Kidd
1966-67 JE Sayers
1967-68 J Stewart
1968-69 E Hywell-Jones
1969-70 KJ McConnell
1970-71 GI Thomas
1971-72 Dr DS Gordon
1972-73 TM McCammont
1973-74 JB Smith
1974-75 JT Henderson
1975-76 J Addison
1976-77 Prof. CW Davidson
1977-78 J Coward
1978-79 THJ Terry
1979-80 BV Howard
1980-81 VJ Ross
1981-82 WC Thomson
1982-83 R Coackley
1983-84 Dr AM Hall
1984-85 RD McColl
1985-86 J Davidson

1986-87 SH Tempest	1993-94 Prof. HW Whittington
1987-88 JB McLean	1994-95 Eur Ing JD Fyvie
1988-89 MC Hately	1995-96 J Lewis
1989-90 JA Errett	1996-97 RA Matthews
1990-91 A Speight	1997-98 JS Grant
1991-92 Prof. ND Deans	1998-99 KW Watson
1992-93 A Smith	1999-2000 Prof HW Whittington

Honorary Secretaries of the Scottish Centre

1900-07 E George Tidd	1953-60 JHP de Villiers
1907-13 JE Sayers	1960-62 DR Rollo
1914-37 J Taylor	1962-68 JK Wheeldon
1937-45 RB Mitchell	1968-73 LEJ Green
1945-48 RB Mitchell &	1973-81 THJ Terry
HV Henniker (jointly)	1981-87 WT Warnock
1948-50 HV Henniker	1987-93 SJ Thompson
1950-53 CS Buyers	1993-99 KB Watson

References

1. Appleyard, Rollo: *History of the Institution of Electrical Engineers (1871-1931)* Pub. The Institution of Electrical Engineers, 1939, p.17

2. ibid.　　p.106

3. ibid.　　p.108

4. ibid.　　p.323

5. Munro, D.S., Taylor, E.O. *Jubilee Recollections, The First Fifty Years 1899-1950 and the Last Decade 1949-59,* (The Scottish Centre of the Institution of Electrical Engineers, 1960), p.5.

6. Appleyard, Rollo: *History of the Institution of Electrical Engineers (1871-1931),* The Institution of Electrical Engineers, 1939, p.192.

7. Parker Smith, S. *An All-Electric House,* IEE Journal, Vol.64, No.351, March 1926, pps.289-301.

8. *The Radio and Electronic Engineer, Golden Jubilee of the Institution of Electronic and Radio Engineers.* Vol 45, No.10. October 1975

9. Minutes of meeting of Scottish Section of BritIRE dated 27th June 1945

[Most of the information in this history has been gleaned from the IEE Scottish Centre Committee Minute Books which are thin on the background and personalities involved. A more personal account will be found in *Jubilee Recollections, The First Fifty Years, 1899-1950* by DS Munro and *The Last Decade, 1949-1959* by Professor EO Taylor. Both gentlemen were very active in the affairs of the Institution and flesh out the bare facts of the minutes with their personal involvement.]

Addendum A
The Institution of Electronic and Radio Engineers
- by David Dick OBE, DIC, CEng, FIEE

Radio engineering started early in this century when Marconi and others were making rapid advances with this new technology. Initially communications at sea and between radio amateurs were its principal applications. The inauguration of the British Broadcasting Company in 1922 brought wireless into many homes in this country, although rather later than in the USA and Europe. By 1925, many of those who considered that their specialist interests were sufficiently different from those catered for by the Institution of Electrical Engineers decided to form their own institution 'distinct from the inhibiting influence of older engineering traditions and teaching' (8); thus the *British Institution of Radio Engineers* was born.

The membership roll of the first decade included many famous names in the world of radio such as **HJ Barton-Chapple, SR Burbridge, WE Miller, Admiral of the Fleet The Earl Mountbatten of Burma**. Two Scots appear in this roll, **HG Henderson** and **WA Jones** whose membership spanned well over forty years and who became the prime movers in the establishment of the Scottish Section.

Although Scotland would not see television until the 1950s the war had introduced many of its engineers to radio, radar, navigational aids and electronic instrumentation. Furthermore, Scotland now had an indigenous electronics industry. Thus, on 27th June 1945, a meeting of the BritIRE was convened in Glasgow, at which were present its President, **Leslie McMichael** (of McMichael Radio fame), the Director and Secretary, **GD Clifford** and fourteen Scottish members. **Andrew Bogie** formally proposed the formation of a Scottish Section and **HG Henderson** seconded the motion which was carried unanimously. It is interesting to note that during the meeting the President, Leslie McMichael, recommended that:

> *the programme of meetings should tend toward generalisation,*
> *instead of papers or lectures on highly specialised subjects in*
> *which there could not be as great an interest in Scotland as in*
> *other sections where more opportunity was available for*
> *practical work in the highly specialised fields* (9).

In the event, the first two lectures were; *Quartz Oscillators* by **P Vigoureux** and *Ultra High Frequency Techniques* by **Professor MG Say**.

Council approval for the formation of the Scottish Section was planned for its next meeting on 29th June 1945 but this had to be postponed because of the *Victory Japan* celebrations and formal approval was granted in a letter dated 8th September 1945. The first chairman was **A Redpath** and the Honorary Secretary was **HG Henderson**. Meetings were held alternately in Glasgow and Edinburgh and interspersed with industrial visits. This pattern continued uninterrupted for several decades, the lecture programme, visits and exhibitions reflecting the changes in technology.

The Institution was incorporated by Royal Charter in 1961, when its President was **Lord Mountbatten,** and celebrated its Golden Jubilee in 1975 when **HRH The Duke of Kent** was President. By 1987, following the murder of Lord Mountbatten and the death of GD Clifford, the BritIRE, which had been renamed the *Institution of Electronic and Radio Engineers* (IERE) in 1964, decided to amalgamate with the IEE. This decision was taken partly because the interests of the IERE had increasingly broadened from radio engineering *per se* to include electronics and control engineering and a joint programme of lectures with the IEE had been arranged for several years. The IEE had increasingly developed its interests towards 'light current' engineering and with some pressure from the Engineering Council to streamline and reduce the number of professional institutions the decision was taken to wind up the affairs of the IERE and to unite with the IEE. The Scottish Section committee members under the chairmanship of **Alan Smith** and honorary secretary **George Griffiths** now became leading members of committee of the Electronic, Computing and Control Section of the IEE's Scottish Centre.

Addendum B
The Institution of Manufacturing Engineers
by TD West MA, CEng, MIEE

By the early 1900s, the 'big three' - the Institutions of Civil, Electrical, and the Mechanical Engineers - were well established, but no Institution had any section devoted to the production of hardware

Following discussions during World War I, a meeting of those engineers engaged in production was convened in London on 26th February 1921. The outcome was a decision to form *The Institution of Production Engineers*. The first President was **Cecil Hammond**. At this meeting many issues were raised which still persist, for example: the name and ethos of the Institution and the status of its members. The title 'Institution of Production Engineers & Managers' was rejected as unwieldy. The word 'Production' was criticised as being narrower than 'Manufacture'. It was hoped that election to Membership would give improved status and recognition to production engineers. Their wide range of duties and responsibilities were noted, and it was envisaged that membership would encompass all grades of practitioner and that the ethos would not veer to the academic.

Other issues were the role of the provinces, the publication of a magazine, the need for a clubroom, the desirability of social events, the establishment of an information bureau including a library and a reading room, and funding. Proposals to become a specialist section of the IMechE, or to amalgamate with the Engineers Clubs in the larger towns, were not taken up.

Up to World War II only apprenticeships and practical courses were available, but the technology was developing, and Higher National Certificates, Diplomas, and BScs were natural educational developments. The Institution grew in membership, and local 'chapters' flourished in large manufacturing centres. The Institution conducted its own examinations and admitted members from all over the world.

The title 'engineer' has always been used (unhelpfully) as a generic term for all workers in engineering, and it was believed desirable to differentiate between the holders of Certificates, diplomas, and degrees. All three grades qualified for membership of the IProdE, and are now eligible to join the *Manufacturing Section of the IEE.*

The first meeting of the Glasgow Section was held on 21st October 1930; this was soon followed by independent Sections in Edinburgh and Dundee. These, and the overarching Scottish Region, continued until 1995.

The IProdE received its Royal Charter on 26 March 1964, and ceased to be merely a limited company. Unfortunately, funding became critical, especially after 1973, and several cost-cutting manoeuvres failed to solve the problem. A merger with the Institute of Industrial Managers (IIM) in 1987 was one proposal and the proposal to merge with the IMechE was re-examined in 1985, but the vote went against it.

In 1990, the Institution changed its title to **The Institution of Manufacturing Engineers (IMfgE)**, to reflect the nomenclature change in America and academe.

In 1995 the IEE, following discussions with the IMfgE, proposed an amalgamation and both memberships voted to include the IMfgE as the 'Manufacturing Section' of the IEE. This Section now has a total

UK affiliation of almost 40,000. In Scotland there are 2000 members, and programmes of lectures, visits and social events are organised under the Section Chairmanship (1999-2000) of **Dr U.Bititci,** University of Strathclyde.

Chapter 2

The Education and Training of Electrical Engineers in Scotland

(i) Electrical Engineering Education before 1960
by WEJ(Ewart) Farvis CBE, CEng, FRSE, HonFIEE

In matters of technical and higher-technological education, as indeed with its primary and secondary education, Scotland led the way. By the end of the 19th century several regions of Scotland had become quite heavily industrialised and there was a problem for the Government of how best to provide appropriate educational support for developing an efficient work force through the provision of higher education, mainly by evening-class study. There was already in place a number of small technical colleges for craft training but the pressing need was for more advanced courses suitable for the engineering apprentices, designers and managers. The creation by the Scotch Education Department (as it was then called) of a select group of well-equipped, well-managed and favourably funded advanced teaching centres, which they named Central Institutions, proved by the end of this century to have been a huge success and an imaginative solution to the industrial higher-education problem.

Doubtless the SED planners of the time had been consciously or unconsciously influenced by John Anderson's revolutionary plan at the end of the 18th century to found a very different kind of 'university' in Scotland from the University of Glasgow in which he had served: one where students could gain *useful* knowledge.

The Universities

Three of the four ancient universities of Scotland were founded as ecclesiastical colleges. St Andrews University came first in 1411, then Glasgow University in 1451 and Aberdeen University which was founded by Papal Bull in 1495 as "a University complete in all its Faculties: Theology, Law, Medicine and Arts". Edinburgh was last and uniquely was created the by Town Council as the 'Tounis College' in 1583.

It can therefore easily be appreciated why the small St Andrews

University, in its quiet location south of the Tay, had no inclination to give serious attention to a proposal in 1871 that it might be able to satisfy the higher educational needs of the booming city of Dundee, which only a university could provide, in subjects like chemistry, mathematics, engineering and technical subjects. That must have seemed a preposterous suggestion to the St Andrews Senatus. Fortunately for Dundee two elderly members of the wealthy Baxter family had been working on a plan to found a separate college in Dundee for teaching Arts and Science subjects - but specifically not Divinity, which was well catered for on the other side of the Tay. The inauguration of their new **'University College, Dundee'** (UCD) took place on 5th October 1883. Engineering was one of the subjects to be taught to degree level but the College was not yet entitled to award its own degree. They could however prepare students for the London External degree which was already well established for use throughout the British Empire (though not yet in Electrical Engineering).

The first engineering professor at the new UCD was **JA Ewing,** as Professor of Engineering and Drawing. He was still in his twenties, born and schooled in Dundee and he had won a scholarship to study engineering at Edinburgh University. He helped **Lord Kelvin (Sir William Thomson)** in overseas cable-laying projects, and in 1878 took an appointment as Professor of Mechanical Engineering and Physics at Tokyo University where he devised instruments for measuring earthquakes before coming to the UCD Chair in 1883. It can be seen from the first Calendar of the College (1883-4) that with the collaboration of **Professor Steggall**, who held the Chair of Mathematics and Natural Philosophy, a course of lectures in Electrical Engineering was made part of the 3-year course recommended for all engineering students who wished to obtain, externally, a university degree. This is how the Calendar entry appeared:

'Professors Ewing and Steggall will make arrangements for a Special Course in Electrical Engineering. The lectures will embrace the following subjects:
(1) Telegraphy and Telephony. The Construction, Testing, and Working of Land and Submarine Telegraphs.
(2) Dynamo-Electric Machines: their Principles, Construction, and Regulation.
(3) Practical Measurements of Electrical Quantities, Current and Energy, Meters, etc.
(4) Electric Lighting. Arc and Incandescent Lamps.
(5) The Electric Storage and Transmission of Power, Efficiency of Electric Motors, Electric Railways, etc.
Students of Electrical Engineering will also be required to spend a large part of their time in Laboratory Work.'

This is quite remarkable when one realises it was as recent as 1876 that **Alexander Graham Bell** had patented his telephone in the United States, and that Joseph Swan had developed his incandescent lamp only in 1878. What is particularly intriguing is to find the course needed the combined contributions of the Professor of Engineering (who had personal experience of cable-laying and testing) and the Professor of Mathematics and Natural Philosophy. It was in Natural Philosophy departments that the principles of electricity and magnetism would have been taught. The reference to engineering students wishing to take a university degree, externally, is also interesting. There was not only the London University External BSc degree possibility but also a helpful link with Edinburgh University.

In 1886 an arrangement had been made whereby two years of study at UCD followed by the third year at Edinburgh would qualify for the Edinburgh *Science* degree. It might have been this arrangement that gave St Andrews a change of heart; for in 1895 (St Andrews Ordinance No.20) St Andrews authorised the granting of a degree of BSc in Engineering to UCD engineering students! Ewing left UCD for Cambridge in 1890 and was succeeded by **Professor TC Fidler MICE** who was an authority on bridge design. Professor Steggall thereafter took full responsibility for teaching electrical engineering. It was not transferred back to the Department of Engineering until 1928, when an Honours Degree was introduced. It seemed important, when preparing this review, to include this mention of how the new UCD made a pioneering contribution to the teaching of electrical engineering in Scotland. It is also interesting to find that in the 1930s **Mr J Conway**, Head of the Department of Electrical Engineering at the nearby **Dundee Technical College**, gave the UCD lectures in Electrical Machines.

In 1948 their Honours Degree course was lengthened to four years, at the time when **Professor EG Cullwick** was appointed to the new **Watson-Watt Chair of Electrical Engineering**. This appointment, together with the teaching staff, and shortly a fine new building with modern laboratories, started a new era for elctrical engineering in UCD. Professor Cullwick's special interest, in which he was an acknowledged authority, was electromagnetics. Although it did not affect the development of the electrical engineering courses in any way, in April 1954 UCD was renamed Queen's College. The recommendations of a 1951 Royal Commission had led to the dissolution of UCD and its Board of Governors, and it became part of St Andrews University (10 p.108). Finally on 1st August 1967 the University of Dundee received its Royal Charter and became autonomous.

Glasgow University has the longest history of all the Scottish universities for teaching Engineering yet, like St Andrews, its Senatus looked askance at the original proposal. Poor **Lewis Gordon** the first, quite young, Professor of 'Civil Engineering and Mechanics' (appointed in 1840) had to convince the Senatus of his suitability by delivering for them a dissertation in Latin! He maintained a Civil Engineering practice in Glasgow, but he had quite a rough ride at the University. For accommodation and his teaching he was allotted a small attic room, though admittedly he had very few students. Although a lecturer for Electrical Engineering was appointed as early as 1898, there was no Professor of Electrical Engineering until the appointment of **Professor GWO Howe** much later (1921). He was a somewhat aloof but very able mathematician/physicist with specialist interests in electromagnetism and radio. He did much technical writing and is reputed to have contributed over 300 papers and other items to the journals of learned societies. He was the editorial authority behind the monthly journal *Wireless Engineer and Experimental Wireless.* It is curious to find, though, that these up-to-date topics on which he wrote so much seem not to have been introduced into the lecture syllabus.

The number of engineering students had substantially increased between the two wars, with the result that there was good reason to create a separate Faculty of Engineering. Its first meeting was held on 3rd October 1923. It was doubtless this reorganisation that permitted a well-defined Department of Electrical Engineering to be established, with Professor Howe as its first Head. He brought much credit to the Department and several of his students rose to prominent positions, some in industry, others in universities and research establishments.

Before moving on to the 1940s and the Second World War years there is a fundamental point about 'boundaries' or 'ownership' that is worth going back to. It will be remembered that during the period from about 1850 to 1900 considerable interest was being shown by Lord Kelvin (William Thomson, as he then was, Professor of Natural Philosophy in the University) in the development of Telegraph Engineering. It was his contribution to the laying of the first Atlantic cable, and its testing, which earned him first a knighthood. Yet he was basically a physicist, not an electrical engineer. It may also be remembered from what has been written of the early years of University College Dundee that after the departure of JA Ewing the teaching of electrical engineering was done by Professor Steggall, the Professor of Natural Philosophy. This kindred link between Physics and Electrical

Engineering has persisted, and had become so evident by the 1980s that the IEE actually began to encourage physicists to apply for membership. Lord Kelvin certainly became one of the idols of our Institution, and rightly so. He clearly had a taste for invention: it is said that he had built up a portfolio of over 50 patents in a period of 40 years.

Returning to the situation in Glasgow University for the teaching of Electrical Engineering, it was back in **Professor Barr's** tenure of the Regius Chair of Engineering, well before Professor Howe's appointment, that the first Lectureship in Electrical Engineering was established, in 1898. This was a key appointment, for that was the period of great industrial prosperity in the West of Scotland, when the manufacture of electric motors gave new employment prospects for young men who had learned the principles of electrical design. From the turn of the century, therefore, when the Scottish Section of the IEE was formed, Glasgow University would have led the field in providing the electrical engineers needed to support the growing electrical industry in Scotland. The quality of the courses in Electrical Engineering would have been greatly strengthened after the appointment of Professor Howe and the founding of the separate Department of Electrical Engineering two years later, with further additions to the electrical teaching staff. When Professor Howe retired in 1946 he was succeeded by **Professor Bernard Hague**, who held the Chair until his death in 1960. He, too, had a great influence on the quality of the teaching of Electrical Engineering. His lectures were popular, and a feature that was greatly appreciated by his students, was his unusually neat blackboard work (blackboard technique is not one of the attributes stipulated, or tested, when making lecturer or professorial appointments in universities!) Professor Hague was the author of several seminal textbooks but did not institute any departmental programme of research. He did, however, strongly encourage individual research and publication.

A period of one academic year elapsed before the appointment of **John Lamb** to the James Watt Chair in 1961 as the next Professor of Electrical Engineering. Under Lamb's driving influence there was a long period of steady expansion in the departmental research, into new areas of electronics in particular, requiring much expensive specialist laboratory equipment, large research grants and additional space.

In **Edinburgh University** the development of a degree course in electrical engineering followed lines quite different from those in Glasgow. With some diffidence (as in Glasgow) the University took a cautious step in the direction of 'moving with the times', following the great 1851 Exhibition in London, by appointing **George Wilson** as 'Professor of Technology' in 1855. It proved to have been either unwise or unpopular, for when Professor Wilson resigned in 1859 it was decided to abolish the Chair. Certainly when one reads the list of lecture courses set out in the Calendar there is nothing that reads like engineering. It had much more to do with varieties of materials, *viz.* 1 Mineral Technology, II Vegetable Technology, III Animal Technology. It seems that the University was encouraged to try again having received a gift of money from **Sir David Baxter** of Dundee to found a Chair of Engineering. (This was the same Baxter who later, with his sister Mary, gave the large benefaction for establishing University College, Dundee.) The donor selected **Fleeming Jenkin** as its first occupant. He was appointed in 1868 and proved to be a high-level 'all-rounder' and undoubtedly a sound engineer.

From the 1871-2 Calendar we read the course of study for the degree of BSc in Engineering was:

First Year:	Mathematics 1
	Geometrical Drawing
Second Year:	Mathematics 2
	Natural Philosophy
	Engineering 1 or 2
	Mechanical Drawing
Third Year:	Surveying and Levelling
	Natural Philosophy (advanced)
	Engineering 2 or 1
	Chemistry

There is nothing obviously electrical there, unless perhaps hidden within Natural Philosophy. However, in the Calendar for the following year there is one item in a long list of lecture topics 'Manufacture of telegraph cables, apparatus and stores'. Here was a touch of electrical engineering of that period. Under that list of lecture topics came this significant Calendar entry:-
"Engineering Works and Factories will be visited by the Class, under the guidance of the Professor."
Telegraph cables would have been a topic Fleeming Jenkins knew something about. He had collaborated with Lord Kelvin (then Sir William Thomson) on the laying of the first Atlantic cable, and between 1861 and 1868 he had practised as a consultant in telegraph and general engineering. The government employed him as a consultant during

the transfer of the telegraphs to the Post Office. He had contributed, too, with **Sir William Thomson** and **James Clerk Maxwell**, to a series of experiments to determine standards for electrical measurements. He died in 1885. In session 1886-7, under **Professor Armstrong**, the new *Regius* Professor of Engineering, there was, for the first and only time, a course of 20 lectures on 'Electrical Engineering' attended by 24 students. It was under Professor Armstrong that the first engineering laboratories were set up. He died in 1900.

The next holder of Edinburgh's Regius Chair of Engineering was **Sir Thomas Hudson Beare** and during his long tenure (1901-1940) there were many important changes, not only by several additions to the lecturing staff but also to course structures and a move into the fine new purpose-built Sanderson Building, devoted solely to Engineering, one of a group of Science Buildings on the King's Buildings site on the south side of Edinburgh. This new block of lecture rooms, staff rooms, drawing office, workshop, and suite of well-equipped spacious laboratories was to serve Engineering well to the end of the century, by the construction, almost decade by decade after 1950, of several substantial extensions to provide much-needed growing space for the addition of Chemical Engineering in the late 1960s and the expanding Electrical Engineering from 1950.

The most significant change introduced by Hudson Beare, as far as Electrical Engineering was concerned, was his plan to concentrate his attention primarily on Civil Engineering. Rather than appoint additional staff to develop the courses for Electrical and Mechanical Engineering he made affiliation arrangements so that the specialist electrical and mechanical lectures and laboratory work would be given from 1902 by 'approved' staff of the **Heriot-Watt College** in their Chambers Street building. He would have known that his students who wished to specialise in Electrical, or Mechanical Engineering were in good hands, because he himself had experience of the College and its teaching staff by his earlier appointment (1887) as Professor of Engineering at Heriot-Watt College at the early age of 28 (he stayed there only two years before taking the Chair of Mechanical Engineering in University College London).

By the early 1930s he was in a position to make additions to his teaching staff to enable the specialist Mechanical Engineering lectures to be taught in the Sanderson Building along with his Civils by sharing his laboratories. Hudson Beare died in 1940 (at age 80), but the affiliation arrangement for the 'Electricals' continued right through until

1950. No appointment had been made for the Regius Chair vacancy to be refilled until the disruptions caused by World War II were over.

Ronald N Arnold, a mechanical engineer, took up his appointment as Regius Professor of Engineering in 1947. One of his first moves was to bring the electrical engineers back full-time to his own Department, by appointing an electrical lecturer. His aim, too, was to bring electronics into the electrical engineering curriculum and to initiate research - for there had been no engineering research done before the War. The new Professor had ambitious plans to produce strong research teams in all three branches of his Department of Engineering. The author was appointed 'Lecturer in Applied Electricity' in September 1948, and by session 1950-51 new courses in electrical engineering were being taught wholly in the Sanderson Building, with a strong bias towards electronics and communications.

By 1950 a policy for electrical/electronics research had been agreed with Professor Arnold, the newly-appointed **Principal Sir Edward Appleton**, and with the Professor of Natural Philosophy. A first step was the development of a full-time **Postgraduate Diploma Course in Electronics and Radio'**. The proposal for ear-marked support was put to the University Grants Committee (UGC) and was approved for government funding. Four new members of teaching staff with the appropriate range of experience were appointed, as well as two more technicians and a secretary. The University provided a small number of post-graduate student scholarships and the course was launched the following year. Its aim was to establish an advanced course which firms like Ferranti could use as part of their graduate training schemes. It might also attract freshly-graduated engineers, mathematicians and physicists who might wish to add a 'top-up' qualification before seeking employment. A special attraction would be that on the radio side the lectures on the ionosphere were to be given by Appleton himself, those on solar physics by staff of the Royal Observatory. A short group of lectures were contributed by the department of mathematical physics. The course was launched in 1951 and was well attended - not only by the registered students but by the resident staff and, for parts of special interest to them, by final-year students. Out of this inter-disciplinary course there grew Edinburgh's first electrical research programme, on cosmic-noise absorption in the ionoshpere. It involved setting up a receiving station with recording equipment in preparation for taking part in the British co-ordinated programme of radio research in the forthcoming International Geophysical Year (IGY). Having completed the design of the special receiving and recording equipment, and the design and testing of a suitable high-gain directional aerial system, the equipment and aerial units were transported to a convenient hill-top site in Shetland so that the effect of an aurora could be recorded. Postgraduate students and the senior technician paid regular visits during a period of about two years.

No sooner had the Diploma course been successfully established than an invitation came from the Electricity Council to consider applying for grant support for research projects in their field of interest. Here was an opportunity to start research on the power side, which would save the electrical research from becoming totally light current orientated. After discussion with the Principal and the Council Chairman when he visited Edinburgh, the author submitted a proposal for a research project that would involve Bruce Peebles, a local manufacturing firm of heavy electrical plant, as well as affording him the chance to apply his post-war electronics interest to his pre-war interest in gas discharges. He had gained earlier works experience on airbreak and oil-circuit-breakers. The proposal was approved by the Electricity Council, and they supported the research generously for several years, in which time three research students obtained higher degrees, a strong working relationship with Bruce Peebles had developed and, by the end, the research led to a UK Patent for computer controlled units which would minimise or even eliminate arcing in power circuit-breakers. The South of Scotland Electricity Board provided the necessary heavy-current transformer and cable to supply a small temporary laboratory in an open area of the King's Buildings site.

In these ways, throughout the 1950s, the electrical group of the Department of Engineering built up its teaching strength of Lecturers, Senior Lecturers and support staff, and established post-graduate projects in radio propagation, gaseous electronics and arc control which produced quite a large number of MSc and PhD higher degrees. In 1959 a much-improved 5-year Block Grant from the UGC allowed the purse strings of the University to be loosened a little and University-wide expansion bids were encouraged. Engineering was among the favoured departments and Professor Arnold decided the time had come for Engineering to be sub-divided into three separate departments with a suite of new buildings to accommodate the expansion. He, the Regius Professor, would head Mechanical Engineering, and the new Chairs of Civil Engineering and of Electrical Engineering were duly advertised.

In September 1960 the author was appointed to the Chair of Electrical Engineering and Head of the new, separately-organised Department of Electrical Engineering. The start date was lst January 1961. It had taken just under 100 years from the appointment of Fleeming Jenkin, the first Edinburgh University Professor of Engineering, to create this first Professor and Department of *Electrical* Engineering!

In 1964 it became clear that there needed to be a review of policy for the departmental research. The integrated-circuit era had begun: from now on the electronics teaching and research needed to be changed completely. Fabrication techniques would need to be taught, and if there were to be research projects involving fabrication these would require an in-house set of expensive furnaces, a 'clean' measurement and assembly area, with expensive microscopes, chemical balances, fume cupboards, toxic etchants etc. The decision was made to switch from encouraging a broad range of electrical research to a focused research programme in this revolutionary new kind of electronics - **Microelectronics**. That would become the future departmental specialisation, but it would require a very large grant and the blessing of the University to convert laboratories and appoint experienced additional members of the teaching staff, with physics or chemistry qualifications who could teach and research in the science of *semiconductor materials.*

Following the death of Sir Edward Appleton a new, younger, Professor Michael Swann had been installed and he gave full backing to this necessarily sudden change of direction, which he saw could be of value to Scottish industry for the training of staff and even for placing research contracts.

Finally, **Aberdeen University** was the last of the 'old' universities to include Engineering in its degree courses. It had always claimed to be the 'most Scottish' of all the Scottish universities and, from its founding in the 15th century, had always accepted it had a distinctive regional responsibility to serve primarily the educational needs of the Highlands and Islands because of its geographical location. It did not seem that a university course for gaining a degree in Engineering was one of those needs. Times changed and modified that judgement, for there developed a regional need for civil engineers. The University responded, but not until well into the 20th century, by establishing the **Jackson Chair of Engineering** in 1923 and appointing Professor Blackadder, a Civil Engineer (1924-40) to fill it. His Department occupied a building specially designed for it, in Marischal College, with laboratories equipped for Materials Testing, Hydraulics and Heat Engines.

At that time, and for a long time afterwards, the courses in mechanical engineering and electrical engineering were taught at **Robert Gordon's Technical College** by 'approved' teachers. The situation for electrical engineering was therefore similar to the arrangement at Edinburgh University with the Heriot-Watt College between 1901 and 1952, except that in Aberdeen the University appointed the Lecturer(s) who were to do the course teaching at Robert Gordon's College. Blackadder was succeeded by Professor Jack Allen who in turn was followed by Professor TM Charlton. All three were civil engineers. It was not until 1962 that **Professor JF Eastham**, distinguished for his research record in the design of novel types of electrical machines, was appointed by the University. But his appointment was to a second Chair of Engineering, not a Chair of Electrical Engineering; so there was still no University Department of *Electrical* Engineering by 1960.

Research

There is to be found in one of the histories of the Scottish Universities this succinct reminder to higher-education teachers of the importance of their engaging in research.

> *Every great department in a modern university must be a centre of research as well as instruction. No university teacher who is not himself actively engaged in providing advancement in knowledge and discovery in his subject can fail to escape stagnation on his own part and loss of interest on the part of his students. It is the duty of a Professor not only to engage in research but to train his staff and post-graduate students in the difficult art of research* (7 p.44)

It will be remembered, too, how the SED when setting up the Central Institutions had expressed the hope that in due course these favoured colleges would engage in research.

Sadly the record shows that, after the innovative start by Fleeming Jenkin with Sir William Thomson in the late 1860s there had been very little electrical engineering research in the Scottish universities until the 1950s. Between 1900 and 1950 there had of course been the two world wars of 1914-18 and 1939-45 with the consequent departmental disruptions and staff shortages. Each of those wars had been followed by an overcrowding bulge of students. Moreover, between these wars, Scotland had experienced a long and damaging economic depression resulting in financial stringencies in both universities and colleges.

The 1950s, however, were years of recovery. By 1950 a gradual influx of lively young staff had begun to supplement or replace the overworked and ageing teachers who struggled through the hard times of the 1930s and 1940s. Most of these young men would have gained experience, either in industry or in the services, of the exciting wartime innovations in electronics, communications and control, so that there was soon a movement towards course revisions and extension, student individual projects, and post-graduate research. The 1960s were years of unprecedented expansion. Research in departments of electrical engineering really took off, both in Scottish universities and CIs.

The Central Institutions

Towards the end of the 19th century so great was the government's concern that Britain might be having its industrial supremacy threatened through growing international competition that it was seriously considering a proposition to establish a national 'industrial university'. Clearly, the **Scotch Education Department (SED)** had been thinking along the same lines, but more in terms of establishing something similar for each of its main industrial centres, namely Glasgow and the West of Scotland, Edinburgh, Dundee and Aberdeen.

Already by the 1850s there had been established in Scotland a number of local technical colleges for providing 'Continuation Classes', in technical and artistic studies. By 1900 the SED formed a policy for co-ordinating these contributions to higher technical education and in 1901 it introduced the 'Code of Regulations for Continuation Classes'. This Code gave the SED the power to grant financial aid to any technical college giving *advanced instruction linked with industry.* These favoured colleges were to be known as **Central Institutions (CIs)** and the first three to be so honoured straight away in 1901 were:

(i) **The Glasgow and West of Scotland Technical College** (established in 1886).

(ii) **The Heriot-Watt College** in Edinburgh (established in 1886).

(iii) **The Dundee Technical Institution and School of Art** (established in 1888).

Two years later (1903) **Robert Gordon's Technical College**, Aberdeen (established in 1884) made a fourth (16 p.15).

When establishing these Central Institutions the SED expressed the hope that they be:

allowed to develop under their own initiative they would become

47

worthy to rank ... in quality and advancement of work under their own initiative with the best of their kind in the country. It is from such institutions, and the opportunities of research and discovery which they will naturally afford, that decisive advantage to the industry of the country, in so far as that is dependent on educational arrangements, is to be looked for. (13 p.4)

An important additional requirement laid on each of them was that courses of instruction and management, should be supervised by a *Board of Governors* consisting of representatives of local industry and local government. This was a very significant difference from the universities who, to a large extent, enjoyed academic autonomy from the start. It was interesting, also, because here was the same kind of thinking that had characterised **John Anderson's** 18th-century plan for the reformed and *useful* 'university" which he had defined in detail in his will, dated 7th May 1795.

The Glasgow and West of Scotland Technical College was the largest of the Central Institutions, both for students and facilities. By the early 1900s many of its Engineering students had become captains of industry at home and played such important roles in the development of mills and factories in India, that in 1912 King George V granted a name change to the **Royal Technical College (RTC)**. As early as 1892 they had appointed their first Professor of Electrical Engineering, **Professor Andrew Jamieson (1843-1912)**. He was one of the group of members involved in the setting up of the **IEE Glasgow Section** in 1899. He had had experience as a young man as a jointer and tester on Atlantic cable ships. He had retired in 1899 but he helped in the initial years of the Section, by reading several papers and contributing to the discussions. He was succeeded in the Chair of Electrical Engineering by **Professor Magnus Maclean** who was much more of a scholar than Jamieson, having had early experience in the University working under Sir William Thomson (Lord Kelvin) in the Department of Natural Philosophy. He gave good years of service to the IEE Glasgow Section. 'It is significant that the quality of the work of the College led to recognition of its independent role by the University Grants Committee (UGC) in 1919' (17 p.15).

Professor McLean retired in 1924 and was succeeded by **Professor Stanley Parker Smith** who occupied the Chair of Electrical Engineering, with great distinction. The name *Parker Smith* was engraved in the minds of several generations of electrical engineering students world-wide, in colleges and universities, through his book *Problems in Electrical Engineering, with Answers* which reached seven editions and two reprints by 1961. His retiral in 1948 marked 'the end of an era' for electrical engineering in the RTC. He was now asked to execute and supervise the Staff College of the North of Scotland Hydro-Electric Board at Faskally House in Pitlochry for the specialised training of young engineers, who owed the excellence of their training to his thorough and rigorous teaching.

Unlike the other Central Institutions there had been the beginnings of research under Parker Smith, arising out of his extensive consultancy work, mainly associated with electrification of the railways. Research really took off, however, in the Royal Technical College department of Electrical Engineering with the appointment of **Professor Frederick M Bruce** (1948), who was already well known for his industrial high-voltage research contributions. Until 1964 successful students were awarded either the degree of BSc from Glasgow University and/or the College's own Associateship (ARTC) or Diploma. The College had acquired such a fine reputation for strong links with industry, for the quality of its teaching and for its growing research programmes that there was complete justification for the government's decision to grant it university status. It became the first Scottish technological university in 1964, and was named **The University of Strathclyde**. How pleased John Anderson would have been! It had taken more than a century-and-a-half to be brought to fruition, but his legacy instructions had finally been fulfilled.

The Heriot-Watt College in Edinburgh had been providing advanced-level teaching in electrical engineering subjects from 1895, when **Francis Gibson Baily** was appointed Professor of Electrical Engineering. Before Baily's appointment any teaching of electrical engineering students had been the responsibility of **Francis Grant Ogilvie**. He was the first Professor of Physics and Electrical Engineering and was also Principal of the College. However, in 1890 he gave up his teaching to concentrate on the administration of the College and was succeeded by **R Mullineaux Walmsley**. It was Professor Baily, who held the Chair until 1933, who really laid the foundations for the teaching of advanced electrical engineering for which the College became famous. That reputation was enhanced still further by the appointment in 1933 of his young, demanding, energetic successor **Professor MG (Dick) Say**. Say, a product of Imperial College London, had been appointed as Research Assistant to Professor Parker Smith at the RTC, to research problems of railway electrification. His continuous efforts to raise the qualification standards of electrical engineers, not only by his inspired teaching but through years of work for the IEE examinations, made Heriot-Watt College 'the place to go to' for an internationally-recognised qualification in the power aspects of electrical engineering. He included in his busy professional life a year as Chairman of the Scottish Centre (1949-50). When Professor Say retired, in 1961, his Assistant Professor **Eric Openshaw Taylor** was promoted to the Chair of Electrical Engineering and continued the sound teaching of the power side of electrical engineering for which the Heriot-Watt College had earned such an enviable reputation. The particular contributions which Professor Taylor made to electrical engineering in Scotland were the sterling work he did towards the founding of the **Scottish Electrical Training Scheme (SETS)** and his series of Saturday morning advanced lectures on Power Systems. These were always well attended by engineers from the power industry. He, too, was a staunch supporter of the IEE Scottish Centre and Chairman 1957-58.

Considering the quality of the College's teaching of Electrical Engineering it is surprising to find that so little, if any, research was initiated. Their concentration was clearly on their teaching; there was no time for research. Successful students were awarded the College Associateship (AHWC) and the Higher National Diploma with day-release. Part-time evening students gaining ONCs and HNCs with 'advanced endorsements' would be qualified students for corporate membership of the IEE.

The Dundee Technical Institute was developed alongside, but distinct from, University College Dundee. There was no attempt for them to integrate. Both were teaching Electrical Engineering, though at different academic levels. By additions to the staff after the 1914-18 War, when there was a large intake of students enrolling for the day classes, a full course of study in Electrical Engineering was available. There was, by then, a London University External BSc degree in Electrical Engineering in place, and the brighter students might choose to direct their studies to gain that degree.

The major development in technical education during the inter-war years 1920-1940 had been the establishment of the National Certificate and Diploma awards, so Dundee Technical College and School of Art, as it was called in 1909, would have shaped their courses mainly towards these awards which, with additional requirements ('endorsements') could qualify students for corporate membership of the IEE. There was a period of austerity in the years after World War II, but throughout the 1950s, and again through the early 1960s, sufficient progress had been made in teaching to an advanced level that the College gained the approval of the **Council for National Academic Awards (CNAA)** to work for the national CNAA degree in Electrical Engineering. Here, too, was a Central Institution that had, as yet, no record of research, but by the later 1960s, following the appointment of **Dr HG Cuming** as Principal, this deficiency was rectified.

Robert Gordon's Technical College was designated as one of the Scottish Central Institutions in 1903. It already had a well-earned reputation for providing courses of technical education appropriate to the industrial and commercial requirements of the Highlands and Islands region which it had served since 1885. (There had been an **Aberdeen Mechanics Institute** since 1824, for providing day and evening courses in scientific, technical and commercial subjects for apprentices, clerks and others, and this education work had been transferred to Robert Gordon's College in 1884.) A **Mr John Gray**, a local factory owner, had offered to provide a building for a school of science and art, on condition that the College Governors provided a site for it and named it 'Gray's School of Science and Art'. That building, which was opened in 1885, enrolling 96 students for day classes and 322 for evening classes, provided the much-needed purpose-built accommodation for housing the Robert Gordon Technical College.

There was at that date no concentration of heavy industry, as there was in Glasgow, but the College, as it developed under the guidance of a Board of Governors, was able to earn Central Institution status at an early date. It had such a good record that when Aberdeen University began teaching Engineering (1926) it chose to send its mechanical and electrical students to Robert Gordon's College for the teaching and laboratory work. That arrangement continued right through to the 1960s. In Electrical Engineering the instruction was to degree level, but they also taught for the National Certificate and Diploma awards. Research did not figure in their programme until the 1960s, when, like the other Central Institutions, the College was approved for the CNAA degree, and was finally granted full university status in 1992.

Paisley Technical College, though founded as early as 1900, was a latecomer to the select group of Central Institutions. It had determinedly avoided begin drawn into the conglomerate of colleges that had become the **Glasgow and West of Scotland Technical College**, but it suffered badly financially as a result of that stubborn, but understandable determination. With considerable sacrifices and accommodation discomforts through the years, the College had succeeded, by the end of World War II, in establishing a good reputation for its teaching of Electrical Engineering. **Ian Shepherd** was appointed Head of Department in 1947, ably assisted by **AH (Sandy) Morton.** Both names have become linked, and deservedly so, to the quality teaching of Electrical Engineering in Scotland. By their devoted endeavours, in the face of all manner of difficulties, Paisley Technical College was given Central Institution status in 1950. That same spirit of devoted endeavour which had earned the SED approval carried them through, with several new staff appointments and laboratory additions, into the 1960s. The Paisley courses in Electrical Engineering had been directed mainly to the degree award obtainable by taking the London University External BSc (Eng) in Electrical Engineering. There was no great difficulty, by continuing with the same determination to achieve high enough standards, for Paisley to be accepted for the award of the CNAA degree in Electrical Engineering during the 1960s. By that time the staff were developing research, which really blossomed through the 1970s. Their hard survival struggles of the early years had been very appropriately rewarded when the College was given the status of becoming one of the new Scottish technological universities, The University of Paisley in 1992.

Educational Requirements for IEE Corporate Membership

Until 1965 in Scotland, as in the rest of Britain, a school-leaver with the ambition of one day becoming a professional engineer had the choice between enrolling for a full-time 3- or 4-year course in a university, or alternatively for a full-time or part-time course in a technical college. What is the difference? Universities would claim they provide *courses of study* whereas technical college courses in the same subject would be slanted more towards *instruction.* In a university the studies are more concerned with the 'why' of the subject whereas in a technical college they would be biased towards the 'how'. Would both types of course, if successfully completed, qualify the student to become a professional engineer? The professional institution makes that decision.

For electrical engineering the IEE would check against their list of Educational Requirements and might require further study.

It is interesting to note that at the founding of the IEE (1871), when it was called the Society of Telegraph Engineers, there were no educational requirements at all, as can be seen from this extract from the Rules for Member and Associate.

CONSTITUTION

1. THE SOCIETY OF TELEGRAPH ENGINEERS shall consist of Members, Associates, Students, Foreign Members and Honorary Members.
2. MEMBERS - Every Member shall have been previously elected as an Associate of the Society, and shall come within one of the following conditions:-
   (a) He shall have been regularly educated as a Telegraph Engineer, according to the usual routine of pupilage, and have had subsequent employment for at least five years in responsible situations.
   (b) Or he shall have practised on his own account in the profession of Telegraph Engineer for at least two years, and have acquired a degree of eminence in the same.
   (c) Or he shall be so intimately associated with the science of Electricity or the progress of Telegraphy that the Council consider his admission to Membership would conduce to the interests of the Society.
3. ASSOCIATES shall be of more than twenty one years of age, and this class shall include persons whose pursuits constitute branches of Electrical Engineering, who are not necessarily Telegraph Engineers by profession, but who are, by their connection with Science, qualified to concur with Telegraph Engineers in the advancement of professional knowledge.
4. STUDENTS shall be persons not under eighteen and not over twenty-one years of age, who are serving pupilage to a Telegraph Engineer, or who are studying Natural Science, and are duly recommended by a Member.
   (Journal of the Society of Telegraph Engineers, Vol.1, p.10.)

In those far-off days it seems that more stress was laid on practical experience and 'pupilage' than on formal education. It is very different now, a century later; but so is electrical engineering!

To illustrate the wide range of acceptable qualifications for Members of the Society of Telegraph Engineers in the 1880s who automatically became IEE Members at the change of name, the following can be cited:

Gray, Professor A, FRS .... Glasgow, North Britain
Robertson, Robert BSc(Edin) MInstCE ..... Glasgow, North Britain
Alexander, Richard

Richard Alexander's case is interesting and probably typical for that period. From his Obituary Notice in the IEE Journal for 1931 we learn: He was born in 1870 and on completing his education at George Heriot's

School his first employment was on the operating side of the local telegraph system. After completing part-time study of the scientific and technical aspects of telegraphy at the Heriot-Watt College he was transferred in 1898 to Edinburgh district engineering office. In 1903 he was sent to London as an engineer during the period of great pressure which followed the establishment of the P.O. London telephone system. Eight years later he was promoted to the post of Sectional Engineer at Edinburgh, an appointment which he held for 17 years. By the late 1880s, although the Society had undoubtedly acquired prestige - for Britain could claim pre-eminence in telegraph engineering through its successful pioneering development of submarine cables and their laying - the younger members of that Society began agitating for a change of name, pointing out that the recent invention of the telephone and, more importantly, the development of Swan's incandescent-electric lamp, could lead to the founding of a rival electrical society. Time has proved that it was indeed a wise decision for the STE to change its name, with effect from 1st January 1889, to the **Institution of Electrical Engineers** (4 p.53), for there rapidly grew a huge demand for electrical lighting installations, with an accompanying demand for generators to supply them. Thus the era of electric power began just when the STE became the IEE. In 1899 the Glasgow Local Section was founded, with the eminent Lord Kelvin as its first Chairman (1900-01). So it was understandably the power aspect of electrical engineering that became the main interest of its local members. It remained so right through to the 1960s and beyond.

The colleges provided evening courses of instruction in electrical engineering, mostly for technicians, with a bias towards electric power. As well as these technician courses, there was a need for courses on the design of electrical plant. These could be provided by some of the technical colleges, again in the evenings. But there was an opportunity for the universities to play their part: they could develop a more advanced, theoretical approach to the design of electrical plant in courses which could be attended full time by keen young school leavers, always providing they had the qualifications necessary for university entrance. Lack of a pass in a foreign language, for example, would debar entrance to a Scottish university. For these people certain technical colleges had made provision for full-time day classes in addition to evening classes.

Soon after the change of name and the Council's decision to found four Local Sections, the President received an invitation from the President of the Institution of Civil Engineers to nominate two IEE

Council members to the **Engineering Institutions Joint Committee**, of which he was Chairman, for the purpose of considering questions relating to the education of engineers. Such a detailed and elaborate inquiry was undertaken as a result that it was not until 1906 that the Committee of Inquiry submitted its report. The Council of the IEE could not fail to be influenced by the recommendations.

It is worth noting that, in 1868, the Civils had made an inquiry into the systems of engineering education in America and in foreign countries. Yet another inquiry was made by the Civils in 1891 on the facilities for engineering education in the universities and colleges in the British Dominions. In 1897 they established a system of examinations for the Students and Associate Members of the Institution of Civil Engineers. This showed the importance their Council attached to the higher education of Civil Engineers.

As a result of the impressive 1906 report of the Civils, the IEE Council set up an Examinations Committee (1908) to report on whether there should be an examination for corporate membership. The Committee's report was positive and in 1911 the Council agreed that the Institution should develop its own examination for Associate Membership. The first of these annual IEE examinations was set in 1913.

The main reason behind the decision of the professional institutions to set their own qualifying examination had been the variable standard and syllabus content of technical college courses. The institutions would now be able to bring about a more uniform standard. Provision had been made for gaining exemption, one obvious case being the holding of a university degree in electrical engineering. The brighter college students could gain automatic exemption therefore by studying for the London University External BSc(Eng) degree in Electrical Engineering, which had been introduced in 1907. From the Institution's standpoint, between their own examination and the London External BSc(Eng) degree a measure of control on course standards in the technical colleges had been achieved. A number of the technical colleges in Scotland provided courses and facilities for their students to take the London External degree as the normal educational qualification, but the numbers taking this external examination were never very great.

Unfortunately teachers in the higher grade of college were uneasy about the imposition of wholly external examinations (though students, whose aim was acceptance by the Institution, would see the merit of the arrangement!) The teachers much preferred to have greater freedom, some flexibility and some participation in the examining. They also would have liked performance of course work to be taken into account.

It was to meet these valid criticisms that the Board of Education introduced in 1924, with the co-operation of the Institutions, the National Certificate and Diploma courses as an alternative qualifying system. Through its assessors the IEE still exercised a measure of control, because college courses had to be 'approved', as did the examination results, before the Certificates and Diplomas were awarded.

By the early 1950s quite a high proportion of the IEE's new members satisfied the educational requirements through National Certificates. The alternative was to pass the Institution's own examinations, which were in three parts. Part I was taken jointly with Civils and Mechanicals. Part II had four compulsory 3-hour papers: (i) Electrical Engineering 1, (ii) Electrical Engineering II, (iii) Mathematics and (iv) either Engineering Physics or Mathematics. Part III had two 3-hour papers, one in a wide choice of electrical engineering subjects, the second in 'Advanced Electrical Engineering'. Parts I and II could be excused by exemption through ONC, leaving only Part III to be passed. There was complete exemption from Parts I, II and III by the possession of a university degree of an approved university, which included the London External BSc(Eng.), or the Associateship of an approved College, such as the Central Institutions. These Institution examinations were no longer needed after the CNAA degrees were instituted in 1966. The last Part III examination was held in 1967. The examing role was then taken over by the Council of Engineering Institutions (CEI) and subsequently the Engineering Council (EC).

Summary

It has been shown how the Electrical Engineering degree and Associateship courses in the Scottish universities and Central Institutions developed over the sixty years from 1900, though in order to understand the situation in 1900 it was necessary to refer back to some landmark events in Scottish higher education in previous decades. The college courses, even at that early date, were accepted by the IEE as meeting their educational requirements for corporate membership. Soon the three major professional engineering institutions became concerned about the variation in standards in the various colleges across the country as a whole, so together they developed their own externally-set qualifying examination. Although they allowed an alternative exemption route this external influence ensured a greater uniformity of standard and was a fair way for the IEE to control the minimum level of academic attainment required for corporate membership. The introduction of the National Certificate route followed. The examinations for both the Ordinary and the Higher National Certificates were allowed to be taken internally but were externally assessed. Throughout the whole of this early period to 1960 it had been accepted by all the professional institutions that the possession of a university engineering degree was automatically acceptable as a membership qualification. (Later, even that route was under Institution 'control' for standards acceptability, through the introduction, nationally, of degree-course Accreditation).

During those first sixty years of the 20th century the Scottish colleges and universities had to survive the severe disruptions and staff overloading through two world wars and the Great Depression of the 1930s. These serious set-backs which naturally killed any hope there might have been to develop research programmes, seemed not to have affected the basic content of the electrical engineering curriculum which, until the end of World War II, had been biased heavily towards machines and power supply topics. This weighting was entirely appropriate when preparing graduates for employment in the well-established electricity supply industry in Scotland or in the larger manufacturing firms. But the growth of a very different light-current industry during the 1950s called for a marked change to their electrical engineering curriculum if the colleges and universities were to provide the new electronics companies, like Hewlett-Packard, Motorola and MESL, with more appropriately educated graduates. Fortunately, this call for change to a more balanced light-heavy mix corresponded with an influx of new, young staff additions in the colleges and universities in Scotland, many with good training in the modernised armed forces, others from industrial research departments, who were themselves eager to introduce new ideas into the courses. Additionally, post-graduate research programmes were at last able to be encouraged so that, by 1960, research became an expected feature in all Scottish universities and the CIs.

It will be seen in Section (ii) of this chapter just how determinedly the universities and CIs responded to the call for change and how remarkably the 'traditional' boundaries of Electrical Engineering were expanded or even brushed aside in later decades of the 20th century.

References

1. *The History of Scottish Education*, Vol.2, by James Scotland.
2. *Scottish Education 1696-1946*, by H M Knox, publ. Oliver and Boyd, 1953.
3. *Technical Education*, by P E R Venables, publ. G Bell & Sons, London, 1955-
4. *A History of the Institution of Electrical Engineers 1871-1971*, by W J Reader, publ. Peter Peregrinus Ltd, London, 1987.
5. *The University of Glasgow 1451-1951*, by J D Mackie, publ. Jackson, Son & Co, Glasgow.
6. *Engineering at Edinburgh University 1673-1983*, by Ronald M Birse, publ. The School of Engineering, University of Edinburgh, 1983.
7. *The Fusion of 1860: A History of the United University of Aberdeen 1860-1960*, Ed. by Douglas Simpson, publ. Oliver & Boyd, 1963.
8. *Aberdeen University 1945-1981*, Ed. by John D Hargreaves, 1990, publ. Aberdeen University Press.
9. *University Education in Dundee: A Centenary History*, by Donald Southgate, publ. Edinburgh University Press, 1982.
10. *University Education in Dundee 1881-1981*, by Michael Shafe, publ. University of Dundee, 1982.
11. *John Anderson's Legacy*, by John Butt, publ. Tuckwell Press with University of Strathclyde.
12. *Dundee Institute of Technology: The First 100 Years*, publ. Dundee Institute of Technology, 1989.
13. *RGIT past, present and future, 1903-1978*, publ. RGIT Aberdeen, 1978.
14. *Forward by Degrees: the University of Paisley 1897-1997*, by Evelyn Hood, publ. University of Paisley, 1997.
15. *History of a Faculty*, by C A Oakley, publ. University of Glasgow.
16. *Scienta et Opera* by RB Strathdee, publ. RGIT Aberdeen, 1971
17. *A Decade of Progress 1964 - 1974* Publ. University of Strathclyde, 1974

Some IEE Scottish Knights

Sir Edward MacColl (1888-1951)
Deputy Chairman and
Chief Executive NSHEB (1943-51)

Sir Robert Watson-Watt (1892-1973)
inventor of RADAR, Superintendent
Radio Research Station, Slough

Sir George Macfarlane (1916-)
Director of Royal Radar
Establishment, Malvern,
Deputy President IEE,
Director of British Telecom

Sir Donald McCallum (1922-)
Director & General Manager Ferranti
Ltd, President Scottish Council
(Development & Industry)

Sir Duncan McDonald (1921-1997)
Chairman Northern Engineering
Industries plc

Admiral Sir Lindsay Bryson (1925-)
Controller of the Navy

(ii) Electrical and Electronic Engineering Education 1960 - 2000
by David King BSc, DipER, CEng, FIEE

A Growing Discipline

An Honours BSc graduate in Electrical Engineering from Edinburgh University in 1960 would have completed a three-year full time course. The whole of the first year and more than three-quarters of the second year was taken in common with mechanical and civil engineers. Only the second year Electricity course and the third year material were exclusive to the electrical students. The words transistor, digital logic or computer did not appear in any of the taught material but the student would have experienced a few lectures in electronics which were based on thermionic valves.

However, a new era was dawning for future Edinburgh graduates, as the BSc course had just moved to four years full time, with the additional year allowing space for new material like transistors. Similar moves were taking place in the other Scottish tertiary educational centres with Glasgow University changing its Ordinance to a three-term, four-year BSc in session 1959-60.

The forty years since 1960 have experienced the birth of the computer age and the explosive growth in electronics and communications applications. In 1960 Electrical Engineering was generally a small part player, in comparison to Civil or Mechanical Engineering, with fewer staff and students. The growth in staff and students over the last forty years has completely changed the position. Electrical Engineering is now the big player in the Engineering disciplines and in the Universities. At **Strathclyde University** the department of Electronic & Electrical Engineering is currently the largest in the University with 46 academic staff, over 600 undergraduate and 200 postgraduate students. In 1960 Edinburgh produced four BSc(Hons) Electrical Engineering students while in 1999 the figure was 67 BEng and MEng, Honours Electronics and Electrical Engineering students.

What's in a Name, University or College or Central Institution?

Strathclyde University (formerly the Royal College of Science and Technology) and the **Heriot-Watt College** both obtained University status in the mid 1960s. They joined four other Scottish Universities, Aberdeen, Edinburgh, Glasgow and University College, Dundee (which was then attached to St. Andrews University) where students could obtain full time degrees in electrical engineering. At this time **Dundee Institute of Art and Technology**, **Robert Gordon's Institute of Technology** and **Paisley Technical College** ran courses leading to a degree equivalent electrical engineering qualification. In the 1960s the Universities gave very little encouragement to part-time undergraduate study. They offered little or no courses or formal work in the evenings and did no sub-degree work. The Scottish Colleges Napier, Glasgow, Dundee, Paisley and Robert Gordon's took on board the part-time teaching of students studying electrical engineering through day-release or evening study for Ordinary and Higher National Certificates (ONC and HNC) and Higher National Diploma (HND) awards.

With the expansion of higher education the Colleges were encouraged to increase the number of their students studying at degree level. The power to award degrees is incorporated in the charter of a university so the Colleges did not by themselves have the power to grant a degree. As part of the expansion of higher education a new UK wide body was established which was not a university, but had a charter to award degrees. This body, the **Council for National Academic Awards (CNNA),** could validate courses submitted to it. By the early 1980s all of the above Scottish Colleges had electrical engineering degree courses which were CNAA approved (1).

Initially, Scotland did not use the term 'Polytechnic' and the Colleges were termed **Central Institutions (CIs).** In Scotland the CIs formed the one half of what became known as the 'Binary System' of Education with the universities making up the other half. In 1992 both Napier College of Science and Technology in Edinburgh and the Royal College of Science and Technology, Glasgow were allowed to call themselves Polytechnics and in 1993 they were given charters to become universities in their own right. Napier Polytechnic became **Napier University** and Glasgow Polytechnic became **Glasgow Caledonian University**. The charters for **The Robert Gordon University**, the **University of Paisley** and the **University of Abertay, Dundee** quickly followed. Reference is now made to "old" and "new" universities within higher education and there is no longer a binary divide.

BSc or BEng or M.Eng or Sandwich

Due to continuing new developments engineering is a dynamic subject which never stands still. The name given to the degree awarded to electrical graduates has also changed over time. For example, a 1960 graduate from the Heriot-Watt would have been awarded an

Associateship in Electrical Engineering from the Heriot-Watt College. By 1966 the award would be a BSc in Electrical Engineering from Heriot-Watt University. In 1983 the undergraduate award for four or five years study would be either a BEng or a MEng in Electrical and Electronic Eng. The BEng and MEng titles came about as a result of the Finniston Report (1980) (2), which reviewed the education and training of chartered engineers. The change to Electrical and Electronic Engineering was due to the Heriot-Watt University changing its departmental name to reflect the growth of electronics. Similar name changes to include electronics were made by most of the other electrical engineering departments in Scotland. **Aberdeen University** is unique among the older universities in that it has maintained its single Department of Engineering with an integrated engineering department structure and a commitment to a broad-based degree.

To try to ensure that the CNAA courses and the institutions offering them were not seen to be simply copying universities, strenuous efforts were made to design courses which were different from those offered by the universities. One very obvious difference was to include an industrial training element in the course structure. The industrial training was 'sandwiched' between periods of academic study, so these courses were called **sandwich courses**. They were either 'thin sandwich' where there were two periods of twenty weeks in industry or 'thick sandwich' where there was one forty-eight week period in industry. Consequently these courses were one year longer than the corresponding full time courses (1).

Course Developments - from the 'And Gate' to the PC

For the last decade of the millennium one has come to take the all-embracing nature and intrusion of digital computers into one's daily life for granted. Since the digital computer is a piece of complex electronic equipment, how the hardware is manufactured and operates is naturally something which is now well covered in university electronic engineering courses. The flow of the relevant material into both undergraduate and post-graduate courses began gradually but very quickly became a flood. Digital logic gates and integrated circuit technology first appeared in course material in the late 1960s and computer hardware courses and the minicomputer in the early 1970s. The terms chip, microprocessor and microcomputer started to make regular appearances in examination papers in the late 1970s. 16-bit microprocessors and the first PC (personal computer) were on the scene by 1980 and by the mid-1980s PCs were no longer just a topic covered in lectures but had become an educational tool.

The acquisition of departmental computing equipment mirrored the evolution of new course material. In the 1960s the author's department could access the Heriot-Watt University's Ferranti SIRIUS Main frame using punch card equipment. Around 1969 the Department of Electronic and Electrical Engineering purchased its first mini-computer, a Honeywell H316, which was accessed by a paper tape reader and was used as a specialist piece of laboratory based equipment. A Digital Equipment PDP-45 minicomputer was obtained in the early 1970s and this was given a dedicated room and operated in a multi-access capacity for staff and student use.

By 1980 the facility had been enhanced and staff could access the departmental computing facilities from a terminal in their room. By the late 1980s the terminal had been replaced by a PC on each member of staff's desk from which they could also access the departmental main frame, large number-crunching computer facilities, libraries and the **world wide web**.

Software

The term software was not used when the author took his first programming course as a post-graduate student on the Diploma in Electronics and Radio at Edinburgh University in session 1960/61. The language used was called *Autocode* and was used to programme a Ferranti Pegasus computer. His next encounter with software was with *Machine and Assembly code* with mini computers and microprocessors in the late 1960s and 1970s. The languages FORTRAN, BBC BASIC, PASCAL and C all found favour within electrical departments, at one time or other, from the 1970s into the 1990s, as departmental facilities became more powerful and numerous. Almost all the electrical students graduating in the last twenty years will have come in contact with the computer operating system called UNIX. **Fred Heath** became Scotland's first Professor of Computer Engineering at Heriot-Watt University in 1971. He brought the DEC PDP-45 minicomputer to the 'Watt' and was responsible for sending the author to the USA in 1974 to meet up with Messrs Ritchie and Thomson (the developers of UNIX) at Bell Telephones, New Jersey. As a result of this meeting Heriot-Watt became the first university in the UK to run UNIX.

Undergraduate Studies

During the 1970s the developments in computing, digital electronics, microprocessors and microelectronics produced an explosion in new course material relevant to electrical engineers. Existing course structures were adapted to include much of the new material and many academics of this period will well remember the arguments about removing existing course material to accommodate new material on, for example, operational amplifiers. Chemistry was an early casualty on many courses while Physics and Mechanics also suffered large cuts in course hours. One dropped course, which the author has fond memories of, went under the title of 'Student Lecture'. This was a course at the Heriot-Watt at which every third year student had to stand, in front of the rest of the year and give a twenty minute talk followed by questions on a non-electrical topic of their own choice. Non technical topics were encouraged and the author can remember sitting in on topics such as Bee-keeping. Many former students will remember being questioned on their talk, by **George Boal**, who organised the course for many years. George reckons that he must have listened to about twenty different talks on Seine net fishing, which seemed to be the favourite topic of the Norwegian students. George also remembers a very interesting talk by **Roy Leitch** (now a Professor at Heriot-Watt) about his travels around the world in the late 1960s long before such journeys became fashionable.

Although a lot of the new material found its way into optional courses in the third and fourth years of the mainstream electrical engineering courses it soon became apparent that more specialist courses were required to cover the full range of electrical engineering. Early examples of such innovations were Heriot-Watt's BSc in Computer Engineering and the BSc in Offshore Engineering which produced their first graduates in 1976. In the 1980s and 1990s the technical developments brought about by the computer and the microelectronic revolution produced ever increasing job opportunities and an increasing numbers of students entering electrical engineering. Competition for the students encouraged departments to

(a) design specialist courses with titles that included the buzzwords like mechatronics

(b) design attractive multi-disciplinary courses with other sister departments.

Typical examples of the above are the BEng in Mechatronics from **Abertay University** and the BEng in Electronic Engineering and

Physics from the **University of Glasgow**.

Scottish part-time students aiming for IEE recognition were catered for when Glasgow College, in the 1980s, started and obtained IEE accreditation for a multi-disciplinary suite of BEng courses. The course took five years with students attending one day a week for a full twelve-hour day from 9.00am until 9.00pm. The long day did not stop the dedicated students travelling from distant parts; one student made the weekly return trip from Inverness.

Postgraduate Studies

There were few post-graduate course opportunities for students in the 1960s and the vast majority of the students who stayed in higher education after their first degree studied for a MSc or PhD by research. Things quickly changed in the following decades and first degree graduates are now spoiled for choice in terms of post-graduate Diploma and MSc course opportunities both full and part-time.

An early course well worthy of mention was the MSc/Diploma Course in Digital Techniques Heriot-Watt. This course started in 1969 as a two-year part-time course when the digital revolution was still in its infancy. Industrialists were consulted on both the course structure and content and the course was designed to attract students working in local industry where the nature of the work was moving steadily from an analogue to a digital base. The course, which operated on Fridays during term time from 2.00 p.m. until 7.00 pm, was very successful and at its peak, in the mid-1970s, it attracted an annual intake of over 80 students. The majority of the students came from the local East of Scotland firms such as Ferranti, Hewlett Packard and Marconi but others travelled from Glasgow firms like Barr and Stroud. The course was one of the earliest MSc courses run off campus, when in 1971, at the request of a number of electronic firms in Fife, it started in **Glenrothes Technical College**. It ran in parallel with the Friday course with the four hours of Friday lectures being repeated in two-hour slots on Tuesday and Thursday evenings. Three cohorts of students took the course over the six years that it ran in Glenrothes. From the early 1970s the course has also been run as a one-year full-time course and over the past twenty years many of the graduates from this course have gone directly into research positions in the Heriot-Watt University's Department of Electronic and Electrical Engineering. The course still runs in 1999 with much of the original structure intact under the title of **MSc in Digital Systems Engineering**.

Bernard Howard was the first organiser of the course and a great deal of its success was due to Bernie's energy and the enthusiasm with which he covered the subject material. It was not surprising that many former students often refer him to with affection as 'Mr Digital Techniques'.

In the early 1980s government funds were made available through the Science and Engineering Council to mount **Information Technology MSc** courses for students who had graduated from non-computer based disciplines. Most of the Scottish electrical engineering departments took advantage of the funds and included an Information Technology course of some form in their course portfolio. The Information Technology route allowed a number of the CI's to gain experience of post-graduate course work. The range of MSc/Diploma courses now available in 1999 is highly impressive - MSc in *Information Systems* from Robert Gordon, MSc in *Electronic Circuit Design* from Dundee, MSc in *Mechatronics* from Abertay, MSc in *Computer Communications* from Napier, MSc in *Maintenance Engineering* from Glasgow Caledonian and MSc in *Electronic Product Design for Manufacture* from Paisley plus a selection of other titles from the old Universities.

Driving Forces

Over the last forty years a number of individuals have made highly important contributions to the tertiary education sector in Scotland. In choosing only two such individuals for a mention it is appreciated that there are several others who but for lack of space would be well worthy of a mention.

John Lamb, arrived at Glasgow University, as Head of Department and James Watt Professor of Electrical Engineering in 1961. With his eight-strong team of researchers and a van load of equipment from Imperial College, London he set to work on viscoelastics, microwave materials and devices, control and computing and power systems. Under his inspiring and far-seeing leadership he took his department into new areas of research in integrated optics, molecular beam epitaxy of semiconductors, ultra-small electronics and optical structures, bioelectronics and power electronics. His death in December 1991 was a great loss to the university. (3).

W.E.J. (Ewart) Farvis (4) became the first occupant of the Chair of Electrical Engineering at Edinburgh University in October 1960 and held the post until his retiral in 1977 when Jeff Collins succeeded him. In September 1948 Farvis had been appointed to be 'Lecturer in Applied Electricity' which was the first specific teaching appointment in electrical engineering at Edinburgh, so Farvis can certainly be looked upon as the Edinburgh architect of electrical engineering with his establishment of the new

and separate Department of Electrical Engineering on 1st January 1961.

Prior to 1960 Farvis's main area of research was in gaseous electronics, however, in the early 1960s he moved his and the new department's research into, the more industrially relevant, solid-state devices and materials science areas. Integrated circuits were in their infancy and Farvis recognising their potential decided to take the bold decision, in April 1964, to concentrate the research work of the department in this area. As the staff complement was gradually expanded during the 1960s and 1970s this focused approach necessitated the selection of new academic staff whose interests were in microelectronic devices and fabrication. In 1964 the Department was awarded its first research contract by the Department of Science and Industrial Research into thin film microelectronic devices and in 1966 the University Court made £14,300 available to allow the construction of a clean room for solid state integrated circuit processing.

Farvis clearly recognised the importance of industrial links and armed with a new clean room, in October 1967 he started a Microelectronics Post-Graduate Retraining Course. The course was the first Microelectronics course from a UK university. It was modular and specifically designed to suit industry. The lecturers were, in the main, specialists from industry and industrial specialists also supervised the laboratory instruction. An expert from Bell Labs in the USA was flown over for a week to teach the latest CAD chip layout developments. The course attracted no academic award, however, it ran successfully for three sessions and was much appreciated by the fee-paying industrial participants since the material covered was highly relevant and much sought after at the time.

Farvis continued to foster industrial links and in 1968 he obtained a five-year, £130,700 'pump-priming' grant, from the Wolfson Foundation to establish a Microelectronics Liaison Unit. This unit operated alongside the department with a remit to encourage academic-industry interactions and its establishment allowed the appointment of two part-time Visiting Industrial Professorships and additional professional staff. The Liaison Unit, which soon developed an international reputation as a centre of microelectronics expertise, was renamed the Wolfson Microelectronics Institute in 1978 and floated as the private company *Wolfson Microelectronics* in 1985.

During the 1960s the department grew in both size and stature and in 1970 **J.H.Collins** became the department's second professor when he was appointed to an SRC research professorship which was subsequently converted into a personal chair in 1973. Collins established new research activities in signal processing with acoustics and magnetic devices, which complemented the existing microelectronic activities. By 1975 the department was an international leader in the vertical integration of microelectronic systems  from their design through fabrication to application. For the past twenty-five years the department has maintained its microelectronics international reputation. During this period growth has increased with support grants which are now measured in £millions.

Ewart Farvis retired in 1977 but he was still active for several years as a consultant with industry and giving service on government bodies as well as IEE committees and working parties.

Research

Research work has always played an important part of the work of the 'older' universities and since the 1960s research funding has been a major force in feeding the growth in departmental staffing. By contrast, the CI's received very little research funding as their prime role was seen to be one of teaching and training. However, all of the accredited BEng courses, within the CI sector, were required by the IEE to be supported by research work and some useful work was conducted with minimal funding. Now, the 'new' universities' departments are building on this experience to gradually increase their research bases.

University of Glasgow

The promotion of research work into integrated optics and molecular beam epitaxy by John Lamb has been mentioned earlier and it is difficult to pick out particular individuals within teams of researchers over a thirty year span. However, **Professor Chris Wilkinson** is mentioned for his excellent research with Electron Beam and X-rays and his contribution to the Nanoelectronics Research Centre. **Professor Peter Laybourn** and **Professor Richard De La Rue** have done excellent research in the integrated optics area. **Professor TJE Miller** created the SPEED (Scottish Power Electronics and Electric Drives) Laboratory in 1987 and the laboratories electric motor design work is a good example of the co-operation of academia and industry. Glasgow has also carried out good quality research in Systems Engineering and Bio-Electronics.

University of Edinburgh

Edinburgh currently has first class research groups in Silicon Technology, Integrated Systems, Signals and Systems, Energy Systems and a Centre for Communication Interface Research. Edinburgh has been active in microelectronics research since 1968 and is recognised world wide as a leading centre. In 1978 the Edinburgh Microfabrication Facility was established to act as a foundry supplying customised integrated circuits for research. Recently, a new £4.2 million building has opened which forms the core component of the Scottish Microelectronics Centre and keeps Edinburgh in the forefront of microelectronic research. Over the years Edinburgh's facilities have supported many excellent researchers one of particular note being **Professor Peter Denyer** for his work with CMOS imaging chips which resulted in the 'spin off' company called *Vision* with its single chip colour camera.

Strathclyde University

Strathclyde, as the university with the largest number of electrical engineering academics, has built up a first class research record over a broad section of the electrical/electronic sector. The research is organised through a number of Centres and Divisions. The research carried out by the **Centre for Electrical Power Engineering** (CEPE) has been built up over a thirty year period under the leadership of **Professor David Tedford** and **Professor Owen Farish**. In 1996 Rolls-Royce set up its University Technology Centre in Power Engineering to operate in parallel with the CEPE and in the same year the CEPE won the Queen's Anniversary Prize for Further and Higher Education. In recent years the research work of the Communications Division under the leadership of **Professor John Dunlop** and **Professor Geoffrey Smith** has blossomed with excellent work on mobile telephones and ATM networks. Other strong research areas are the Industrial Control Centre, the Optoelectronics Division and the Signal Processing Division.

Heriot-Watt University

Heriot-Watt was conducting low cost underwater vehicle research before oil was found in the North Sea. The oil discovery brought the funding which laid the foundation of much of the research carried out in the last thirty years. Three successive heads of department, **Professor Gordon Nicoll, Professor Colin Davidson** (Chairman IEE Scotland 1976-77) and **Professor George Russell,** encouraged this research which has now moved into related fields such as under water robotics, applications in computer vision and intelligent control systems (ref. Chapter 3).

Good research work has also been done on microwave ferrite devices and microwave arrays.

The above four universities have the biggest research groups however, over the past forty years all of the other universities have made significant research contributions. In the 1960s the Satellite Receiving Station at **University College, Dundee** produced the first television weather maps from satellite images. Dundee also produced good research by **Dr Arthur Cruickshank**, on reluctance motors, and **Professor Brian Makin** on Electrostatics.

The more recent work at the **University of Aberdeen** by **Professor James Penman** on Condition Monitoring and **Professor Spracklin** on network protocols is well worthy of mention.

Among the 'new' universities the School of Electronic and Electrical Engineering of the **Robert Gordon University** is the largest electrical section and it is active in research over a broad field. This School recently completed a major project to measure the earth's gravitational field by sending experiments into space on the NASA Space Shuttle.

With their history of part-time students the 'new' universities all have strong industrial links and most of the work they do would be classified as industrial research. Much of the collaboration with industry is around specialist units such as the **EMC Centre** at the **University of Paisley** and the Advanced Materials Centre at **Napier University** or it is channelled through the Teaching Company Scheme (TCS).

The start of the new millennium sees tertiary education well set to be in the forefront of future world research and development with the establishment of the **Alba Centre** in Livingston. This centre is a collaboration of government, industry (Cadence Design Systems) and four Universities (Edinburgh, Glasgow, Heriot-Watt and Strathclyde). It will deal in system-on-chip (SoC) technology and will lead the way in world class research into System Level Integration and the retraining of graduates to use the SoC technology.

Quality Assurance and Assessment - Quality Assessment of Teaching and Learning

In 1992 the binary divide between the 'old' universities and the CIs was removed and all the Scottish Tertiary Educational Institutions received their funding from the **Scottish Higher Education Funding Council (SHEFC)**. The drive for efficiency and value for money resulted in a quality assessment process where each subject cognate area in the universities was examined by teams of SHEFC assessors. In Scotland the cognate area of Electrical and Electronic Engineering was one of the first subjects to be assessed with the SHEFC assessors visiting the departments during 1992/3. The SHEFC Reports were published in June 1993. On a three-point scale of excellent, satisfactory or unsatisfactory, three Universities, Edinburgh, Heriot-Watt and Strathclyde, obtained excellent ratings for their teaching and learning while the other eight universities obtained a satisfactory rating (5). Overall, the teaching and learning of Electrical and Electronic Engineering within the Scottish Universities came out with a good clean bill of health. Preparing for and taking part in the assessment process was found to be very resource intensive and to date the quality assessment process has not been repeated.

Research Assessment

Government research funding is finite and in 1986 and 1989 the University Grants Committee, and in 1992 and 1996 SHEFC (the government bodies responsible for distributing the research funds) conducted research assessment reviews. These reviews provided a subject rating of the quality of an institution's research work and subsequent research funding is distributed taking this rating into account. In the Electrical and Electronic Engineering subject category the Universities of Edinburgh, Glasgow and Strathclyde have all consistently performed well in the reviews. In the latest 1996 review Edinburgh, which has always achieved a top rating, was one of three

UK Universities with the top 5*A rating which equates the research quality to attainable levels of international excellence in the majority of the sub-subject areas. In 1996 Strathclyde was also rated in the international excellence area with a top 5B rating (6)

IEE Accreditation

Around 1960 most of the Scottish higher educational establishments which produced graduate or graduate equivalent electrical engineers moved to four year full-time courses. Students graduating with a BSc(Ordinary) or equivalent qualification in Electrical Engineering from these courses met the existing entry educational requirements for Corporate Membership of the IEE. From 1974 Corporate Membership of the IEE also allowed registration as a **Chartered Engineer (CEng)** with the **Council of Engineering Institutions (CEI)**.

In a response to the Merriman Report (1978) (7) the educational entry requirement for IEE Corporate Membership was raised in 1982 to a 2nd class honours degree or equivalent. At the same time the IEE moved to a more formal arrangement and set up an Accreditation Committee to inspect the standard of courses that wished to have accreditation. Electrical Engineering Departments who wanted their students to meet the minimum IEE educational standard were invited to apply to have their courses accredited. The application was followed by a two-day accreditation visit to the department by a small group of experienced IEE members from the Accreditation Committee. If a department's application was successful then the course would normally receive accreditation for a four- or five-year period.

In response to the Finniston Report (1980) and the Council of Engineering Institutions Standards and Routes to Registration (SARTOR) document the accreditation requirements have received further alteration. Courses are now expected to be BEng degrees and must incorporate within their curriculum the practical Engineering Application (EA) elements of EA1 and EA2. The more practical oriented courses at the 'new' universities took the inclusion of the EA element in their stride while some of the more theoretical courses at the 'old' universities needed more adjustment to maintain accreditation. The Merriman Report introduced the concept of the **'enhanced' M.Eng Degree** and stated that it should be the future minimum acceptable standard for corporate membership. Merriman thought that a decade from 1978 would be a suitable timescale for the new higher educational standard to be applied. SARTOR 97, the recently published Engineering

Council document, lays down a new standard of a minimum educational level of MEng or equivalent for future CEng registration. As this standard will apply from early in the new millennium it has taken more than two decades, not one decade as suggested by Merriman.

Over the past forty years the Scottish University Departments of Electrical Engineering have had a good record in obtaining and maintaining IEE accreditation of courses designed for students who wish to progress to CEng status. SARTOR 97 sets out a new challenge and all Universities, 'old' and 'new', will redesign their courses to meet the minimum MEng or equivalent standard.

References

(1) Unpublished Essay on Public Sector Higher Education, Peter Bainbridge, 1999.

(2) Finniston Report: *Engineering our Future*, Department of Industry, 1980.

(3) Obituary - Professor John Lamb by Peter Laybourn, *The Independent* Newspaper, 23rd Dec.1991.

(4) Typed notes on History of Electrical Engineering at Edinburgh, Peter Grant, circa 1983.

(5) Report on Quality Assessment in Electrical and Electronic Engineering, SHEFC, June 1993.

(6) 1996 Research Assessment Exercise The Outcome Unit29, NISS-Joint Funding Councils of UK, 1996.

(7) The Merriman Report: *Qualifying as a Chartered Electrical Engineer*, IEE Publication, 1978.

(iii) The Scottish Electrical Training Scheme (SETS)
- a personal view

by Douglas S. Deans BSc, C.Eng, MIEE, Dip.EE

The Scottish Electrical Training Scheme (SETS) was set up in January 1957. It was the brainchild of far-seeing engineers and academics including **Duncan McDonald** of Bruce Peebles Ltd, **Eric O Taylor** Assistant Professor of Electrical Engineering, Heriot-Watt College.

It provided a unique opportunity for graduates in Electrical Engineering or Applied Physics to gain their required two-year graduate-apprenticeship training here in Scotland instead of otherwise having to apply to one of the large manufacturing firms in England such as British Thompson Houston or Metropolitan Vickers, possibly never to return to Scotland.

About ten member companies collaborated by pooling their individual training resources therby providing new graduates with the opportunity of sampling several different working environments prior to making an informed choice of permanent employment with one of the member companies. Young graduates thus obtained training and experience in a wide range of modern engineering expertise in such as power generation and distribution, installation, marine systems, machine and transformer design, cable manufacture, advanced avionics, instrumentation and control.

During their first year the graduates became full-time employees of SETS and spent periods of training with four or five of the member companies, by choice and arrangment with the SETS Chief Executive, who tailored the training to suit the expressed interests of each graduate intake. Towards the end of their first year each trainee would apply for a post with the member company of his choice to complete his second year of 'in-company' graduate training.

Although at that time it had no offices, no students, no trainees and no concrete administration planning, it had appointed its first Organising Secretary **Major General JEC McCandlish CB, CBE, CEng, MIEE**. Throughout the subsequent years John McCandlish would prove to be the driving force and, as averred by one of the Governing Directors, 'the architect and master builder of SETS'.

The SETS in association with its Members provided the practical part of the training required by those intending to become professional electrical engineers (Chartered Electrical Engineers). It was operated by the SETS organisation on behalf of the members.

The original structure, which changed little in the subsequent years, comprised John McCandlish as Chief Executive and Secretary with a small secretarial staff working in offices at 127 St Vincent Street, Glasgow. The management team included a board of governing directors, one being provided by each member company, and a group of advisory directors made up mainly of eminent academics from many of the Scottish universities and colleges. Finally there was the Executive Committee always referred to as *EXCO*. This committee usually met monthly and comprised the personnel from the member companies and academic world who were directly involved with student training. *EXCO* members were the students' contact personnel at university or whilst training with one of the member companies.

The operation and activities of the member companies covered all aspects of electrical engineering in Scotland and students could experience training in manufacturing, both heavy and light current, generation, transmission, distribution and contracting. In giving this training SETS was able to provide the route to attractive careers in electrical engineering in Scotland for many graduates. By assessing each member company's needs in employing graduates the numbers of trainees for each year could be determined. In other words no more graduates would be accepted than the total requirement of the members' needs and in that way, subject of course to satisfactory reports, all graduates completing training were assured of a career with one of the member companies. I doubt if nowadays one could use words such as 'assured' and 'guaranteed' in relation to employment and careers.

My own happy association with SETS began in early 1965 and little did I realise at the time how much it would shape and influence my future life and not all from an engineering standpoint. My electrical engineering studies for the first three years took the form of a sandwich course. The courses, very popular in these days, closely linked the academic and practical aspects of engineering, something that I came to appreciate more in subsequent years. The benefits that SETS could offer to students was a fully planned, but nevertheless, a flexible training programme for the entire academic period. The pattern of training given was that recommended by **The Institution of Electrical Engineers**. It was divided into three distinct phases (described later) but these divisions were not rigid and time spent on each phase could be adjusted to suit the ability and progress of each trainee. In my own case the

SETS training programme admirably fulfilled the stricter requirements of the sandwich course and the heady incomes from a summer on the buses was left to our student colleagues from the less stringent Universities.

As mentioned above one great asset of SETS was the diversity of work of the member companies and the opportunity for trainees to experience a wide range of electrical engineering activity before committing themselves to a particular branch of the profession. During my four years with SETS there were nine member companies and the wide range of their expertise can be seen from their names listed below.

    The Belmos Company Ltd.
    Bruce Peebles & Company Ltd.
    Ferranti Ltd
    The Harland Engineering Company Ltd.
    Honeywell Controls Ltd.
    James Kilpatrick & Son Ltd.
    North of Scotland Hydro-Electric Board.
    Scottish Cables Ltd.
    South of Scotland Electricity Board.

SETS Conference 1958, *courtesy Prof.WEJ (Ewart) Farvis*

Given that each of the companies could offer training in design, production, development, research and sales, it can be seen that the scope and quality of training was endless.

Vacation Training - three phases

As previously mentioned training programmes were set up in three distinct phases but with flexibility to accommodate personal ability and progress. The three phases of vacation training would be completed prior to graduation. The first phase was a period of basic workshop training during which knowledge was gained, both in theory and practice, of materials and machine tools used in the industry. The second phase developed and expanded this knowledge and trainees gained experience of a wide range of manufacturing, operating and testing duties in both mechanical and electrical engineering. As this developed students would begin to appreciate the work and responsibilities associated with professional status. Finally, the third phase was a period of objective training directed towards equipping the trainee for his first executive post. Typically students would be working in engineering offices, development laboratories and undertaking junior engineering duties.

Graduate Training

After completion of vacation training and following successful graduation a further full year of graduate training would then be undertaken with SETS. Again flexibility was the key and if a graduate was still uncertain as to where his or her interest might lie then training could be carried out with a number of selected member companies. Usually, however, after three years vacation training graduates had already chosen their particular career and after discussion would join the appropriate company for the full year's training. Invariably this would be followed up with a full-time post in the company. My own training followed that format as I had decided before completion of my studies that I wanted to pursue a career in electrical installation design and contracting and so my graduate training was with **James Kilpatrick & Son.**

I had completed three years vacation training and was a few months away from commencing my year's graduate training when Mr. McCandlish retired. On the 1st May 1968 **Mr Dennis Smith CEng, FIEE, MIE Malaysia** took over as Chief Executive and Secretary.

SETS was unique. It provided electrical engineering careers or the stepping stones to those careers for hundreds of electrical engineers in Scotland and at the same time enabled the member companies to be assured of a good flow of well-trained graduate engineers to meet their own needs. I have understandably, in a book of engineering history, emphasised SETS engineering attributes, but it gave more than that. As a SETS trainee or graduate you were a member of a family. There were social events, graduate days and a wide range of activities. As has often been said there is more to being an engineer than academic excellence and perhaps it was the SETS family that provided these other all-important ingredients.

SETS influence

I mentioned above that SETS influenced and shaped my life as well as my career. In 1967 I undertook a period of vacation training with Bruce Peebles Ltd and on the first day reported, as one does, to the Company Engineering Training Officer, **A Dawson** [his then secretary Miss Mary Smith will, by next year, have been Mrs Deans for 30 years!]

Finally, let me close this nostalgic look at SETS much as I started with a reference to JEC McCandlish. His every action was for the good of SETS. Everything he did influenced SETS down to his unique way of numbering paragraphs in his letters, a clear throwback from his Major-General days. When writing for the last time in the renowned SETS Bulletin issued to commemorate his years with the organisation I will always remember him signing off ' I am, Sir, your obedient servant.' It was to be the last time I ever saw that written. He was indeed an officer and a gentleman, he was of the old school, but more importantly he *was* the *Scottish Electrical Training Scheme*.

The Dissolution of SETS

Over the years some of the original companies left the scheme and others joined. Also the coverage was extended, and the title was broadened to the *Scottish Engineering Training Scheme*. Sadly, however, after privatisation of the electricity supply industry the South of Scotland Electricity Board withdrew its membership as from 31st December 1990. At the 141st and final meeting of the Board of SETS, under the chairmanship of **James Beckett**, on 23rd March 1992 the board resolved to have its name struck off the Register of Companies.

Chapter 3

(i) Frontiers in Electrical and &Electronic Engineering Research in Higher Education
edited by
Professor DJ Tedford OBE, OM(Poland), FRSE, CEng, FIEE

Introduction

Like any centenary, that of IEE Scotland could be treated as an abstraction, a categorising of dates in its history and that of related bodies. In a very real sense, however, it focuses attention on what has become a living tradition, a large number of organic units formed not just by a long line of pioneering innovators who in the past shaped industries and universities, but also by the many engineer researchers of to-day whose extensive work will be self-represented later in this chapter.

Research in electrical engineering over many decades has shown itself to be ready to investigate any problem and keen to produce new advanced devices, even when it meant redefining its locus. To refer to boundaries in this context could be quite facile, as it is well known that most of the research in universities had been centred around electrical power until after the manifold military successes of radio, radar, and countless other electric wonders in the second world war. Thereafter, the all-pervading influence of electronics was accorded explicit recognition and grew profoundly. The broad Electronic Age followed the Radio Age, and within two decades 'electrical' research in departments all over the country was covering a range of disciplines from electromagnetism, geophysics and radio astronomy at one end, through surface physics/chemistry and biophysics, to control theory and optimisation, artificial intelligence, computer design and robotics at the other, to name but a few.

There are now no distinct borders in this eclectic field, especially in an age where fax, voice mail, and e-mail have blurred the edges of continents and time zones. Multimedia technology has allowed interaction with computers through a combination of all forms of presentation (text, graphics, sound, touch etc.), and is resulting in the blending of major industries such as computing, broadcasting, entertainment, consumer electronics, education, filming, and so on. The home TV set can now also be a powerful computer system, and e-commerce is becoming a *sine qua non* at every level. Communications and IT developments alone, in hectic cross-disciplinary research activity, are leading to profound redefinitions of such concepts as community, library, banking, and even university itself.

Another internal challenge that has been successfully overcome is that relating to the two major categories of devices (based on physics and engineering) and systems (based on mathematics) which were once distinctly separate. In the latter, mathematical modelling is at the core, with areas such as control, signal processing, communications and computing as crucial components; and in all of these our universities have made notable contributions. The devices side, by tradition (for example in semiconductor and component manufacture), has had a much larger empirical content, and experience and experimentation have often been used to produce a trial processing system which could then be fine-tuned to good effect and at relatively low cost. However, as capital costs in manufacturing have soared, so also process yields had to be dramatically improved. This has provided good reasons for our researchers to explore the applications of sophisticated signal processing and control techniques to the materials processing and manufacturing scene. The establishment in 1998 of the Alba Centre, including the Institute for System Level Integration (SLI) with four major universities involved, was a major front-edge Scottish initiative to drive the future of electronic design with advanced commissioned research, professional development training, and post-graduate education in SLI and System-on-Chip (SoC) Technology.

Thus the field is ever challenging and almost without bounds, and from the frontiers of our university laboratories, as each academic research group briefly speaks for itself below, one can reflect on the trends of the recent past, the problems of the present, and the visions of the future. For further detailed information you are invited to visit the individual university/department websites and/or contact the researchers involved.

University of Aberdeen Department of Engineering

History

The Department is the only Integrated Engineering Department in the Scottish system, and although it is part of a University now in its sixth century, it was founded as recently as 1922. For the next 50 years the principal focus of the Department was in the areas of civil and mechanical engineering, and it was not until 1972 that the first professor of electrical engineering, Professor JF Eastham, was appointed. In 1985 Professor CT Spracklen took up the first Chair of Electronics. Since then, the Department has been active in all these areas of engineering research, building upon the particular opportunities that the Departmental structure provides for interdisciplinary work, and developing a close relationship with the offshore oil and gas industry. The current Head of Department is Professor J Penman who is an electrical engineer and there are three other professors of electronics and electrical engineering in post - Professors Player, Spracklen and Vas.

Current R&D Activity (in E&EE)
The Intelligent Motion Control Group: Leader – Professor P Vas.

Research in methods for the sensorless control of electrical machines and drives, particularly via techniques employing vector control and direct torque control through the use of fuzzy systems and genetic algorithms.

The Condition Monitoring Research Group: Leader – Professor J Penman.

Application of methods based on higher order spectra, wavelets and neural computing to improve the operational performance and availability of industrial plant and processes.

The Electronics Research Group: Leader – Professor T Spracklen.

Development of satellite and mobile communications protocols; the silicon implementation of large neural arrays for real world problems; the development of parallel algorithms for fast signal and image processing; and the development of a holographic camera for deep ocean recording of biological diversity.

The Engineering Physics Group: Leader – Professor M Player.

The microstructures of polycrystalline thin films; laser induced breakdown spectroscopy for non destructive testing; ultrasonics and signal processing; and impedance tomography for characterisation of cores.

Special Research Units
The Scottish Offshore Materials Centre is currently being commissioned by the Department for research into instrumentation and materials performance under conditions of high temperature and pressure. This is possible through a grant of £773,000 from SHEFC,

and is aimed at the new challenges being encountered by the oil and gas industry. It will bring together the expertise across all areas of the Department, and will result in increased collaboration with our supporters in the project at Edinburgh University (Geology) and Heriot-Watt University (Petroleum Engineering). The case for the Centre received wide support from the industry.

Active Links with Industry

The Department has strong industrial connections in all areas, and has developed them significantly in recent years through mechanisms like the DTI-funded Teaching Company Scheme (TCS). There are 12 such schemes active in the Department, and it is acknowledged by DTI to be the most successful TCS activity in the UK transferring technology to the oil and gas industry. Examples of the schemes include the use of neural computing and artificial intelligence methods to improve operational performance (with AMEC Process and Energy), and the development of high speed signal processing for sonar systems (with Fugro UDI).

Most research is supported and driven by industrial requirements. Other examples include:

The Holomar Projects - in collaboration with Quantel of France and Nemko of Norway.

Work on Sensorless Drives - supported by GEC Traction, Control Techniques Ltd and Texas Instruments.

The GRANIT Project – which won a John Logie Baird Innovation Award in 1998 and for which the Department received a Millennium Product Award in December 1999. Involves the use of signal processing techniques to test the integrity of ground anchorages and rock bolts. It is the subject of major licensing agreement with AMEC Civil Engineering.

The Department is currently involved in research projects sponsored by 24 different industrial organisations.

Research Active Personnel (whole Department)
Academics 33; Research Fellows 31; Research Students 58.
Research Grants (whole Department)
Currently Number >50; Total Value £4.25m.

(Submitted by Professor J Penman)

University of Abertay Dundee
School of Science and Engineering

History

Research in amorphous semiconductors was introduced in 1972 by Dr J Marshall who established a group producing some of the first PhD graduates in the then College. In 1987 he moved to a Chair at the University of Wales at Swansea. Charles Main, one of Dr Marshall's former colleagues at Edinburgh, joined the group in 1981 and the Edinburgh link was continued with the appointment of Steve Reynolds to a lectureship in 1987.

In 1983, Allan Gillespie and Peter Martin joined the UK Free Electron Laser (FEL) project and subsequently participated in the development of the highly successful FEL at the FOM Institute of Rijnhuizen near Utrecht. A few years later, Allan Gillespie established a research group in optical signal processing and photonics.

Research in electrical power became established during the 1980s through Leslie Crowe's work on distribution systems, then extended into electromagnetics and motor design with the arrival of Chinniah Rajanathan from Imperial College in 1986. Suheyl Ozveren came from Durham in 1990 to carry out work on decision support systems for power system planning. The University has a long tradition in mechatronics through the pioneering work of John Milne and latterly through the extensive modern work of David Bradley who arrived in 1998 from the University of Wales at Bangor.

Current R&D Activity (E&EE)

Photonics: Leader – Professor A Gillespie

Optical information processing – object recognition using optical correlators, display technologies and display characterisation, human factors engineering – presentation of information in control rooms, the requirements capture phase of the design process. The EPICentre has been recently established for research and technology transfer in these areas.

Industrial relevance: helping engineers design systems to present information in a manner that is easy to assimilate, e.g. in lap-top computer displays, control room design.

Amorphous Semiconductors: Leader – Dr C Main

Modelling and experimental research into the electrical conduction processes in thin film amorphous and organic semiconductors. Si:H pin structures, transient and modulated photocurrent density of states spectroscopies, high stability solar cells.

Industrial relevance: developing technologies underpinning the design of new types of solar cell sensors and displays.

Electrical Machines: Leader – Dr C Rajanathan

Electromagnetics. Finite element modelling of shaded-pole motors aimed at supporting customised design to meet client specifications. Development of novel linear actuators incorporating dsp control for positioning systems.

Industrial relevance: development of motors for domestic applications such as vacuum cleaners and highly reliable actuators for use in industrial control and vending machines.

Electrical Power Systems: Leader - Dr S Ozveren

Applications of neural networks and expert systems to power system engineering problems as well as the development of comprehensive decision support systems for power system planning. Industrial relevance: development of systems to aid electricity supply companies predict demand and so deploy their generation assets in a cost effective manner.

Signal Processing: Leader – Mr A Sapeluk

The development of speaker recognition and verification systems using neural networks and dsp platforms.

Industrial relevance: voice control of instruments, for example, for use by surgeons in operating theatres, providing an alternative to PIN numbers for bank auto-teller machines.

Mechatronics: Leader – Professor D Bradley

The application of systems engineering to a wide range of practical problems, for example, artificial intelligence governor for a hydro-electric power generating plant, intelligent networked healthcare systems, the development of an autonomous robot excavator.

Industrial relevance: increased efficiency of power station operation, provision of enhanced level of care for people living in sheltered accommodation.

Special Research Units

EPICentre (Electronic & Photonic Information Control):

A research and technology transfer centre for physical and human factors associated with display technologies; complex supervisory control in a remote distributed sensing environment; secure fault-tolerant advisory systems. Funded by a SHEFC Research and

Development Grant, European Regional Development Fund (ERDF) and Scottish Enterprise Tayside.

MIST Centre (Manufacturing & Intelligent Systems Technology):
A research centre for mechatronics and engineering design, and for providing support for technology transfer in product design, development and manufacture. Funded by ERDF, Dundee City Council and Technology Ventures.

Active Links with Industry:
Spin-off Company – Voice & Signal Systems Ltd
Teaching Company Scheme with TVI Europe
Design of electric motors with Turk Electric
Working closely with members of Tayside Engineering Forum and Scottish Enterprise Tayside to develop flexible part-time engineering course provision (BSc Engineering and MSc Mechatronics with Project Management).

Research Active Personnel
Academics 10; F/T Research Students 10
Research Grants (from all sources)
Currently Number 13; Total Value £1.44m.

(Submitted by Professor P Martin)

University of Dundee
Department of Applied Physics and Electronic & Mechanical Engineering

History
Electronic and Electrical Engineering has a long and distinguished history at the University of Dundee, having been established shortly after the original foundation of the University in 1882. Prominent among the earliest professors was Sir James Alfred Ewing, well known for his pioneering work on instrumentation and cryptography and for his contribution to the establishment of the discipline in Japan. Later in the twentieth century the Department played host to vital radar research under the leadership of Sir Robert Watson-Watt who had himself been educated at Dundee. More recently the Department has attained international renown for the development of the amorphous silicon solar cell and the thin film transistor (TFT) by Walter Spear and the late

Peter LeComber. These devices resulted from their ground-breaking achievement in discovering that amorphous semiconductors can be successfully doped, and helped to establish the current multi-billion dollar market in flat-panel displays.

Current R&D Activity

Research in electronic and electrical engineering is conducted in a multi-disciplinary environment, and as such it benefits from expertise in physics, chemistry and materials science, as well as from the traditional disciplines.

Remote Sensing and Environmental Monitoring: Leader – Professor AP Cracknell

Combines expertise in satellite communications, instrumentation development and data analysis. The Group is renowned for its contributions to environmental applications, including the development of climate models and studies of erosion in coastal regions.

Analytical Electron Microscopy and Surface Analysis: Leader – Professor AG Fitzgerald

Uses its extensive range of surface analytical and electron microscopy equipment to elucidate the behaviour of a large number of materials, including amorphous silicon, synthetic diamonds, and high temperature superconductors. It has also made fundamental contributions to the quantification of microbeam analysis.

Materials Research: Leader – Professor JA Cairns

Concerned with the design and fabrication of advanced photomasks (including X-Ray masks) for the production of next-generation integrated circuits and also with the production of gas sensors using micro-fabrication technology combined with the incorporation of novel chemical compounds.

Amorphous Materials: Leader – Dr RAG Gibson

Builds on the strong traditions of amorphous silicon research in the Department to extend its expertise into developing methods for the production of improved thin film amorphous silicon devices and also into the commercially important area of large area electronics.

Micro-engineering: Leader – Mr BL Lawrenson

Makes use of the excellent departmental lithography facilities, housed in specialist clean rooms, to fabricate complex structures of micrometre dimensions in order to produce novel sensors and also to study fundamental phenomena, such as the measurement of interfacial stresses between metals and silicon.

Applied Electrostatics: Leader – Professor B Makin

Investigates electrostatic aspects of micro-fabrication, in which materials processing, using finite element techniques for analysis of electrostatic fields, is directed towards the production of micro-sensors with medical and surgical applications.

Medical Engineering: Leader – Professor J Hewit

Collaborates closely with colleagues in medicine and surgery to develop improved instrumentation. Of particular interest is minimum access (so-called 'keyhole') surgery and advanced robotics, the latter having the potential to play a major role in the operating theatre of the future.

Organic Semiconductor Research: Leader – Dr DJ Goldie

Investigates the use of thin film organic semiconductors for a range of applications, including large area imaging and displays, chemical sensors, and biosensors. These applications depend on a detailed understanding of the mechanisms involved in the electronic transport properties of the materials.

Electron Spectroscopy: Leader – Dr DJ Keeble

Uses electron magnetic resonance to study the properties of a range of electronic materials, including diode structures. It also employs the technique of positron annihilation to probe thin films, such as ferroelectrics.

Artificial Intelligence Techniques: Leader – Dr B Ramsay

Including neural networks, the research is directed to a range of applications, such as combined heat and power systems and advanced manufacturing methodologies.

Special Research Units

Advanced Materials Centre:

This is being set up in collaboration with Scottish Enterprise, in order to assist with the transfer to industry of some of the potentially exploitable research generated within the group. This includes technology for the production of advanced photomasks and X-ray masks, which will be required for the production of next-generation integrated circuits.

Active Links with Industry

Department has a long history of interaction with industry, covering a wide range of applications. Special links include:

Compugraphics International (photomasks)

Zeneca (organic semiconductors)

Merck (liquid crystals)
Philips, Xerox (amorphous silicon)
BP (photovoltaic and memory devices)
British Telecom (memory technology)
NCR (cashpoint machines)

Research Active Personnel
Academics 17; Research Fellows 17; Research Students 17
Research Grants (from all sources)
Total Value (1996-99) £4.75m (mainly from EPSRC, SHEFC and industry).

(Submitted by Professor JA Cairns)

University of Edinburgh
Department of Electronics and Electrical Engineering

History

The Department of Electrical Engineering was formed in 1960 with Professor Ewart Farvis as the first holder of the Chair of Electrical Engineering. By 1967, cleanrooms had been constructed to establish a research facility for the fabrication of solid state integrated devices and an associated postgraduate diploma in microelectronics. The 1970s saw the growth of microelectronics research within the department including the setting up of the Wolfson Microelectronics liaison unit which was founded to provide a direct integrated design service for industry. The arrival of Professor Jeffrey Collins initiated a research programme in analogue signal processing and research in microfabrication was enabled with the £10 million support grant from SERC to help acquire world class equipment for VLSI microcircuit technology. The two decades of 1980s and 1990s have shown the growth of the Department in a wide range of electrical engineering disciplines at research level and the creation of both research institutes and limited liability companies.

The main commercialisation activities by members of academic staff are the spin-out of Wolfson Microelectronics Ltd in 1985, the founding of VLSI Vision Ltd in 1990 (acquired by ST Microelectronics in 1999), and the formation of Elektrobit UK in 1999. Several others of our graduates have their own companies. In 2000, it is planned to open the Scottish Microelectronics Centre (SMC), a new £5m purpose-built campus building for microcircuit processing and commercialisation of our microelectronics research via the associate company. The quality of the Department's research can be judged by its being continuously top rated in the UK Research Assessment Exercises in 1989, 1992, 1996, finally being awarded the coveted 5* accolade plus 1st Prize in the 1996 OST Industry/Academe Collaboration Competition.

Current R&D Activity

Centre for Communication Interface Research: Leader – Professor MA Jack.

This is a multi-disciplinary research institute which undertakes collaborative research and development in all of the essential components of the speech and language communication technologies including speech and natural language processing, speech language understanding, dialogue engineering, interactive multimedia and virtual reality.

Integrated Systems: Leader – Professor AF Murray.

Its activities fall into four inter-related areas, viz., neural computation, analogue VLSI, VLSI image sensing and processing, and digital system design. The group has strong interests in the neural field, both in software and hardware innovations and also in the development of image sensors fabricated using standard CMOS technology.

Silicon Technology: Leader – Professor AJ Walton.

This group covers the activities across a broad spectrum of microelectronics ranging from technology CAD to deep sub-micron devices. In addition to the process and device research related to silicon IC technology, it is also active in the field of amorphous silicon and scanning electron microscopes.

Signals and Systems: Leader – Professor B Mulgrew.

The research is focussed on fundamental signal processing theory for a wide range of applications. A major aspect of the sustained effort on nonlinear signal processing algorithms has been a move from multi-layer perceptron structure to radial basis function network for which a systematic method of training has developed.   The group also has interest in adaptive array processing for airborne radar and for CDMA communication systems, and has participated actively in the Mobile VCE, a multi-university virtual centre of excellence in mobile and personal communications.

Energy Systems: Leader – Professor HW Whittington.

The group's activities are broadly divided between policy studies and the development of hardware and software in the field of electrical power systems. Geographically the work has covered a wide range including United Kingdom, European continent and a range of developing countries. The group has particular expertise in the design and implementation of small-scale hydroelectric schemes. Within the area of power electronics, the specific interests include electronic power supply, design and manufacture.

Special Research Units
The Centre for Communication Interface Research (CCIR).
Microelectronics Image and Analysis Centre (MIAC)
ALBA Centre for System Level Integration (collaborative venture)
Scottish Microelectronics Centre (SMC)
Scottish Energy and Environment Institute

Active Links with Industry
There are many industry links; the following are indicative:
CCIR collaborates with over 200 European companies in the DIALOGUES project
Mobile VCE involves collaboration with 24 companies or providers of mobile cellular services.
Numerous individual research contracts and teaching company schemes with microelectronics manufacturing, electronic,
communications, and radar companies.
Research Active Personnel
Academics 31; Other Research Staff 47; Support Staff 22; PhD Students 50
Research Grants (from all sources)
Average Annual Value for 1996 to 1999 is £2.7m.
(Submitted by Professor P.M. Grant)

Glasgow Caledonian University
Department of Engineering

History
Research stemmed from a modest beginning in the early 1970s at the then Glasgow College of Technology when only a few of the academic staff were research orientated. Their work reflected particular interests centred on signal processing and high voltage engineering. Since then,

and following various metamorphoses, research activity has expanded to cover a wide range of fields in Electronic & Electrical Engineering where >60% of the academic staff are now regarded as research active.

Current R&D Activity (in E&EE)

Although there are specific areas of research interest, the Department prides itself in its ability to provide a flexible response to research/development problems and prefers not to "categorise" research active staff. The work within the electrical/electronic area tends to be application orientated and, as such, often involves multi-disciplinary teams, reflecting different ranges of skills. Examples of this include:

The Insulation Diagnostic Group: Leader – Dr IJ Kemp

The Group has research interests ranging from fundamental investigations into the mechanisms of degradation of solid insulating systems (primarily polymerics) to the development of novel instrumentation systems to monitor the condition of insulating systems of high voltage plant under in-service stress conditions. This range of work involves, at one end of the spectrum, staff with a strong physics/chemistry background, and at the other, staff with strong signal processing/software development skills. In addition, the development of novel sensors/transducers can involve the application of a very diverse range of skills in this research area, e.g. electromagnetic skills in anatomic design and development.

Intelligent Technologics Group: Leader – Dr BJ Beggs

Within this research grouping, staff, primarily with backgrounds in electronics and communication, have addressed a range of research/development problems. One example of this has been the development of strategies/instrumentation to monitor street lighting and communicate degradation and failure to a central monitoring site. They have also been very active in researching and developing security systems and, specifically, for intruder recognition and detection.

Other areas of research interest within the electrical/electronic domain range from power electronics research (dc brushless motors) and power systems analysis on the electrical engineering side to advanced signal and antenna research on the electronics side. However, the preferred option is not to categorise these into groups.

Active Links with Industry

Most research is funded by external sources, primarily by industry with which the Department has developed numerous industrial contacts over the years. A good example of this is the link with the National Grid Co plc which has recently yielded more than £500,000 of direct funding for research into new strategies/instrumentation for condition monitoring of high voltage plant. However, this is just one example and others can be seen on our website.

Research Active Personnel (E&EE)
Academics 16; Research Fellows 2; Research Students F/T 10, P/T 10
Research Grants (from all sources)
Currently Number 12; Total Value >£1m (primarily from industry and EU)
(Submitted by Dr I. Kemp)

University of Glasgow
Department of Electronics and Electrical Engineering

History
Research in the Department has arisen from various drivers. One important driver was the establishment of device fabrication techniques (semiconductor layer growth, lithography and dry etching) initially for integrated optical devices (starting around 1972). A programme to find the limits of electron beam lithography (1980) led naturally to applications and so to research into high speed electronic devices. The provision of a large area electron beam machine (1990) completed the array of technologies necessary for a world class fabrication facility. The application of this fabrication technology to biology and medicine (starting in 1982) opened the world of bioelectronics.

Current R&D Activity
Nanoelectronics Research: Convenor of Management Committee – Professor C Wilkinson
Covers a range of related studies, including:
Ultrafast Systems (Dr I Thayne)
Design, fabrication and characterisation of high speed III-V semiconductor devices and monolithic integrated microwave circuits at frequencies between 44 and 150 GHz. Application are in communications and mobile phones.
Atomic Force Microscopy (Dr J Weaver)
Microscopy using a scanning probe is giving a new glimpse into the

world of the very small. Generic ways of making the probes so that optical, magnetic and temperature information can be acquired on an atomic scale have been developed.

Quantum Transport (Drs J Williamson and A Long (Physics)

Quantum mechanical effects become more evident in device characteristics as device sizes and operating temperatures are reduced. The behaviour of nanometre sized devices is being investigated with the ultimate aim of incorporating them in integrated circuits.

Dry Etching (Professor C Wilkinson)

Dry etching is used by industry to transfer patterns into semiconductors. The research group has developed new processes that avoid dry etching damage and the science behind why they do so.

Molecular Beam Epitaxy (Professor C Stanley)

Semiconducting films of precisely defined doping density and layer thickness are grown by Molecular Beam epitaxy. Present research includes growth of shallow modulation doped layers for high speed devices and 500 layer structures for cascade lasers.

Electron Beam Lithography (Dr S Thoms)

Development of electron beam lithography to its ultimate resolution and reproducibility.

Device Modelling (Dr A Asenov).

The aim of semiconductor device modelling is to predict the performance of realistic devices accurately. Efficient manufacture depends on good models so that device design can be right first time.

Optoelectronics Research: Convenor of Management Committee – Dr J Marsh

The objective is to develop technologies for optoelectronics which emulate the success that silicon-based electronics has achieved with integration: increasing speed, reliability and functionality. Themes are: high-speed semiconductor lasers; single frequency lasers; high power lasers; extended cavity semiconductor lasers; modulators, switches and amplifiers; and control of the band-gap of a semiconductor optical waveguide, allowing the fabrication of photonic circuits on a single chip. Several groups are involved:

Nonlinear Optics (Dr C Ironside)

In non-linear optics, the intensity of the optical wave changes the optical properties of a material. GaAs/GaAlAs based material has been used to demonstrate all-optical switching, spatial and temporal propagation, mode-locking and gain due to polarisation coupling.

Planar Silica Micromaching (Professor Stewart)

Silica on silicon is a flexible technology for integrated optics with many potential applications. In collaboration with BT Labs, rare earth doped glasses for lasers and amplifiers have been developed. The hybrid integration of such devices with silicon micro-machined structures and CVD diamond films for sensor and packaging applications are also under development.

Photonic Band Gap Materials (Professor R De La Rue)

Photonic Arranging atoms in a periodic array produces crystalline material with different properties to the original atoms; similarly an array of structures cut into an optical material produces material with new properties. Opals and insect wings are examples that occur in nature: here they are being used to make better lasers and to suppress non-wanted modes in antenna feeds.

Theory and Modelling of Optical Devices (Professor J Arnold)

Theory and simulation occupy important roles in the activities of this research group, with a particularly high level of interaction with experimental research both within the University of Glasgow and with external collaborators. The group has active programmes in nonlinear optics (semiconductor theory and laser dynamics) and applied electromagnetics.

Bioelectronics Research: Leader – Professor J Cooper

Covers the following activities:

Biological Sensing (Professor J Cooper)

Nanofabrication is particularly suited to this area since the dimensions of fabricated structures and of biological molecules are of the same order of magnitude. To make diagnostic devices, it is necessary to modify a transducer surface (e.g. any electrode or a waveguide) with a biological molecule (e.g. an enzyme or an antibody) such that any degree of molecular recognition between the biological molecule and a sensed species will be communicated as a signal. Integrated electrochemical and optical biosensors have been developed in the group. This area of biochips is the subject of intense industrial interest.

Biological Manipulation (Dr H Morgan)

Forces can be exerted on biological cells using electric field gradients from micro-electrodes-dielectrophoresis. This phenomena is being applied to the automatic sorting of cells and viruses of different types and to a more complete understanding of the dielectric properties of living matter.

Cellular Engineering (Professor C Wilkinson and Adam Curtis (IBLS)).

Biological cells are strongly influenced by the topography of the surface on which they lie and this topography can be formed using nanofabrication. For example, a biodegradable membrane, patterned with narrow grooves by embossing has been developed as a prosthesis for the repair of tendons.

Control and Systems Engineering: Leader – Professor D Murray-Smith
Research in this area is organised on a Faculty basis. Two themes are active in the Department of E&EE:

Analogue VLSI (Professor J Sewell)
Work on simulation tools for switched-networks and mixed-mode systems has produced very versatile and efficient software suitable for analysis of large systems containing many nodes and utilising numerous clock waveforms. These suites of simulation programs are supplied commercially to companies.

Evolutionary Computing (Dr Yun Li)
The application of ideas from biology has proved very successful in producing new strategies for control and communications and is attracting strong industrial interest.

Power Electronics: Leader – Professor TJE Miller
Electro-mechanical components are controlled by electronic circuitry to produce more efficient machines and systems. The SPEED group produces motor design software that is used worldwide by leading manufacturers. Present research covers high speed brushless motors, and reluctance motors, both synchronous and switched.

Special Research Units

Centre for Systems and Control. Faculty wide
Centre for Economic Renewable Power Delivery. With E&EE Strathclyde, SHEFC funded.
Centre for Cell Engineering. Virtual Centre in collaboration with the Institute of Biological Sciences and the Department of Orthopaedics at University of Glasgow and the Department of Applied Chemistry and the Bio-engineering Unit at the University of Strathclyde.
Institute for System Level Integration. Part of the ALBA project and established jointly with Edinburgh, Strathclyde and Heriot-Watt universities.
Centre for Systems and Control. Set up by Glasgow University (GU) with members from E&EE, Mechanical Engineering and Computer Science Departments
Centre for Device and Process Modelling. Funded by GU to expand

links with the semiconductor industry, particularly in Scotland. A wide range of commercial software has been donated to it.

Centre for Music Technology. Funded by GU to promote research and support laboratory work in joint degree with Department of Music.

KNT Ltd. Wholly University-owned company undertaking commercial contracts in nanofabrication area.

CST Ltd. Joint Glasgow University/Strathclyde University company for research and limited scale production in optoelectronics.

Active Links with Industry

KNT Ltd, CST Ltd and the Centre for Device and Process Modelling have very strong connections with external commercial companies as they are direct suppliers of R&D as well as products.

Some other examples are:

GEC-Marconi Materials Technology, Caswell is the only UK supplier of III-V MMICs and fruitful links have developed in recent years.

Joint research programmes exist with DRA Malvern and Thompson-Thorn Missile Electronics.

Motorola has shown considerable interest in the Department's scanning probes, and thermo-couple probe with 50 nm resolution was tested in Arizona.

In Optoelectronics there are strong interactions with Hewlett-Packard, BT, Mitel and Siemens.

In the Healthcare and Pharmaceutical area cooperation is largely with Glaxo-Wellcome, Unilever, Kodak (UK), Smith and Nephew, and Johnson and Johnson.

Modelling research is carried out in collaboration with Motorola, Siemens, IBM, and Mitel Semiconductors, and the major vendors of simulation software – Avant and Silvaco.

Research Active Personnel

Academics 38.5; Research Assistants 57; Research Students 95.

Research Grants (from all sources)

Currently number 60; Total Value £13.9m.

(Submitted by Professor C.Wilkinson)

Heriot-Watt University
Department of Computing and Electrical Engineering

History
Education and training of Electrical Engineers was established at Heriot-Watt College around 1890. By the mid-twentieth century, a substantial department existed, resulting from the work of Professors MG Say and EO Taylor.

In 1966, the College was granted its University Charter and the Department of Electrical and Electronic Engineering was further expanded under Professor GR Nicoll. The move from Chambers Street to the new Mountbatten Building in 1966 saw growth in postgraduate courses and extensive research. The discovery of North Sea oil stimulated research on underwater vehicles, close relationships with the local electronics companies encouraged radar and microwave systems, and industry funded a high-voltage laboratory under the direction of Professor B Salvage. By 1980, GT Russell had established the Subsea Automation research area, Professor J Helszajn Microwave Engineering, Professor AJ Sangster Radar Antenna research and Professor FG Heath Computer Engineering. Research activity covered a wide range of funded programmes with a large complementary postgraduate teaching programme, and Professor CW Davidson had introduced a five-year MEng course.

The next decade saw significant acceleration of research in machine vision, robotics, intelligent systems and image processing. Professor SJ Yang created a new activity in micro-machines and Professor RR Leitch strengthened his work on intelligent systems. The area of power electronics was introduced with the appointment of Professor BW Williams, and an industrial Chair was funded by NCR to which Professor RJ Clarke was appointed.

The present 'joint' Department was formed after the move to the Riccarton Campus in 1992. Recently the appointment of Professor DM Lane has continued the tradition of subsea automation. The research work continues to expand, the latest developments being in micro technologies and system level integration, together with multi-disciplinary work on imaging systems.

Current R&D Activity
The Department has 7 research groups:

Micro-Engineering: Leader – Professor AJ Sangster

Incorporating electrostatic micro-actuators, integrated microwave antennas, miniature microwave integrated circuits and VLSI devices for, in particular, minimally invasive medical applications. The group is also involved in the development of optically interconnected electronics for high speed integrated circuits.

Electrical Power: Leader – Professor BW Williams

Concerned with high performance induction motor control, snubber energy recovery for power semiconductors, neural networks applied to switched reluctance motor torque ripple and noise reduction, control of electrodynamic actuators for vibration test applications, integrated electro-mechanical modelling of marine propulsion systems, combined AC and DC transmission for offshore oil and gas fields and high voltage electrostatic deposition for abrasive products.

Intelligent Systems Engineering: Leader – Professor RR Leitch

The Intelligent Systems Laboratory (ISL) pursues the synthesis of Artificial Intelligence and Control Engineering approaches to the design and implementation of industrial control systems. It has pioneered the development of a design methodology and approaches to modelling that integrate qualitative and quantitative simulation techniques for model based systems for industrial fault diagnosis, control and training.

Oceanic Systems Engineering: Leader – Professor DM Lane

The Ocean Systems Engineering research group has made major contributions to the interdisciplinary research areas of image processing and interpretation, intelligent control of automated processes, sonar systems and image communication systems. The generic procedures that have evolved have been applied to other areas including radar signal recognition, infra-red image modelling and medical X-ray analysis. Associated with these is significant research activity in Video Image Coding.

Database and Information and Knowledge-Based Systems: Leader – Professor MH Williams

This work includes: database functionality – dealing with object-oriented databases, active databases and spatial database systems; parallel databases - covering performance prediction for parallel database systems and the development of appropriate tools for application sizing, capacity planning and performance tuning; medical information systems - with research in the area of telemedicine, and natural language explanation of medical record data for patients; multimedia/web applications - with research on the MAN to support interactive learning and the development of a framework to create learning environments; and distributed interactive simulation – with data handling strategies for distributed interactive simulation.

Computer Vision: Leader – Professor AM Wallace

Research covers three main aspects:

(i)   *Computer Vision* - involving the development of innovative depth sensors, co-operative intensity and range processing for 3D object recognition and location, parallel algorithms, sensor planning, genetic programming, adaptive control and motion analysis. Applications include subsea robotics, the fisheries sector (fish grading processes), and imaging and metrology for the aerospace industry;

(ii)   *Image Analysis* – including spatial modelling of sidescan sonar data, the application of fractals in data fusion and sonar modelling, subsea and seismic data analysis, infra-red image generation and mission planning, and textural analysis and segmentation. Expertise has been applied to paper fibre analysis, medical imaging, ice floe classification, inspection of road surface defects and sub-surface radar imaging; and

(iii)   *Visualisation* - of 2D and 3D data for human-computer interaction and to aid human solution of problems concerned with image analysis.

Dependable Systems: Leaders – Professor F Kamereddine and Professor R Pooley.

This Group has an interest in all problems involved in the construction of robust, efficient, correct and predictable systems. It focuses on; foundations - especially logic type theory and term rewriting, particularly the use of types in optimisation within functional language compilation and the study of languages that bridge theory and practice; functional programming – functional environments, tools and methodologies for parallel and distributed programming; performance modelling – including work in future communications networks and optoelectronic network based computing with BT, and in the integration of performance modelling with software design methods; automated reasoning and formal verification – in particular the application of proof planning to the verification and synthesis of software and hardware.

Special Research Units

Image Analysis Centre (IAC):

Set up in conjunction with DERA

Microsystems Engineering Centre (MISEC):
   Provides facilities and infra-structure for inter-disciplinary and inter-departmental research in microtechnology with emphasis on systems level integration on a chip, microwave electronics, microelectronics, integrated opto-electronics and micro-mechanics.

Active Links with Industry
   The Department has numerous collaborative research programmes with UK and EC industry in particular, funded primarily by the UK Research Councils, the European Community (through ESPRIT, MAST, FAIR and Copernicus), the DTI and other government organisations, and directly by industry alone.
   Recent funding partners include: DERA; Adobe; Optos; Centre for Marine and Petroleum Technology; NATO; Scottish Enterprise; PWM Drives; GEC Plessey Semiconductors; Royal Society; De Beers Marine; 3D Scanners; 3Com Europe; Thomson Sintra; Hewlett Packard; Scottish Office; NHS in Scotland
   Recent research partners include: British Aerospace; Ultralife Batteries; Guidant Europe (Belgium); ETEL (Switzerland); Cadence; Cray/SGI; Lockheed; IBM; US Navy; Unilever (Netherlands); BP; Shell; ENEL (Italy); GEC Marconi; Technatom (Spain); Labein (Spain); Cogsys; KCL (Finland).

Research Active Personnel
Academics 41; Research Associates F/T 45, P/T 41; Research Students F/T 48, P/T 47.
Research Grants (from all sources)
Current value of active grants:
EPSRC £1,736, 397; EC £880,678; Industry £408,302; Government £346,406; Other £12,000.

(Submitted by Professor R Clarke)

Napier University
School of Engineering (Division of Electrical Engineering)

History
   For several decades, the basic policy on research in Electrical Engineering at Napier University has been to reflect the dominant

industry in Scotland and in particular that in the Edinburgh area. Thus, when the dominant company was Ferranti, research was focussed on telecommunication engineering. Later, the availability of grants under the DTI ECAD initiative allowed research to spread into digital techniques and microelectronic design, and the emergence of Scotland as a world force in the field of electronics manufacturing demonstrated the need for research in this area. Most recently, the vulnerability of Scottish industry to changes in world trading conditions has shown that the development of indigenous R & D must be a top priority. The Technology Foresight Initiative showed that sensors and instrumentation was an area worthy of further research. Other UK-wide developments, such as environmental issues and privatisation of the electricity supply industry, have led to research into electric vehicles and electricity pricing.

Current R & D Activity

Electronics Manufacturing:

The Scottish Electronics Manufacturing Centre (SEMC) provides a research consultancy and pilot manufacturing facility for the Scottish electronics industry. Led by Professor Hunt, a major research project has developed competitive ball grid arrays in both hermetic and non-hermetic formats. Sensors and instrumentation work is led by Dr Binnie, the group's major work being in the area of smart sensors. One project completed was the development of a low-cost infrared camera on a chip.

Digital Techniques: Leader – Professor Almaini

Covers fundamental research into the synthesis and optimisation of digital systems with emphasis on Reed-Muller techniques.

Power Engineering:

Electric Vehicles: Leader – Professor S Gair

Vehicles for energy-efficient, emission-free transport.

Energy, the Environment, and Electricity Privatisation: Leader - Professor D Lidgate

Special Research Units

The Scottish Electronics Manufacturing Centre (SEMC).

Set up in December 1993 with funding from the EU STRIDE programme and Scottish Enterprise Ltd.

The Scottish Advanced Manufacturing Centre (SAMC).

Established at Livingston in 1997 jointly by Napier University, West

Lothian College and Lothian and Edinburgh Enterprise Ltd (LEEL) to provide training facilities for the Scottish electronics industry from craft to post-graduate level.

The Transport Research Institute (TRI)

This was the first Napier University multidisciplinary research pillar. The work on electric vehicles is done in conjunction with the TRI and a consortium of European Universities funded under the EU human capital and mobility programme. A number of other less formal links exist with other universities in Scotland and UK.

Active Links with Industry

In recent years most links with industry have been formalised through the DTI Teaching Company Scheme. Since the prime objectives of the scheme are to increase transfer of technology from academia to industry, and to improve the competitiveness of UK industry and the calibre of personnel entering industry, the Teaching Company Scheme is seen as of most benefit to the development of indigenous companies.

Research Active Personnel

Academics 8; Research Fellows/Assistants 4; Research Students 14 F/T, 15 P/t.

Research Grants (from all sources)

Current Total Value £935,000.

(Submitted by Professor D Lidgate)

University of Paisley

Department of Electronic Engineering and Physics

History

A former Scottish Central Institution, the University of Paisley was formed in 1992 from Paisley College of Technology which celebrated its centenary in 1997. In 1996, the Department of Electronic Engineering and Physics (EEP) was formed by the amalgamation of the former departments of Electrical and Electronic Engineering, and Physics. The mission has consistently been to deliver high quality, industrially relevant, undergraduate and post-graduate education to full-time and part-time students, preparing them to contribute rapidly to their employers' operations. The EEP Department maintains a close coupling with industry, through research projects, commercial operations, its BEng Hons sandwich placement year, and the University's Corporate Partners Programme. Electrical and electronic engineering research has thus developed in support of teaching interests and industrial contacts. Research activities have become more tightly focussed due to the action of the Research Assessment Exercise and are aligned with recommendations of the UK Technology Foresight exercise. Recent and current research activities have been supported by the Chief Scientist Office, the Engineering and Physical Sciences Research Council, the Scottish Higher Education Funding Council, charity and industry funding sources, and several have been nationally recognised by the John Logie Baird, Scottish Innovator of the Year, and SMART Awards.

Current R&D Activity (in EE)

Digital Signal Processing (DSP): Contact - Professor DR Campbell

Current research is aimed at improving the intelligibility of speech by Digital Signal Processing and from this gain information which can be used for the improvement of devices such as hearing aids, hands-free mobile 'phones and hands-free speech input devices.

Sensor Materials and Technology (SMT): Contact - Dr DF Clark

Research involving silicon micro-machining and sol-gel glasses aimed at the development of novel sensing devices to detect combustible gases and having importance for applications in petrochemical and automotive industries.

Electromagnetic Compatibility (EMC): Contact - Mr FS Galbraith

Research to obtain fundamental knowledge about the structural features at chip and board level, which directly influence the electro-magnetic (EM) properties and EM measurement of modern microprocessor devices. This is relevant to safety critical electronic systems in transportation and health care.

Thin Films (TP): Contact - Professor F Placido

Thin film research interests cover a wide range and utilise extensive in-house facilities for film characterisation and deposition. Applications include: dielectric mirrors for use in lasers, head-up displays, eye protection from lasers, and films that offer protective coatings in harsh environments.

Special Research Units

The Electromagnetic Compatibility Centre (unit of national importance)
The Thin Film Centre for Scotland (unit of national importance)
The Applied Computational Intelligence Research Unit (cross-disciplinary).

Active Links with Industry

Substantively these number 7, including:
EMC and DSP projects in collaboration with Motorola MOS Memory and Microprocessor Division.
Sensor projects in collaboration with GMI Ltd and IATROS Ltd.
Thin Films projects with Pilkington Optronics (Glasgow), Pilkington Space Technology (N Wales), RTC Ltd (England) and Deposition Science Inc. (U.S.A.).

Research Active Personnel

Academics 8; Research Fellows/Assistants 4; Research Students 5.5.
Research Grants (from all sources)
Currently number 8; Total Value £1.48m.

(Submitted by Professor D.R. Campbell)

The Robert Gordon University

School of Electronic and Electrical Engineering

History

In the 1970s there was a strong focus on research into *Reliability and Stochastic processes* led by the then Head of Department, Professor P Mars. This involved advanced control theory and the development of reliability simulators. Under the Headship of Professor FG McIntosh in the 1980s, this work continued to grow, and new strategic research areas emerged such as, *Condition Monitoring and Life Management of Electrical Drive Systems*. This research was of strategic importance to the North Sea Oil and Gas industry and Power Utilities in Scotland. In the 1990s, the present Head, Professor ND Deans, encouraged extension of the range of work to include such as High Performance Communication Networks, Protection and Control of Power Systems with Co-generation, and Computational Intelligence. There have always been strong research links with industry and major financial support from BP Exploration, Shell UK, ScottishPower and Scottish Nuclear for the Condition Monitoring work represents a typical example. Technology transfer has featured from the start, and in 1992 the product called *Motormonitor* was awarded the Queen's Award for Technological Achievement. Over 450 systems have now been sold worldwide and the University continues to receive related royalty payments.

Current R&D Activity

Condition Monitoring and Life Management of Electrical Drive Systems: Leaders – Professor WT Thomson and Mr DG Edwards

This has provided industry with on-line condition monitoring systems for diagnosing the health of strategic electrical drives. The new techniques have prevented failures, reduced downtime and operational losses, improved maintenance strategies and ensured the operational safety of drive systems.

Performance Monitoring and Management of Communication Networks: Leader – Dr RA Butler

To improve the quality of digital communications for a diverse range of services and networks including digital video and audio, ATM networks and broadband networks.

Protection and Control of Power Systems with Co-generation: Leader – Dr SK Salman.

The increased use of embedded co-generation schemes requires improvements to protection and control strategies and this is the focus of the research.

Dependable Systems: Leader – Professor ND Deans

This involves the creation of design methodologies which allow engineers to design-in the required level of dependability in the system at the start of the project and not as an afterthought.

Non-Destructive Testing for the Offshore Industry: Leader – Dr GPP Gunarathne

Involves the development of ultrasonic imaging techniques to examine scale deposits in down-hole systems used in the North Sea.

Reliable High Temperature Data Logging Systems: Leader – Mr KS Gow

To develop and design reliable high temperature (250 oC plus) data logging systems for down-hole tools in the oil industry.

Development of Techniques for the Condition Monitoring of Mechanical Structures: Leader – Dr JF Watson

To create and develop new monitoring techniques for mechanical structures such as cranes and bridges.

Computational Intelligence: Leaders – Dr C Macleod and Mr GM Maxwell

Investigating the response of neural networks to the environment in which they are operating.

Special Research Units
The Electrical Machine Monitoring Centre

Active Links with Industry
Typically 20, including:

Nan Gall Technology Ltd, Aberdeen, Waterweights Ltd Aberdeen Defence Evaluation and Research Agency, ScottishPower, Scottish Nuclear Shell UK, BP Exploration, Centrilift, Texaco Wood Group, ESL/Berl, Pheonix, Keatch Chem.

The links are predominately with the North Sea Oil Industry and associated service companies, and the major Power Utilities in Scotland.

Research Active Personnel
Academics 13; Research Students/Assistants 12

Research Grants (from all sources)
Number 10 over period 1997-99; Total Value £450,000.

(Submitted by Professor W.T. Thomson)

University of Strathclyde
Department of Electronic & Electrical Engineering

History
The Department's research history extends back to 1892 with Andrew Jamieson publishing on lightning protection, detectors for the Bell photophone and steamship lighting; so the Department's diversity is rooted in its very foundation. Its industrial links are similarly rooted; by 1917 the Marconi Company was sponsoring classes in Magnus McLean's department. Stanley Parker Smith succeeded Professor McLean and continued the "applicable research" tradition for over twenty years, setting up one of the first UK laboratories of intrinsically

safe design and enhancing the relationship between the University and local and national industries. He published not only with the IEE, but interestingly also in the Journal of the Institution of Civil Engineers; clearly an early multidisciplinary man.

The post war period continued to lay the foundations for what is now our Centre for Electrical Power Engineering, and in the late 1960s a new Department of Electronic Science and Telecommunications emerged under the leadership of Denis Taylor, formerly chief scientist with Plessey. At this stage though, telecommunications was an optional subject for final year studies. The early 1980s saw the two departments reunited, and there followed a vigorous expansion funded through the "Shift" programme which enhanced both the teaching activity and the research portfolio. The same traditions remain, applying physics and mathematics, encouraging technology transfer, but most of all stimulating a vigorous atmosphere for staff and students to flourish.

Current R&D Activity

The Department's research ethos is firmly rooted in exploring and establishing innovative principles and, where appropriate, pursuing these into industrial application. Its research portfolio spans the principal application sectors of electronic and electrical engineering - namely, energy in the environment, communications and signal processing systems, and sensor systems and control. The research encompasses the fundamental, the applied, technology transfer and licensing, and has stimulated several spin-out companies. Major groupings include:

Mobile Communications: Leader – Professor J Dunlop

The mobile phone will doubtless expand its presence and importance into high capacity services for internet, video and multimedia data all of which consume immensely more bandwidth than the familiar voice communication system. This group has pioneered adaptive techniques for bandwidth utilisation and in parallel the possible use of mobile networks in difficult environments, such as the underground railway. Some adaptive software algorithms are already being licensed to final users.

Broadband Communications: Leaders – Professor I Andonovic and Professor DG Smith

Fibre optic technology is the principal enabler for broadband transmission and current research here focuses on the study of optical transport layers in all optical networks, investigating the evolution of the network to the next phase of speed and traffic capacity through both wavelength and time multiplexing (Professor Andonovic). The broadband communications work also investigates traffic interactions on broadband systems and fault identification in very high speed networks (Professor Smith). Both these generic research areas feed into the design criteria for next generation networks through close interactions with both other academics and industrial institutions in Europe and elsewhere.

Signal Processing: Leader – Professor T Durrani

Embraces fundamental activities in algorithms and architectures using, for example, higher order statistics and wavelet transforms. Fundamental research has been applied to areas as diverse as mobile communications, image processing, seismic signal processing and biomedical signal processing. The resulting systems have found a wide range of applications in, for example, patient positioning, magnetic resonance scanning systems, material testing and noise and vibration control.

Industrial Control: Leader – Professor M Grimble

Covers the application of new techniques to model-based predictive control and H2 and H alpha systems to marine engineering, aerospace and power transmission and generation with demonstrated real gains in process efficiency. The group has also made fundamental progress in the use of non-linear adaptive techniques introducing new flexibilities into control system design and realisation.

Ultrasonics: Leader – Professor G Hayward

Includes transducer and array design for sonar, biomedical and non-destructive testing applications, mathematical modelling of ultrasonic data analysis and sensing for structural monitoring. The research is closely linked to industrial applications and is particularly recognised for its contributions to composite ultrasonic transducer design.

Optical Sensing Systems and Components: Leader - Professor B Culshaw

The research here deals with the development and application of novel sensing techniques for use in areas as diverse as monitoring high performance marine ropes and examining the chemical activity in biological cells. It is complemented by components related activity investigating novel optical sources for measurement systems including, for example, a wavelength flattened high power optical noise source for network testing and advanced guided wave modulators and switches particularly for use in optical routing and the control of sensor networks.

Industrially oriented projects examine sensing for hydrocarbon spillages, water ingress, methane gas and structural assessment in metals and composites.

Micromachined Optical and Mechanical Systems: Leader - Professor D Uttamchandani

Micromachining realises mechanical systems to submicron tolerances including structures such as vibrating elements for sensing and measurement, micromechanical optical routing systems and optically or electrically controlled micro pumps and analysis systems. These will enable a new range of techniques for chemical and biological analysis, optical signal control and high tolerance measurement.

Electrical Power Engineering: covers the following five major themes:

High Voltage Technologies: Leader – Professor O Farish

Here the areas of interest include pulse power technology with applications from laser power supplies to sterilisation systems exploiting subnanosecond pulse generation. In parallel, research on condition monitoring systems for power distribution networks (some in association with the spin-off company Diagnostic Monitoring Systems) examines very high bandwidth, high voltage and current measuring systems. Electromagnetic compatibility forms a third strand, focusing on EMC from large structures such as power switching systems and developing applicable theoretical models.

Electrical Materials: Leader – Dr A Fouracre

Focuses on measurement techniques and systems to assess degradation processes occurring in, principally, solid dielectric materials. Of particular importance have been studies on water treeing in power cables, the performance of insulation exposed to high and low energy radiation, gas discharges, solid insulator performance and conduction properties in polymers.

Intelligent Systems and Protection: Leader – Professor J McDonald

This research covers intelligent systems applications in power engineering for telemetry processing, scheduling and optimisation and integrated protection control and monitoring. Advanced sensors, especially for high power systems and notably those using optical technologies are being researched and evaluated. Power system control and operation to assess the dynamic response of system protection is being studied along with economics and planning, and including, for example, the impact of wide scale embedded generation on power system operation strategies. This work is closely integrated with the electrical power utilities and manufacturers.

Power Systems Research: Leader – Professor KL Lo

New tools and analytical techniques are being developed to better utilise network assets within the power industry. These include not only hardware modelling and analysis but also assessment of the impact of pricing policies especially in the context of privatised networks. This group has specialised in international collaboration particularly within developing countries.

Electrical Machines and Drives: Leader – Professor J Smith

Specialises in machine design and performance analysis and, in particular, in the evolution of power electronic techniques with embedded microprocessor systems for machine control. Such systems will become increasingly important as more flexible and precise control of the electrical power network and its components become more critical with efficient system operation.

Special Research Units

The Department is involved in many such activities. These include:

The Centre for Electrical Power Engineering (CEPE)

The Virtual Centre of Excellence in Mobile Communications

The Centre for Ultrasonic Engineering

The Rolls Royce University Technology Centre in Power Engineering

The Centre for Economic and Renewable Power Delivery (with Glasgow University)

The Texas Instruments ELITE Programme.

The Department also has numerous collaborative research projects within the UK, the EU and internationally.

Active Links with Industry

The Department is linked in research with well over 100 companies worldwide but predominately in the UK and Europe. Examples of different types are:

EPSRC Case Awards (e.g. Bookham Technology on silicon waveguide optical modulators)

Full Scale Research Support (e.g. The Rolls Royce Technology Centre)

Several LINK programmes

Numerous European initiatives involving at least 50 different companies

University Spin-Out companies such as Diagnostic Monitoring Systems, OptoSci, Industrial Systems and Control

Research Active Personnel
Academics 48; Research Fellows/Assistants~50; Research Students 100.
Research Grants (from all sources)
Number of Contracts (at any one time) 100; Total Value £12m to £15m.

(Submitted by Professor B. Culshaw)

(ii) Faraday Beneath the Waves
by Robin M.Dunbar BSc, MSc, MSUT, PhD, CEng, FIEE

The Ocean calls Heriot-Watt University, Edinburgh

Heriot-Watt University made its first electrical contact with the ocean in 1969, when a study (1) was commissioned to find opportunities for electrical and electronic engineering research in a totally new area in the realm of nature described by Jacques Cousteau as 'Le Monde du Silence' (2).

The research activity which followed was highly experimental, in the best tradition of Michael Faraday, exploring the relationships between theory and practice across a broad front of subsea engineering, and this realistic approach continues to be upheld thirty years on, in studies which seek to provide the experimental validation of theoretical models, for example in hydroacoustics (3) and in electromagnetic wave propagation underwater (4).

Foundational studies

In 1969, while completing a research project in mainstream power electronics, **Robin Dunbar** of the [then] Department of Electrical and Electronic Engineering became intrigued by reports of submersible vehicle developments and problems of underwater communications. His head of department, **Professor Gordon Nicoll** fortunately had the same fascination for the application of electrical methods in unusual areas, and he took the bold step of giving Robin free rein to explore possible lines of research for the Department under this new heading. As the study progressed it quickly became obvious that this was an 'Aladdin's Cave' of research opportunities, the study highlighting some areas where contemporary electrical knowledge could provide immediate solutions, and other areas for which no known electrical techniques existed at the time. As a result, the new research direction of **Underwater Technology** was created within the Department, with the objective of seeking solutions to problems of underwater communications, control, navigation and measurement.

It was recognised that the best way forward would be to focus these and other related topics within a substantial 'systems' project, where each element would contribute to one central and significant application area. The area chosen was the development of an unmanned, cable-controlled submersible system which would include all necessary subsystems: vehicle, umbilical cable, surface support equipment, control console, power generation, and underwater navigation equipment. This will be described in more detail shortly, but some subjective comments are important here.

Teamwork

On many occasions throughout the history of the submersibles project those involved saw the guiding hand of Providence and this was particularly noticeable in the formation of the original team that produced Scotland's first submersible, ANGUS.

On one of a series of visits made during the course of the original study, to Admiralty departments, government laboratories, and companies involved in underwater activities, **Robin Dunbar** visited Vickers Oceanics at Barrow-in-Furness, to view and to discuss research problems associated with manned submersibles. It was there that he first met **Robin Holmes** who was working in the 'Pisces' manned submersible research programme, and who had interests in unmanned vehicles. A rapport soon developed between 'the two Robins' and it was not long before Robin Holmes joined the staff of the Department of Electrical and Electronic Engineering at Heriot-Watt University.

The third member of the 'ANGUS' group was **Peter King**. He had joined the Department around the same time and he became involved in underwater magnetic field and other communication experiments with Robin Dunbar. Peter's creative and technical genius, and his sense of humour were soon recognised and he quickly became an integral part of the three-cornered team that created the ANGUS Project.

Looking back over those thirty years it is clear that the success of the project was due largely to the amalgam of the complementary skills and personalities of the two Robins and Peter: skills which were willingly pooled, and efforts beyond the call of duty which were willingly made, to achieve significant technical successes and to gain wide publicity for the University prior to its entering the offshore arena, as North Sea Oil 'took off'.

As a result of the novelty and visual quality of this new and exciting application area of submarine engineering there was wide national and international press and TV coverage in the early days of the ANGUS Project and it is interesting to note that photographs of the ANGUS and ROVER vehicles which were built and operated in the 1970s and early 1980s are still used on occasions to illustrate University publicity material.

The ANGUS Project

'ANGUS', *A Navigable General-purpose Underwater Surveyor* was the name given to both the actual submersible and to the total project. The 'G' in ANGUS originally stood for 'Geological' since there was an association with North Sea survey work being carried out by UK and Norwegian marine geologists. The first ANGUS actually took part in an historically unique set of trials carried out in North Sea and Norwegian waters, where three submersibles or ROV's (Remotely Operated Vehicles) were involved: CONSUB I, an English ROV operated by the [then] Institute of Geological Sciences; SNURRE, operated by the Royal Norwegian Council for Scientific and Industrial Research, NTFK; and the Scottish ANGUS, operated by Heriot-Watt University.

The first ANGUS vehicle (three ROV's were actually produced, ANGUS 001, 002, and 003) was based around a Mk 30 torpedo kindly supplied by the Royal Navy, but fitted with a dummy warhead. The hull was designed to be pressure compensated, high pressure air being supplied automatically to equalise the internal air pressure with the ambient water pressure outside the hull. This enabled electronic control equipment, cameras, and other instruments to be contained in a dry environment, connections being taken to the outside wet environment through water tight connectors or high pressure cable glands.

Propulsion was provided by two ten-inch propellers driven by two 2-kW, 415-volt, 3-phase, squirrel-cage induction motors. The propeller speed control was achieved by varying the voltage fed to the induction motors. The electrical engineering purist will recognise that precise speed control of an induction motor requires proportional frequency variation, in addition to voltage control. This detail led to many interesting and sometimes heated debates with electrical engineering colleagues both within and beyond the University, but satisfactory speed control was in fact achieved by matching the square law torque-speed characteristic of a propeller to the motor characteristic through a non-linear control circuit. A joystick control unit was specially designed to include the necessary electronics, and steering of the vehicle was achieved through a thrust differential between port and starboard motors. In 1999 High Street stores are full of exotic looking joysticks for computer games but thirty years ago the team had to manufacture their own, a rather clever, rugged and reliable unit which has outlasted three submersibles.

The two main propellers provided horizontal thrust for forward and reverse motion and vertical thrusters were added later to give control in the vertical plane. On later ANGUS 002 and 003 vehicles lateral thrusters were an optional extra to provide more flexible control, and by that time speed control of all propellers was achieved through the use of inverters.

Initially, 16mm film and studio TV cameras were fitted inside the vehicle, looking out through a hemispherical acrylic glass window, but later, as funds and suitable equipment became more readily available proprietry underwater TV, 35mm strobe, and 8mm film cameras were housed outside the pressure hull.

An under water trial of ANGUS 001 at Portobello Swimming Pool, Edinburgh
- Robin Holmes left, Robin Dunbar right, *Courtesy of The Herald (Glasgow)*

The actual vehicle was only one part of the total system. Power and control signals were fed to the ROV over a 600-m multicore umbilical cable, image and sensor signals travelling in the opposite direction to monitoring equipment housed in the control console. There was continuous indication of signals such as ambient and differential pressures, levels of lighting and thruster power, and a monitor in front of the operator provided the real time forward view from the ROV. The ROV was operated in a 'free-swimming' mode, in the sense that the cable was pulled through the water by the vehicle, rather than the vehicle being suspended by the cable. Consequently the slack cable tended to form a large loop in the water between the support vessel and the ROV, when the two craft tracked one another in a forward direction. The large hydrodynamic drag produced by the cable provided an ultimate limit on the performance of the ROV, limiting the forward speed to around two knots and restricting the area of the seabed that could be surveyed to a region know as the 'footprint'.

Power for vehicle propulsion and control was supplied by a 5-kW diesel generator through a group of earth-leakage and over-current trips. Such circuit breakers are readily available today but thirty years ago the designers had to procure them from an overseas manufacturer. Great care was taken in the safe design of all power circuits, electricity and water not being the best of friends, and it is a tribute to those original designs that no electrical shock was ever experienced in the laboratory or at sea, although, it has to be said, on many occasions the trips did operate, usually as the result of a water leak!

Water Leakage - a Headache

Water leakage was always a potential problem, saltwater ingress into multiway cable connectors being a particularly irritable problem in the early days of field trials. To give early warning of water leakage into the main pressure hull a highly sophisticated detector was developed. This consisted of a specially machined brass clothes peg fitted with a microswitch, held open by a soluble aspirin. If water entered the hull the tablet dissolved, the switch closed, and alarms sounded. The team look back on this device with great affection since it is the one piece of equipment that colleagues at home and abroad, and many members of the general public remember with an interest that eclipses all other scientific achievements of the entire ANGUS programme!

Funding

Professor Nicoll is to be thanked for his perceptive liberality with departmental research funds over 1969-1971 when early measurements in underwater communications and experiments with the empty torpedo were conducted, in swimming pools and from a trawler hired for the day rate of a bottle of whisky. When the first application for external funding was made by Robin Dunbar in 1971 to the (then) **Science Research Council**, he had to wait until the following year before a committee could be found that would take the step of faith of funding this rather off-beat area of research. Actually, it was the Mechanical and Production Engineering Committee of the SRC that awarded the sum of £10,770 in 1972, to which a further £1000 was added a year later. This was sufficient 'to get the show on the road' and in the summer of 1973 full-scale sea trials were conducted at a trials site on Loch Linnhe, where the vehicle reached its design depth of 200m, *and* returned safely to the surface.

The success of this mission gave other funding agencies confidence in the Underwater Technology Group (UTG), as the team had become known, and support started to appear from other quarters such as the **Department of Trade and Industry** (DTI), the **Department of Energy** (DoE), the **Ministry of Defence** (MoD), **Vickers Engineering**, and **Ferranti Ltd**.

Loading Angus 001 on board RV Clione at Lowestoft, 1975, Peter King (left). *Courtesy of Heriot-Watt University*

In 1974 a fully self-contained long baseline acoustic underwater navigation system was developed which enabled accurate and repeatable surveys to be carried out. In cooperative research programmes with the **Ministry of Agriculture, Fisheries and Food** (MAFF), ANGUS 001 was operated from their ships in various areas of the North Sea to provide mid- water and seabed ground-truthing data for the MAFF scientists as well as giving the ANGUS team valuable trials experience. The ROV was used to make films for the Central Office of Information and for BBC's *Tomorrow's World* and activities continued until the vehicle became trapped near to the seabed during an interesting mission for an Admiralty department in 1975, in Loch Long. The ANGUS 001 ROV was recovered a few months later, and after some cosmetic refurbishment it spent many years proudly on display in the Royal Scottish Museum in Edinburgh.

The change in attitude towards funding, between 1971 and 1975, when the vehicle was 'lost', was quite remarkable. In effect, funds of the order of £50k were made available almost immediately so that the project might continue. This prompted the Team to look to a different design philosophy for ANGUS 002, and a form of construction, which is now familiar to offshore operators, was followed. Instead of a modified torpedo pressure housing, a space-frame design approach was used, with static buoyancy at the top, and with all propulsion, control and sensor equipment mounted compactly in the space below. This produced a very stable platform, and with two horizontal thrusters, four vertical thrusters at the four corners of the frame, and 12kW of power, the ROV turned out to be highly manoeuvreable.

Expansion

The ANGUS 002 ROV which was developed during 1976-78 was widely used in offshore operations for serious offshore inspection work, as well as being the test vehicle for rapidly expanding research activities within the Department. The team expanded and research students had their MSc and PhD projects focused around automatic vehicle control problems, and developments in underwater imaging and communications. To assist in the development of a computer model of the vehicle and its associated cable the entire ROV was used as a test piece in a manoeuvring tank at ARE Haslar (now DERA), where its static drag and rate parameters were measured under typical simulated operating conditions (5).

As research objectives became more ambitious the Team grew in 1978 to include colleagues **Tony Norton, Dave King,** and **George Russell**, who contributed their expertise in the areas of TV systems, microprocessors, and adaptive control systems. Some time later **Professor Colin Davidson** took over as head of department, giving his support and encouragement to the submersibles project and, following Colin's period of duty, **Professor George Russell** took over the reins of the department. In addition he headed up the Marine Technology Centre, a focus for the University's many activities funded by the Marine Technology Directorate, and a link with other universities and companies. As we approach the start of the new millennium **Professor Roger Clarke** is head of a department whose research activities continue to expand, with Ocean Systems more active than ever.

Around the same time as the development of ANGUS 002 the two Robins heard about an aircraft that was reportedly lying on the bottom of Loch Ness. After some detective work by **Robin Holmes**, the aircraft was found and photographed by a mobile camera frame 'PK1' designed and built by **Peter King**. This led to the **Loch Ness Wellington Bomber** project headed by Robin Holmes, the climax of which was the recovery of the aircraft in 1985, and its eventual restoration and display in the Brooklands Museum near Weybridge. This momentous project is described in fascinating detail in **Robin Holmes's** book *One of our Aircraft* (6). Later on, Loch Ness was to become a test site for the ANGUS 003 vehicle, designed and built as a more rugged successor to 002, and as a deep water transporter for 'future concept' vehicles. Loch Ness has continued to be an excellent test site for experimental research activities (7), the mysterious and often foreboding ambience of the location adding spice to the scientific endeavours.

In parallel with this development in the sophistication of the ROV research, during 1977-1980, interest was increasing in research problems associated with cable-less, free-swimming vehicles, where the vehicle would be operated without an umbilical cable. Today, such vehicles are generally referred to as **Autonomous Underwater Vehicles**, AUVs. While this had major advantages in terms of removing cable drag and cable handling difficulties it brought with it the requirements of carrying power on board and of transmitting command and control data to the vehicle, and sensor data from the vehicle. The alternative approach of designing autonomous mission management systems was examined in parallel, as the **Remote Presence v Artificial Intelligence** debate was entered into. This opened up research into techniques of bandwidth compression, to minimise the amount of data required to be transmitted, methods of high data rate underwater acoustics to maximise the possible signalling rate, and knowledge-based systems as an aid to adaptive control techniques. These areas of study, initiated at that time, became the forerunners of the extensive Departmental research work programmes currently being carried out by other colleagues and their international partners in image analysis, through-water communications, and autonomous robotic systems.

As part of the earlier experimental research work carried out to evaluate underwater communication systems a semi-autonomous submersible ROVER was produced which was designed specifically to be carried in a bay within the space frame of ANGUS 003. Recently this vehicle has been re-engineered and re-named **Remote/Autonomous Underwater Vehicle Experimentation and Research RAUVER**, reflecting the continental European influence invading the activities of the Ocean Systems Laboratory, the more up-market name introduced a few years ago for the old Underwater Technology Group.

Looking back and looking forward

From the perspective of an electrical engineer, it is very interesting to look back over the period from 1969, from the pioneering days of the submersible project, to observe how electrical and electronic techniques have developed and how they have been applied to increase the sophistication and reliability of underwater engineering activities, particularly in the areas of remote systems, robotics and communications.

More detail on the early work can be found in *Jane's Ocean Technology* (8), in the McGraw-Hill *Encyclopaedia of Science and Technology* (9), and in an IEE paper of the time (10). Information on current activities can be examined at the **Ocean Systems Laboratory web site, http//:www.cee.hw.ac.uk/oceans/** .

Regarding the period between the pioneering days and the present, there are a large number of papers on robotics (e.g. 11), acoustic communications (e.g. 12), and EM wave and laser subsea communications (e.g. 13) which give a flavour of the wide range of highly significant work that has been carried out over this thirty-year period and which is now being carried forward, supported by UK, European Community, and other international funding agencies.

It is interesting to finish with a mention of a new project which to some extent shows that we have gone full circle, in once again carrying out research work which is of interest to the general public, as well as having technical significance in its own right. Government funding has been received to generate interactive displays of ROVs and underwater sounds and communications at *Deep-Sea World*, a highly successful sea life exhibition at North Queensferry, close to Edinburgh, under the thematic umbrella of *Partnerships for Public Understanding of Science*. **Professor David Lane** is co-ordinating the ROV activity, and **Ronald McHugh** and **Robin Dunbar** are contributing the *Sounds of the Sea* interactive demonstration. It is hoped that this venture will rouse the technical curiosity of young people in the same way that the original experiments caught the imagination of the public all those years ago, and that it will encourage these future scientists and engineers to view electrical engineering applied to the ocean, as a wonderfully exciting area of opportunity.

References

1. Dunbar RM, *A Survey of Underwater Technology*, Heriot-Watt University Department of Electrical and Electronic Engineering RM70/4.

2. Cousteau J-Y, *Comment on autographed artist's impression of ANGUS 001*, 1973.

3. Dunbar RM, McHugh RM, de Malet Roquefort S, Bathgate, L, *High level control of automated oceanographic and acoustic equipment and experiments*, OCEANS 94, Brest, France, Vol.1, pp.678-682, Sept 1994.

4. Dunbar RM, Skelland ND, *Modelling and measurement of CW and chirp ELF/VLF electromagnetic fields transmitted by submerged line, loop and contour antennas in the presence of reflecting and stratified boundaries*, MARELEC 99 Conference, Brest, France, DERA/GESMA/ICL, pp.175-186.

5. Fyfe AJ, *Planar motion mechanism experiments to determine the stability and control derivatives of the unmanned cable-controlled submersible* ANGUS, IOE/HWU/Department of Energy Report No. OT/R/7957, 30th August 1979

6. Holmes RT, *One of our aircraft : the story of 'R for Robert' the Loch Ness Wellington*, Quiller Press, 1991.

7. Dunbar RM, Linnett, LM, Rzhanov Y, Bell J, *Computation and visualisation of historical geographical data for acoustic channel modelling*, Proc. GeoComputation 97, SIRC, University of Otago, NZ, pp.217-225, 1997.

8. *Jane's Ocean Technology* 1978, ed. R.L.Trillo, pp.172, 173.

9. *Oceanographic Submersibles*, McGraw-Hill Yearbook of Science and Technology, 1977, pp. 318-320.

10. Dunbar RM, Holmes RT, *ANGUS*, Electronics and Power, JIEE, Vol.21, No.7, April 1975, pp.433-436.

11. Lane DM, et al, *Mixing simulations and real subsystems for subsea robot development*, OCEANS 98, IEEE, Nice, France, September 1998, pp.1382-1391.

12. McHugh R, Shaw S, Taylor N, *Azimuth ambiguities in broadside and squint mode synthetic aperture sonar*, IEE Proc. - Radar, Sonar Navig., Vol. 146, No.2, April 1999, pp.113-119.

13. Dunbar RM, Tennent AW, Wade S, *A duplex laser location and communication system for wideband real-time signalling between AUVs*, 7th Int. Symp. Unmanned, Untethered Submersible Technology, Univ. New Hampshire, USA, Sept. 1991, pp.253-263.

(iii) A Review of Researches in Medical Electronics
edited by Dr James Dripps BSc, PhD, MIPEM

Introduction

This is my 20th year of research work in medical electronics. I came from a background of military Research and Development work which is an excellent training ground for young engineers, particularly if you gained your experience in the excellent environment of what was then the Ferranti Radar Group at Crewe Toll in Edinburgh. I came to medical electronics hoping to find an application for my electronics training which had the potential to benefit society in general and our National Health Service (NHS) in particular. Every medical electronics project I have seen has this potential, however, I eventually learned that only a small fraction of the R&D work which is successfully undertaken actually finds its way into routine clinical practice. It seems that I shall have to settle for the satisfaction of publishing some 40 papers on various aspects of medical electronics (mainly signal processing). However, the four (real) contributors to this part of the book have the added satisfaction of having worked on major projects which have contributed to and possibly even significantly advanced routine clinical practice.

Geographically, these projects span the whole of Scotland, coming from Research and Development centres in Aberdeen, Edinburgh, Glasgow and Inverness. They span a wide range of applications from the glamorous imaging modalities - Magnetic Resonance Imaging and Ultrasound - through to small ECG ambulatory monitors to the kind of equipment which is not normally seen by the public, but which must work with absolute reliability - Endoscope Disinfection Machines. I shall let them tell their stories in their own words.

Nuclear Magnetic Resonance and Magnetic Resonance Imaging in Aberdeen

The history of Magnetic Resonance in Aberdeen dates back to the time when Professor John Mallard took up the Chair in the early 1960s. He brought some Electron Spin Resonance equipment from Hammersmith, where he worked previously. About 1970, a PhD student, Roy Gordon (now a head manager of Oxford Research Systems) embarked on the construction of an NMR spectrometer, under my supervision, with the idea of measuring relaxation times of samples of biological tissues. This progressed well, and towards the end of his studentship, Paul Lauterbur brought out his classic paper in *Nature* in 1973 with the idea of using gradients to form images. We were excited by this, and within three weeks we had devised a simple field-gradient system, and formed a one-dimensional image of a set of four capillary tubes of copper sulphate solutions. Not only that, but the tubes contained different concentrations of CuSO4 and we were able to see the differences in relaxation times (T1) on our 1-D image, using an inversion-recovery sequence.

This was the point of no return. Roy, unfortunately, left us to take up a post in Canterbury, but I continued the work, along with occasional students on projects. We obtained a permanent magnet which allowed us to go up to mouse-size; a full field-gradient set was made along with dedicated electronics; this enabled us to produce crude 2-D images and tackle some of the practical problems of imaging. It resulted in our famous "mouse" picture which thrilled Professor Mallard, and he lost no time in spreading the word about Aberdeen's research.

We decided to jump to full-size human imaging and we applied for a very "blue skies" grant from MRC to construct a machine; amazingly we were awarded it! In 1999 I can only thank the prevailing attitude towards science at that time. The magnet was a four-coil resistive design between ourselves and Oxford Instruments; it was their first attempt at any kind of whole-body magnet, and I believe it started them on their way to their present success and dominance in MRI magnets.

We completed the system in 1978, but the particular pulse sequence we had chosen was really bad for movement artefacts, so, although we got recognisable images of phantoms, our attempts on living humans were unacceptable. By this time we had formed a team including Glyn Johnson (now in New York doing MRI research) and Bill Edelstein (now a key researcher in International General Electric, USA), and this setback worried us. However, we came across a minor paper from Richard Ernst's group (the Nobel Prize winner) which tentatively suggested an imaging technique related to his 2-D spectroscopy method. This redirected our thinking and we came up with the so-called "Spin Warp" method, which needed very little change to our apparatus, and it WORKED! This was during late 1979.

During 1980, we were very busy improving the machine, presenting things at conferences, and getting medical people interested, in particular, Dr Francis Smith, a radiologist, who became a primary asset to the team for anything on the medical side. In August 1980, we scanned our first patient (who had terminal liver cancer); we could not only see the immense differences from a normal liver, but even discovered a secondary tumour in the spine, which had not been found in prior tests.

We believe that this was the world's first clinical whole-body MRI scan, although other groups had already imaged volunteers. Interest from medical staff in the hospital (ARI as it was then) spread like wildfire, and we had over 1000 patient referrals in the two years before our second, and more clinically oriented MRI system was built and commissioned in the hospital. We were amazed at how few patients rejected being scanned on our rather "Heath Robinson" apparatus; in part we think that this was because we always had a nurse or doctor inside the screen next to the patient during scans.

Our Mark II instrument was funded by Asahi Medical of Japan, who also sent three of their engineering staff to work with us on constructing it; they did not restrict our publications (as many industrial sponsors seem to), but every detail of the instrument was sent back to Japan, where a duplicate was being constructed. This was a very fruitful collaboration on both sides.

The Mark II machine served in the hospital from late 1982 to 1990, when it was replaced by a commercial Siemens "Impact" 1-Tesla MRI scanner. It was kept in operation by our Medical Physics Department staff, but it was starting to become unreliable by the late 1980s, and was falling well behind the "state of the art" in MRI just before the Siemens imager replaced it.

Dr Francis Smith obtained a second MRI system in the mid 1990s and set up his own unit in another Aberdeen hospital; this is an open-plan low-field system, and is finding a lot of use in Orthopaedics and Sports Medicine.

The Medical Physics magnetic resonance research has diversified into new avenues such as Overhauser Imaging (which combines electron spin resonance with MRI) and new techniques in the old field of Electron Spin Resonance (ESR), in particular the interaction of free radicals (which are easily detected by ESR) with the body.

(Submitted by James MS Hutchison)

Electrocardiography Developments in Edinburgh

The electrocardiogram (ecg) is a signal, often less than 1 mV in amplitude, which can be detected using electrodes on the body surface in which each heart beat generates a sequence of waves reflecting the contractions of the heart muscles. Usually the ecg is printed out on paper for a few beats for doctor interpretation. In the early 1960s the technique of Ambulatory Electrocardiography emerged in which a small magnetic tape recorder was carried by the patient to record the ecg for hours, later extended to 24 hours. The tape was replayed at higher speed and the accelerated ecg signal viewed on an oscilloscope to detect disturbances of heart rhythm, typically the presence of premature heart beats and beats in which the waveform was distorted indicating their origin in the wrong part of the heart. Detection of certain of these disturbances is important because of the risk of further deterioration of the rhythm leading even to cardiac arrest but difficult because of the very large number of heart beats (typically 100,000/day) and the poor signal/noise ratio associated with patient movement.

By the mid-1960s at the Department of Medical Physics and Medical Engineering in Edinburgh University Dr JM Neilson was working on the problem of automatic electronic analysis of these ambulatory ecgs and in 1969 he patented a hybrid analogue computer which detected and timed each beat in the ecg and compared its waveform with the characteristic shape of that patient's 'normal' beat, pioneering the use of both pattern recognition and noise adaptive processing. Particular sequences of premature and distorted "ectopic" beats characterising classic rhythm disturbances were automatically recognised and reported to the operator. In collaboration with *Reynolds Medical Limited* of Hertford this machine was made available world wide as the "Pathfinder" arrhythmia analyser in 1975 which analysed ambulatory ecg tapes at 60 times the recording speed. Succeeding models of the Pathfinder still lead the field and in its current all digital, multiprocessor form processes 24 hours three-channel ecg signals at up to 1000 times the original recording speed.

To accompany the Pathfinder Analysers Neilson developed an improved miniature 24-hour tape recorder, the "Tracker", which records two channels of ecg signals, a paced beat detector channel and a data channel recording the exact time at each point of the tape.

The amplitude of the "ST segment" part of the ecg at each beat reflects the presence periods of "ischaemia" i.e. inadequacy of the blood supply to the heart muscle which occurs in patients with coronary artery disease.

In 1968 Neilson was the first to demonstrate electronic apparatus for tracking continuously these ST segment changes and in due course this capability was added to the Pathfinder Analysers.

Even in the absence of rhythm disturbances due to abnormal, ectopic, beats the heart rate varies continuously in response to the body's requirements under the control of the autonomic nervous system. In some diseases this control system itself becomes deranged leading to the possibility of dangerous heart rhythm disturbances. In the 1980s medico-scientific interest focused on Heart Rate Variability (HRV) as an indicator of this control activity. Neilson developed a new measure of HRV (sNN50) based on the rate of the larger beat to beat changes in heart rate characteristic of the faster acting branch of the autonomic nervous system and developed his analysis system to track this measure continuously during 24 hour ecg analysis. With Dr DJ Ewing of the Department of Medicine at Edinburgh University applied this sensitive and specific measure to the study of the effects of diabetes on control of the heart, later extending this work with colleagues in the University and international collaborators to a wide range of heart diseases.

Arising out of this work his interest turned to the possibility of continuous tracking of the duration of the electrical activity associated with each individual heart beat, the "QT" interval, which reflects largely the electrical recovery of the heart muscle after each contraction. Abnormalities in this interval are particularly associated with the risk of serious rhythm disturbances. A technique was developed for this purpose and incorporated into the Pathfinder Analysers in 1995 and was well received by users.

Disappointed nevertheless by the observation that the 24-hour variation of the QT interval reflected mainly its known relationship to the prevailing heart rate, the inventor began to focus on the nature of this relationship. The physiological lag between changes in heart rate and the response of the QT interval was investigated and a way found to correct this complex lag continuously in the QT Interval signal. This revealed for the first time that the underlying relationship between QT interval and heart rate varies continuously throughout the day and differs among heart diseases.

A new QT/ Heart rate Analyser specifically for use in the wide field opened up by this discovery is scheduled to be made available by *Reynolds Medical* early in the year 2000.

Collaboration between Neilson and the University and *Reynolds Medical Limited* as their industrial partners has been fruitful for over

30 years and during that time has been recognised twice by Queen's Awards for Export Achievement and one for Technology.

(Submitted by Jim M. Neilson)

The Development of Medical Ultrasound

It has been estimated that ultrasound accounts for forty per cent of all medical diagnostic imaging and there may be as many as 500,000 scanners in the world. As the first successful steps were taken in the 1950s this represents an astonishing rate of growth.

The foundations of ultrasound were laid by the Curies, Paul Langevain (1872-1946) and the pioneers of echo sounding and submarine location in the 1910s and 1920s. The loss of the *Titanic* and submarine warfare stimulated research on underwater acoustics. Then World War II brought advances in electronics and by the late 1940s ultrasound was being applied to the detection of flaws in metal components. A-Scan instruments were developed by Firestone at the Sperry Corporation, in Japan by Ichida and in Scotland by Sproule at *Kelvin and Hughes*. By 1948 the medical potential had been recognised. From this point advances were dominated by a few individuals and small groups; in Sweden Edler, Hertz (cardiology) and in Glasgow Donald, MacVicar and Brown (obstetrics and gynaecology), in Denver Holmes and Howry (general medicine). The use of Doppler ultrasound for fluid flow measurement can be traced back to the 1940s. A decade later Satomura in Japan was measuring blood flow.

Prior to his arrival in Glasgow Ian Donald's attention was drawn to the medical possibilities of ultrasound during a lecture in London by JJ Wild from Minneapolis. In Glasgow one of Ian Donald's patients put him in touch with the heavy engineering firm of *Babcock & Wilcox* and experiments ensued with the company's 'supersonic' flaw detector. Next came co-operation with Tom Brown of *Kelvin & Hughes* and this resulted in the development of the first contact scanner. The transducer on this machine was moved by hand in one plane while being kept in contact with the patient thus avoiding the water bath favoured by other experimenters. Brown not only saw this as a natural development from industrial practice but also necessary to work with the sick elderly patients in Donald's gynaecology wards; Brown described the first images as "rather disappointing". Nevertheless in spite of scepticism from the medical profession *Kelvin and Hughes* produced a small number of static scanners. This was known as the Diasonograph. Later the ultrasound interest was acquired by *Nuclear Enterprises* who very successfully produced many hundreds of scanners in a number of versions. These slow cumbersome machines established the place of ultrasound and showed its possibilities in obstetrics and gynaecology, general medicine, cardiology and ophthalmology. All these were explored and clinical techniques were developed and tested.

Then in the early 1970s the real-time revolution started. At first the images had few lines, poor resolution and a limited field of view and were aimed at visualising moving structures. Only gradually was it realised that real-time could be of value on any part of the body. The advantages are now clear: easy to use and learn to use. The machines are smaller and easier to demonstrate and install. These advantages led to wider acceptance, increasing sales and increased investment in research and development. An early active participant in this advance was *Diagnostic Sonar Ltd* of Livingston. Some years later this firm split resulting in the formation of *Dynamic Imaging Ltd,* also in Livingston.

Looking back it can be recognised that 'real-time' started in 1950s with Wild's transducer oscillating at a few sweeps per second while scanning in a water bath around a patients' neck. The first array appeared about 1965; a 10-element concave transducer built by East German ophthalmologist, Werner Buschmann and Kretztechnic of Austria. Of much greater impact at the time was the *Vidoson* that appeared in 1967. This remarkably simple machine designed by Richard Soldner of *Siemens* used a transducer rotating at the focus of a parabolic mirror in a water filled enclosure. This was overtaken by a return to the array principle. Bom developed small arrays specifically for cardiology. In 1974 the first commercial linear array scanner appeared; the ADR 2130 from Advanced Diagnostic Research in Arizona. Development became intense, so for example, by 1979 eleven forms of real-time transducer were described and included linear and curved arrays, phased arrays and mechanical designs in which the transducer elements are rocked or rotated. A particular contribution to the range of designs of mechanical methods was the work of McDicken in the Department of Clinical Physics and Bioengineering in Glasgow; this department was the first to organise training courses in medical ultrasound.

In parallel with the development of 2D imaging Doppler progressed from simple fetal heart detectors and blood velocity meters to pulsed systems able to measure flow at selected depths. Then pulsed Doppler was combined with real-time to give Duplex scanners. From these have grown systems giving a dramatic display of flow in colour superimposed on high resolution cross-sectional images.

From the very beginning 3-D has been a goal, now with the power of microprocessors this has become a reality for specialised use. It is tempting to see such achievements as the ultimate but it is more likely that with the continuing co-operation of medics and paramedics, physicists, engineers and industrialists ultrasound imaging will continue to develop and applications advance as rapidly as ever.

The history of medical ultrasound is being recorded by the *British Medical Ultrasound Society* which is developing a historical collection with the assistance of the Hunterian Museum and the Wellcome Unit for the History of Medicine, University of Glasgow.

References

1. Donald I, (1974) *Sonar: The Story of an experiment Ultrasound in Medicine and Biology* Vol 1 No 2, pp109-117
2. McNay MB, Fleming JEE, (1999) *Forty years of obstetric ultrasound 1957-1997: from A-scope to three dimensions.* UMB, 25(1) Jan, pp3-56
3. Holmes JH (1980) *Diagnostic Ultrasound During the Early Years of AIUM.* J. Clin Ultrasound 8:299-308 August 1980
4. Blume, S.S, (1992) Chapter 3 *The Constitution of Diagnostic Ultrasound in Insight and Industry. On the Dynamics of Technological Change in Medicine.* Publ. The MIT Press Cambridge Mass., London, England
5. Herrick JF, *History of early ultrasonic blood flowmeters.* Medical instrumentation Vol 11 No 3 May-June 1977 pp144-148

(Submitted by John EE Fleming)

The "Inverness" Endoscope Disinfection Machine

The endoscope disinfection project began in 1990 and was aimed at improving the reliability of existing disinfection machines. Design was influenced by increasing concern over the harmful effects of glutaraldehyde based disinfectants. The specification for the machine was that it should enable disinfection of a wide range of flexible endoscopes. It was to be mobile and self contained to allow easy transfer between different treatment rooms and operating theatres. Operators would be able to select programmes of washing, disinfection and rinsing.

Disinfection would be achieved by total immersion in glutaraldehyde solution. The internal channels of the endoscope would be irrigated by a guaranteed flow of disinfectant. The machine would use a single, five-litre container of a glutaraldehyde solution such as Cidex. Glutaraldehyde fumes would be contained within a closed system of plumbing, including a scaled lid.

In the development stage, a moulded fibreglass tray was designed to accommodate all the currently available flexible endoscopes. Standard jerrycans were adapted for detergent and rinse water containers. Fluid dynamics was achieved with peristaltic pumps and solenoid valves. For flexibility, the machine was controlled with a commercial microprocessor board. An EL display and "softkey" switches formed a user-friendly operator interface.

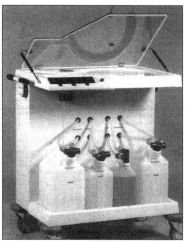

Endoscope Disinfection Machine.
Courtesy of Raigmore Hospital, Inverness

A novel programming language was developed for control purposes. Software continually monitored all inputs (softkeys, pressure switches, proximity switches, liquid level switches) and adjusted all outputs (pumps, solenoids, displays) accordingly.

A prototype version of the machine was tested in Raigmore Hospital in 1992 and the first production model went into service two years later. The machine is in widespread use in the NHS.

(Submitted by Mark Stevenson)

Epilogue

So there we have our four stories. It would take much more space and time to do full justice to all the people who have, through the years, contributed to medical electronics development in Scotland. It appears that in this field, as in so many others, Scotland has made a contribution on the world stage which belies its small size and population.

Chapter 4

Electrical Supply and Transmission

(i) Electricity Generation in Scotland
by Dr Jim Grant BSc, FREng, HonDTech, FIEE

One hundred years ago the generation of electricity for public supply was in its infancy, the largest sets of the day, at the leading edge of technology, being capable of 1,000 kW. The first Scottish public supply was established at Fort Augustus in 1890 and comprised an 18-kW oil engine and a similarly rated water wheel. Six years later, in 1896, the British Aluminium Company commissioned a 5,000-kW DC station at Foyers - this was the first large-scale hydro-electric development in Scotland. Today, the largest sets operating in Scotland are rated at 676 MW. The reliability, efficiency and availability of these modern mammoths are a tribute to the Electrical Engineers who designed them.

The story of the last 100 years in Scotland is told by picking out a number of the significant developments which have taken place in chronological order. The first part of this story deals with "conventional generation" which covers coal, oil and gas-fired thermal plants, gas turbine, hydro, pumped storage and diesel plants The second part is devoted to the development of nuclear power plants in Scotland. Details of all significant generating stations built in Scotland during the last 100 years are included in the tables on pages 146-153.

Conventional Generation
When Lord Kelvin officially opened Neptune Bank power station in Newcastle in 1901, he said:

> *I don't know what electricity is, and cannot define it - I have spent my life on it. I do not know the limit of electricity but it will go beyond anything we conceive of today .*

How right he was. (Neptune Bank, by the way, provided the first public supply of three-phase electricity.)

In Sebastian Ziani de Ferranti's IEE Presidential Address in 1910 he advocated full-scale national electrification to conserve coal, which would be economic if generation achieved a thermal efficiency of 25% at 60% load factor. He predicted 100 stations each of 250-MW capacity with 10 x 25-MW sets. Capital costs would be 0.0776 d/kWh and works costs 0.036 d/kWh with coal at 10 shillings (50p) per ton.

Rannoch Hydro-Electric Power Station
Courtesy Scottish & Southern Energy plc

In 1922 the **Grampian Electricity Supply Company** was granted Parliamentary powers for the construction of hydro-electric plants in Northern Scotland. Two years later the **Lanarkshire Hydro-electric Power Act** provided for the harnessing of the water power of the Falls of Clyde. The Lanark hydro-stations of Bonnington and Stonebyres were commissioned in 1926/27.

The **Lochaber Power Company**, a subsidiary of British Aluminium, completed the first phase of the Lochaber hydro-electric scheme comprising 42 MW of plant in 1929. Its twelve generating sets supplies the smelting process of Alcan Smelting and Power UK and relies on its head of water from dams at Spey, Loch Laggen and Loch Treig through a 15-mile length of tunnel to Lochaber. Of ultimate capacity 85.75 MW, this was the first large scale water power development in the country to be planned along comprehensive lines.

The next major hydro development in Scotland took place in the Stewartry of Kirkcudbright in 1935 when the Galloway hydro-electric scheme was commissioned. The total installed capacity was 103.25

MW from five stations: Tongland, Glenlee, Earlstoun, Carsfad and Kendoon. The installed capacity of the scheme was increased by 2.1 MW in 1985 when the Drumjohn needle valve was replaced with a water turbine

1943 saw the establishment of the **North of Scotland Hydro Electric Board** (NSHEB) as a public corporation. The first chairman being the Rt. Hon.The Earl of Airlie. This was followed in 1947 by the taking into public ownership the supply industry of England and Wales and Southern Scotland; the **British Electricity Authority** being established on 15th August under the chairmanship of Lord Citrine.

The NSHEB commissioned its first new stations in 1948 - at Morar (600 kW) and Lochalsh (1,000 kW). The former is believed to be Britain's first underground station. The year 1950 saw the start up of Sloy station of the Loch Sloy scheme. By the end of that year the Clunie and Pitlochry stations of the Tummel-Garry scheme and the Grudie Bridge station of the Fannich scheme were also in commission. The first fully automatic hydro-electric power station in Europe was commissioned at Gaur Power Station in 1953.

1st April 1955 was vesting day for the **South of Scotland Electricity Board** (SSEB).

Also in 1955 a 12-MW gas turbine of the "closed cycle" type was connected to the system at Carolina Port station in Dundee. The project was abandoned in 1959 as reliable commercial operation seemed unlikely.

In 1956 the SSEB commissioned two 30-MW sets at Barony station in Ayrshire. These were the "first of a kind" in the UK using colliery washed slurry as a fuel. Methil station in Fife, also with 2x30-MW slurry burning units, was commissioned in 1965.

The first example of pumped storage on any considerable scale on the British public supply system was established with the commissioning of a 5-MW generating/pumping set at the NSHEB Sron Mor power station, part of the Glen Shira scheme, in 1957.

The new standard generating voltage (13.8kV) and the 660-MW Generator

In 1958 the first 120-MW units in the UK were commissioned at Blyth 'A' in Northumberland and Kincardine power stations on 23rd and 28th November respectively. Altogether forty-four of these standard units, generating at the new standard voltage of 13.8 kV, were installed in fourteen stations in Great Britain. This was the start of a period of rapid escalation in generating unit size. Prior to 1958 the standard size was 60 MW, by the mid 1960s it had stepped through 120 MW, 200 MW and 300 MW and reached 500 MW. By the early 1970s 660 MW had become the standard size. The impact on the designers and manufacturers can be imagined when one considers that at the time of commissioning the prototype 200-MW units, the 300-MW prototype was on work's test, the 500-MW prototype was in manufacture and the 660-MW set was on the drawing board. It was no wonder that many of these units had a rather chequered early operational performance. A salutary lesson was learnt.

The first 200-MW unit at Kincardine power station was commissioned in 1962. This was the first unit in Scotland to have 'direct cooling' of the copper in the 16-kV stator winding using water. Who said water and electricity don't mix?

Dundee attains the record thermal efficiency - 37.6%

The first of two 129-MW oil-fired units was commissioned at Carolina Port 'B' in Dundee in 1965. This station achieved the highest thermal efficiency of any steam station in the UK in the years 1966/67, 1967/68 and 1969/70 to 1972/73.

Also in 1965 the first of 4 x 400-MW single-stage reversible pump turbines was commissioned at **Cruachan** pumped storage station at Loch Awe in Argyllshire. It operated under a head of **1,195 feet**, at that time the **highest in the world** for this type of plant.

At Cockenzie power station the first of 4 x 300-MW units was commissioned in 1967. The turbine generators were later to have major components replicated at Longannet station which started up in 1970. Its four 600-MW cross-compound units were unusual in having both lines running at high speed, 3000rpm. A unique feature of the station was the fuel supply arrangement - the output from four collieries was despatched to the station stockyard along a computer-controlled underground conveyer system of some 5.5 miles, with automatic blending to ensure consistent ash content.

Foyers pumped storage station on Loch Ness was commissioned in 1974 with two 150-MW reversible pump turbines; this was part of the Great Glen Group of stations under remote control from Fort Augustus.

In 1976 the SSEB commissioned the first of three 676-MW oil-fired units at Inverkip. In later years techniques were developed at this station for fast start-up from both hot and cold standby conditions to improve the economics of two-shift and cold start-up operation.

Scottish engineers export a clever trick - a world first in demagnetising

In September 1974 the mechanical failure of a slip-ring lead retaining wedge on a Cockenzie generator rotor shorted-circuited the majority of one pole of the rotor winding resulting in a unit trip. Investigation revealed the existence of a strong remanent axial magnetic field in the shaft making the unit incapable of rotating without inducing heavy circulating currents which would destroy the bearings. A major demagnetising exercise was therefore essential. The only previous experience to draw on was the demagnetising of a 60-MW set at Uskmouth in Wales in the early 1960s and a 350-MW Tilbury unit in the late 1960s where on both occasions the technique used was to strip down the unit into its individual components and using a variable, reversible DC supply, subject each component to diminishing B/H loops, a process which took thirteen weeks, including the time to strip down and re-assemble the unit. Since the unit had become magnetised in the fully assembled state, it was argued that it should be possible to demagnetise it in a similar state.

The heavy dc power supply and the cables wrapped round the generator rotor ready for demagnetisation at Cockenzie Power Station 1974, *Courtesy of ScottishPower*

The decision was made to attempt to demagnetise the Cockenzie unit in its fully assembled state with the exception of the generator rotor which had to be removed for repair and would be demagnetised separately. This was attempted by wrapping welding cables around the shaft at each bearing, the number of turns used being directly proportional to the cross section of the shaft. The coils were connected in series to a controllable, reversible heavy DC supply to provide a slowly 'alternating' current of variable magnitude. The technique was very successful and the unit was demagnetised in four days. Interestingly, it was necessary to adopt a 'period' of 10 minutes for the alternating current to allow full penetration of the magnetic flux into the large solid masses of metal in the shafts. It was the first time this technique had been used anywhere in the world. The technique was later successfully exported to Australia to demagnetise a Japanese 500-MW set following five weeks of abortive attempts by the original manufacturer using a diminishing 50-Hz supply.

In 1981 Peterhead station was commissioned burning surplus gas and natural gas liquids (after methane separation) for which there were no alternative outlets. The station replaced the proposed Stakeness Steam Generating Heavy Water Reactor (SGHWR) nuclear station when the Government decided not to proceed with that type of reactor.

A prototype water cooled generator was installed at Cruachan pumped-storage station in place of a conventional 100-MW unit in 1982.

A loch is restored (de-acidified) and the fish return

In 1984 a five-year £5-million project, financed by CEGB/SSEB/NSHEB and the National Coal Board, was started at Loch Fleet in Galloway. Loch Fleet had sustained a fish population until the mid-1960s when the fish completely disappeared due to increasing water acidity. At that time afforestation was taking place in Galloway and part of the Loch Fleet catchment area was partially planted with fir trees. During subsequent years the acidity of the loch water had continued to increase. The aim of the project was to determine the actual reasons for the increasing acidity of the water and to attempt to restore conditions which would allow a self- sustaining fish population to be re-established in the loch. In the 1980s there was considerable unease about the impact of 'acid rain', which was being blamed on sulphur dioxide (SO_2) emissions from the power generation industry, and afforestation on land masses sensitive to acidification - areas with no neutralising lime. There were many theories but little supportable evidence of the part played by SO_2 and trees in the acidification of surface waters. The research was carried out by independent, respected organisations and showed that SO_2 and trees played important roles in the acidification process. A new form of corrective treatment was tried - treatment of selected catchment areas with lime. This approach had not been tried anywhere else. The Norwegians had been successful with direct lime treatment of the water but the improvements were short-lived and dependent on the rate of turnover of the water in the loch. At Loch Fleet a single application to selected catchment areas sustained the water quality for at least ten years even though the turn over rate of the loch was six months during which time a self-sustaining fish population was established.

Scottish Nuclear

The prospect of privatisation saw considerable changes being introduced in the North of Scotland Hydro-Electric Board (NSHEB) and the South of Scotland Electricity Board (SSEB) from 1989 onwards. In 1990 a new company, Scottish Nuclear, was set up to own and operate the nuclear plants which had belonged mainly to the SSEB (now Scottish Power) but the NSHEB (now Scottish and Southern Energy) had a partial financial interest in them.

Nuclear Generation

The first artificial splitting of the atom was achieved in 1932 by **Sir John Cockroft** and **Dr ETS Walton**. They used protons to bombard lithium, resulting in the formation of helium. This inaugurated the era of 'atom smashing'. In the same year the neutron was identified by **James Hardwick** - by bombarding beryllium with alpha particles he obtained an unknown radiation that was able to penetrate the nuclei of various substances causing protons to be ejected from them. The particle was called the *neutron* at the suggestion of **Lord Rutherford** - he described it as: *like an invisible man passing through Piccadilly Circus: his path can be traced only by the people he has pushed aside.*

In 1934 **Enrico Fermi** discovered that the effect of radioactivity, induced by neutron bombardment, could be increased by reducing the velocity of the neutrons - moderation of neutron velocity.

In 1936 **Eugene Paul Wigner** developed a theory that in a crystal lattice atoms are displaced when bombarded with neutrons and its shape and dimensions change. Some of the energy lost by the neutrons is stored in the lattice e.g. graphite in a reactor known as *Wigner* *energy*. The real significance would be discovered much later in the Windscale pile fire.

Nuclear fission was discovered in 1938 by the German chemist **Otto Hahn** and radiochemist **Fritz Strassmann** by bombarding uranium (atomic number 92) with neutrons showing that one of the products was a radioactive form of a much lighter element - barium (atomic number 56), indicating that the uranium had split into two lighter atoms.

On 2nd December 1942 the world's first nuclear reactor started up in Chicago. Enrico Fermi achieved a controlled chain reaction by striking a target nucleus, uranium-235, with a low energy neutron, emitting two or more neutrons to initiate further fission. Like Fermi's reactor the first British commercial reactors used natural uranium as fuel and graphite as the moderator.

The year 1947 saw the start up of the first atomic reactor in the UK - the Graphite Low-Energy Experimental Pile (GLEEP) at Harwell.

Nuclear Technology Development in Scotland

Dounreay

When on 1st March 1954 Sir David Eccles, the Minister of Works, informed the House of Commons of the Government's decision to build a nuclear reactor of the breeder type at Dounreay in Caithness, the likelihood was that few amongst his audience had anything but the vaguest notion of where the place actually was. However, over the next 40 years it, was to become a byword for the forefront of nuclear technology not only in the UK but throughout Europe and indeed the world.

In July 1954 **Sir Christopher Hinton**, who until then had been Chief of the Ministry of Supply's Atomic Energy Industrial Group, took control of the newly-established **United Kingdom Atomic Energy Authority** (UKAEA). Three months later the UKAEA took over administrative control of the Dounreay Aerodrome from the Admiralty.

Civil work commenced in early 1955 and the UKAEA took formal possession of the **Dounreay Fast Reactor** (DFR) in 1957. Commissioning commenced at the end of 1958 and on the 14th November 1959, the Control Room instruments showed that the DFR had ceased to be theory - it was now a fact. Electricity was considered to be a by-product and it was October 1962 before power was fed into the grid and July 1963 before the full power output of 14.5 MW was achieved.

From the outset it was apparent that the DFR was only one stage *en route* to the 1,000-MW commercial fast breeder reactors which, it was assumed, would be coming on line during the 1980s. Such were the heady days of optimism when predicted forward load growths of 5% to 7% per annum were the norm.

DFR had two small scale predecessors at Harwell to prove the fundamental physics of fast reactors. This basic scientific information DFR had refined into a working technology. If DFR was applied science the **Prototype Fast Reactor** (PFR) would be applied technology.

Construction of PFR began in 1966. Although the two reactors shared the same basic features of a small core cooled by liquid metal the PFR core was barely three times the size of its predecessor's but it generated ten times more heat - an output of 600 MW as opposed to 60 MW. The PFR was completed in 1973, fuel was loaded early the following year and low power operations began in March 1974. It was connected to the grid in 1975. The conventional turbine-generator plant installed was similar to that installed at Cockenzie and at Longannet power stations although the electrical output of PFR was only 250 MW. This was done to replicate proven plant and to minimise the need for special spares.

In July 1988, the Secretary of State for Energy, Cecil Parkinson, informed Parliament of the Government's decision to cease funding the PFR project beyond March 1994 and, on cue, on 31st March 1994 the PFR shut down for the last time. Thus ended Britain's fast reactor programme.

Chapelcross

In June 1955 the UKAEA made the decision to build a nuclear power station at Chapelcross in Dumfriesshire. This station was based on gas-cooled natural uranium reactors and was designed primarily as a producer of plutonium for military purposes. The natural uranium fuel was contained in Magnesium Alloy 'cans' thereby giving the name *Magnox* to this type of reactor. The final installed capacity was 8x23-MW turbine generators, operating on a dual-pressure steam cycle, supplied by four reactors.

Construction commenced in October 1955 in those halcyon days for the construction industry when there were no public enquiries. At its peak the construction workforce was around 2000. Scottish contractors involved included Babcock and Wilcox, providing the boilers, and Mitchell's on civil works and cooling towers - those concrete *milk bottles* one sees on the right of the M74 when driving south through Dumfriesshire.

The four reactors started up during the period February 1959 and May 1960 and the station was officially opened on 2 May 1959 by the Lord Lieutenant for Dumfries, Sir John Crabbe OBE, MC, TD. During the life of the station the average electrical output has been 193 MW and it has operated with a typical load factor of 92%.

On 11th May 1967 experimental fuel in one channel of Reactor No. 2 melted. The reactor was shut down immediately. A piece of graphite from one of the sleeves lining a fuel channel had partially obstructed gas flow and caused overheating of the fuel. The reactor was out of action until August 1969 because of difficulties in removing the blockage but it has since operated satisfactorily.

In 1971 the UKAEA's nuclear fuel cycle business and the two Magnox stations, Calder Hall and Chapelcross, were transferred to the newly-established British Nuclear Fuels Ltd. (BNFL). The station is now operating under a 'safety case', endorsed by the Nuclear Installations Inspectorate, for operation to 50 years i.e. until 2009/10

Currently the preferred method for decommissioning is 'deferred safestore' involving the early removal of all fuel and external equipment (including the boilers) and weatherproofing the existing buildings for 30 years followed by the construction of an aluminium weather cover 'safe store' to last 100 years. At that time the reactor vessels and cores will be relatively easily dismantled due to the low level of remanent radiation.

Hunterston 'A'

The building of a civil nuclear power station in Scotland was first envisaged in a Government White Paper early in 1955. At that time no country in the world other than the UK had made proposals for a civil nuclear power programme. Calder Hall, the pioneering station in Cumberland, built to produce plutonium with electrical power as a by-product, was still under construction and its first electricity was a year away.

Of the first three stations, each with an electrical output of 300 MW, which set the programme in motion, two were to be built in England and one in Scotland.

Ideal or even suitable sites for nuclear power stations do not exist in abundance. Positive requirements include a large area of level ground, a firm foundation, preferably rock, to carry the great weight of the reactor buildings, proximity to a plentiful supply of cooling-water on a level with the site to minimise the need for pumping, and a substantial supply of fresh water for boiler make-up purposes. In addition it is desirable to site the station near the load centre.

The Hunterston site, on a promontory of the Ayrshire coast near West Kilbride, fulfilled the main requirements and Hunterston was therefore chosen as the site on which to build the Scottish station.

Following a public enquiry, consent for the project was granted in July 1957 and construction commenced shortly thereafter. The first reactor went 'critical' in September 1963 and the second in March 1964. Hunterston 'A' was a very successful station which for many years was in the top ten performers world wide. However, adverse economics caught up with it and, in March 1990, it closed down and is currently undergoing decommissioning along the lines detailed earlier for Chapelcross.

Hunterston 'A' was transferred first to Scottish Nuclear in 1990 and then to Magnox Ltd., which was the company established to retain all the Magnox stations of Nuclear Electric and Scottish Nuclear under Government ownership when British Energy was floated on the Stock Exchange. (British Energy is the holding company which owns Nuclear Electric and Scottish Nuclear). Subsequently Magnox Ltd. was merged with BNFL.

Hunterston 'B'

Hunterston 'B' power station shares the same site with Hunterston 'A'. Construction commenced in 1969 following a public enquiry and the chosen reactor type was the Advanced Gas-cooled Reactor (AGR). This type comprises a graphite core with 308 channels for enriched uranium oxide fuel elements, the core and boilers being contained within a cylindrical prestressed concrete pressure vessel with a wall thickness of 5 metres.

The two turbine generators are rated at 660 MW each with a generated voltage of 23.5 kV. Unit 1 generated electricity for the first time on 6 February 1976 and has operated successfully since. Unit 2 first generated electricity on March 1977. Following commissioning tests and achieving full power operation the unit was shut down for maintenance in October 1977. The gas pressure in the reactor was reduced to atmospheric and it then became apparent that sea water had entered a space inside the reactor pressure vessel but isolated from the core.

Central Control Room of Hunterston 'B' Power Sation
Courtesy of British Energy

There followed a major repair programme taking some 27 months, requiring 480 man-years effort at a cost of £13 million. Since re-commissioning the reactor has operated very successfully. The currently expected decommissioning date is 2011. British Energy's current decommissioning strategy is the 'safestore' approach with the following anticipated timings:

Stage 1 (0-3 years)	defuelling
Stage 2 (3-8 years)	preparation for safestorage
(8-135 years)	safestorage
Stage 3 (135-143 years)	return to green field site

Torness

Torness power station is situated near Dunbar on the east coast of Scotland and is a two-reactor station of an updated Hunterston 'B' design.

Following a public enquiry consent to build was granted in May 1978 and site work commenced in October of that year with construction starting in August 1980. The first unit went to power, on programme, in March 1988. Both units have operated very successfully. The current expected decommissioning date is 2023 at which time British Energy's current decommissioning 'safestore' strategy will be implemented.

What does the future hold?

Having looked back over the last 100 years at the growth of public electricity supply in Scotland it seems appropriate now to look forward to see what might happen in the future. As a guide consideration of the last ten years shows the following:

* Privatisation and deregulation of the industry
* No new major power stations
* The 'dash for gas' (currently a moratorium on large scale gas plants)
* Considerable excess in generating capacity in Scotland
* Considerable cost cutting and performance improvements in existing plants
* The growth in renewable generation
* Expansion of the grid connection with England
* Approval of the grid connection with Northern Ireland

A 660-MW turbine at Torness Nuclear Power Station
Courtesy British Energy

Projecting this scenario forward one can see no new major power stations in Scotland for at least the next 20 years. There will be an increase in the use of renewable technologies on a small scale and possibly some limited development of embedded generation but the main thrust of activity will be on 'life extension' of existing plants with some re-planting/re-powering. Conventional thermal plants can probably achieve a 60-year life, nuclear plants a 40/50-year life and the only life limiting feature on a hydro plant is the dam.

Efforts to export ever more electricity to England and soon to Northern Ireland will continue in order to improve the utilisation of spare, economic generating capacity.

With re-powering/re-planting and eventually a move towards more use of gas, when the moratorium is removed, as the most likely scenario it is interesting to look at the project nearing completion at Peterhead Power Station which demonstrates how efficiency and flexibility improvements can be implemented on an existing site.

Peterhead was commissioned in 1981 and comprised two 660-MW, gas/oil-fired reheat steam units. In 1989 two 115-MW gas-turbine units were added to improve flexibility and reliability to satisfy the 'must take' gas contract. Re-powering offers higher thermal efficiencies by converting existing *Rankine cycle* steam plant, where the fuel burned produces steam in a large boiler, to a combined cycle plant where the fuel is burned in high efficiency gas turbines to produce the electrical energy while the exhaust gas energy produces steam, in a heat recovery steam generator, which is then expanded in the existing 660-MW steam turbine also producing electrical power.

The hybrid re-powering concept adopted for Peterhead involves the retention of the existing main boilers to operate in parallel with the heat recovery steam generator rather than the traditional re-powering arrangement where the heat recovery steam generators simply replace existing boilers. This feature enables the plant to be operated in either pure combined cycle mode providing base load at peak efficiency, or hybrid mode when the existing boiler produces supplementary steam to enable peaking power to be provided but at a slightly reduced level of efficiency.

The scheme is created around 3 Siemens 94.3A gas turbines, each producing nominally 265 MWe, with their hot exhaust gases being passed to a horizontal natural circulation, reheat steam generator.

The anticipated plant performance and efficiency are shown below:-

| Parameter | Existing Plant | Re-powered Plant | |
	Rankine Cycle	Combined Cycle	Hybrid
Load MWe			
Steam Turbine	2x660	360	625
Gas Turbine	-	795	795
Plant Total	1320	1155	1420
Efficiency %	38	55+	51+

In addition, the second steam unit at Peterhead can be utilised when economics dictate that it would be advantageous to operate at the maximum station output of 1550 MWe. It is likely that we will see more schemes of this enlightened nature being developed in the future.

References

1. *Electricity Supply in the United Kingdom - A Chronology.* Issued by the Electricity Council. Fourth Edition 1987.
2. *Electricity Supply Handbook* - Published annually by the Electrical Review.
3. *Dounreay The Illustrated Story* by Stephen Caslunore, published by North of Scotland Newspapers.
4. *Tunnels and Dams - The Story of the Galloway Hydro Scheme* by George Hill.
5. *The development of the repowering Concept at Peterhead Power Station* by IHD O'Donnell.

Table 1
Power Stations Owned by ScottishPower

Name	Year*	Type	DNC/ MW**	Generator Details				Year Decom.
				Sets	MW	kV	Speed	
Pinkston	1901	Hand	-	-	-	-	-	-
	1907	fired-coal	-	-	-	-	-	-
Falkirk	1903	chain	-					
	1921	grate-	1.5	1	1.5	6.6	-	-
	1925	coal	3.0	1	3.0	6.6	-	-
	1941		3.0	1	3.0	6.6	-	-
Kilmarnock	1904		22.0	1	0.5	-	-	
				1	1.5	-	-	late
				1	2.5	-	-	1960s
				1	5.0	-	-	
	1918			1	12.5	-	-	
	1926	Chain	12.5	1	12.5	-	-	
	1940	grate-	30.0	1	30.0	22	3000	
	1943	coal	30.0	1	30.0	22	3000	
Dunfermline	1905	-	-	2	-	-	-	1932
	1919	chain	4.0	1	4.0	6.6	-	1932
	1922	grate-	6.0	1	6.0	6.6	-	1973
	1923	coal	3.0	1	3.0	6.6	-	1973
***	1955		12.5	1	12.5	11.0	-	1973
Yoker	1905	coal	4.0	2	2.0	-	-	1926
	1926	chain	20.0	1	20.0	11.0	3000	1973
	1931	-grate	20.0	1	20.0	11.0	3000	1973
	1937		30.0	1	30.0	11.0	3000	1976
	1939	coal	30.0	1	30.0	11.0	3000	1976
Bonnybridge	1905	-	-	-	-	-	-	-
	1923	chain	12.5	1	12.5	6.6		1973
	1924		5.0	1	5.0	6.6		1973
	1929	grate-	12.5	1	12.5	6.6		1973
	1944		20.0	1	20.0	11.0		1975
	1945	coal	20.0	1	20.0	11.0		1975
Greenock	1909	coal	1.0	1	1.0	-		1931
	1910	fired						
	1919		19.0	-	-	-		1941

*   year First set commissioned

**   DNC- Declared Net Capacity

***   12.5 MW Metropolitan Vickers 1924 set removed from
       Portobello and installed in Dunfermline in 1955

Table 1 (contd.)
Power Stations Owned by ScottishPower

Name	Year*	Type	DNC/ MW**	Generator Details				year decom.
				sets	MW	kV	Speed	
Galashiels	1914	-	1.5	2	0.75	-	-	-
	1924	chain grate-coal	1.875	1	1.875	6.6	-	-
	1929		3.75	1	3.75	6.6	-	-
Clydeshill	1916	chain grate- coal	10.0	2	5.0	11.0	3000	-
	1921		18.75	1	18.75	11.0	3000	-
	1926		18.75	1	18.75	11.0	3000	-
	1935		30.0	1	30.0	11.0	3000	1978
	1941		30.0	1	30.0	11.0	3000	
	1944		60.0	2	30.0	11.0	3000	
	1950		30.0	1	30.0	11.0	3000	demol
	1951		30.0	1	30.0	11.0	3000	
	1955		60.0	2	30.0	11.0	3000	
	1965	gas turb	55.0	1	55.0	11.8	3000	1984/5
Dalmarnock	1920	chain grate- coal	18.75	1	18.75	-	-	-
	1922		118.75	6	18.75	-	-	-
	1929							
	1937		50.0	1	50.0	-	1500	1977
	1938		50.0	1	50.0	-	1500	demol.
	1956		60.0	1	60.0	-	3000	1981
	1957		60.0	1	60.0	-	3000	
Ferguslie	1923	-	16.25	3	-	-	-	1957
+Bonnington	1926	hydro	10.0	2	5.0	11.0	375	
+ Stonebyres	1927	hydro	6.0	2	3.0	11.0	375	
Portobello	1929	chain grate- coal	62.5	2	31.25	11.0		-
	1938		30.0	1	30.0	11.0		-
	1951	p.f.	180.0	3	60.0	13.2	3000	1975
	1956							
++ Tongland	1935	hydro	33.0	3	11.0	11.0	214	-

*   year First set commissioned
**   DNC- Declared Net Capacity
+   Lanark Hydros - run-of-river
++   Galloway Hydro Electric Scheme

Table 1 (contd.)
Power Stations Owned by ScottishPower

Name	Year*	Type	DNC/ MW**	Generator Details				year decom.
				sets	MW	kV	Speed	
++Glenlee	1935	hydro	24.0	2	12.0	11.0	428	-
++Earlstoun	1936	hydro	14.0	2	7.0	11.0	214	-
++Carsfad	1936	hydro	12.0	2	6.0	11.0	214	-
++Kendoon	1936	hydro	21.0	2	10.5	11.0	250	-
++Druhjohn	1985	hydro	2.0	1	2.0	11.0	1005	-
Breahead	1951 ↓ 1953	p.f.	200.0	4	50.0	11.0	3000	1979
	1961	p.f.	60.0	1	60.0	11.0	3000	1979
Barony	1956	slurry	56.0	2	30.0	11.0	3000	1983
Kincardine	1958 ↓ 1953	p.f.	336.0	3	120.0	13.8	3000	1990
	1962 ↓ 1964	p.f.	376.0	2	200.0	16.0	3000	-
Methil	1965	slurry	56.0	2	30.0	11.8	3000	
Cruachan	1965	pump storage	400.0	4	100.0	16.0	2x500 2x600	
Cockenzie	1967	p.f.	1152.0	4	300.0	17.0	3000	
+++Longannet	1970	p.f.	2304.0	4	600.0	17.0	3000	
Inverkip	1976	p.f.	1890.0	3	676.0	23.5	3000	

*   year First set commissioned
**   DNC - Declared Net Capacity
++   Galloway Hydro Electric Scheme
+++ Cross Compound sets 300MW each line

Table 2
Scottish & Southern Energy plc

Station	Station max Output	Unit	Generator Output MW	Voltage kV	Speed rpm	Manufacturer	Year	Turbine type
Achanalt	3.0	No.1	3.0	11.0	336	Harland	1956	Kaplan
Aigas	20.0	No.1	10.0	11.0	188	Bruce Peebles	1963	Kaplan
		No.2	10.0	11.0	188	Bruce Peebles	1963	Kaplan
Allt na Lairige	6.0	No.1	6.0	11.0	429	Harland	1956	Pelton
Cashlie	11.0	No.1	11.0	11.0	500	Eng. Electric	1959	Francis
Cassley	10.0	No.1	2.5	11.0	750	Harland	1959	Francis
		No.2	7.5	11.0	429	Harland	1960	Francis
Ceann-acroc	20.0	No.1	16.0	11.0	375	Eng. Electric	1956	Francis
		No.2	4.0	11.0	500	Harland	1956	Francis
Chliostair	1.1	No.1	0.66	0.415	1000	AEI	1961	Francis
		No.2	0.66	0.415	1000	AEI	1961	Francis
Clachan	40.0	No.1	40.0	11.0	429	Eng. Electric	1955	Francis
Claddoch	0.21	No.1	0.11	0.415	1015	Bk.Cromptom	1950	Pelton
		No.2	0.1	0.415	1000	Bruce Peebles	1950	Pelton
Clunie	61.2	No.1	20.4	11.0	214	BTH	1950	Francis
		No.2	20.4	11.0	214	BTH	1950	Francis
		No.3	20.4	11.0	214	BTH	1950	Francis
Cuaich	2.5	No.1	2.5	3.3	755	Bruce Peebles	1959	Francis
Culligran	24.0	No.1	2.0	11.0	755	Bruce Peebles	1963	Francis
		No.2	22.0	11.0	300	Eng. Electric	1963	Deriaz
Deanie	38.0	No.1	19.0	11.0	375	Eng. Electric	1964	Francis
		No.2	19.0	11.0	375	Eng. Electric	1964	Francis
Dalchonzie	4.0	No.1	4.0	3.3	334	Bruce Peebles	1958	Kaplan
Errochty	75.0	No.1	25.0	11.0	429	GEC	1956	Francis
		No.2	25.0	11.0	429	GEC	1956	Francis
		No.3	25.0	11.0	429	GEC	1956	Francis
Fasnakyle	69.0	No.1	23.0	11.0	375	Eng. Electric	1952	Francis
		No.2	23.0	11.0	375	Eng. Electric	1952	Francis
		No.3	23.0	11.0	375	Eng. Electric	1952	Francis
Finlarig	30.0	No.1	30.0	11.0	375	BTH	1955	Pelton
Foyers p/s	300.0	No.1	150.0	-	273	ASEA	1975	Francis
		No.2	150.0	-	273	ASEA	1975	Francis
Foyers Falls	5.2	No.1	5.0	6.35	756	Bruce Peebles	1968	-
	-	No.2	-	-	-	-	-	-
Gaur	6.0	No.1	6.0	11.0	-	BTH	1953	-
		No.2	0.4	11.0	750	BTH	1953	Francis

Table 2 (contd.)
Scottish & Southern Energy plc - Hydro-Power Stations

Station	Station max Output	Unit	Generator Output MW	Voltage kV	Speed rpm	Manufacturer	Year	Turbine type
Gisla	0.72	No.1	0.72	3.0	-	AEI	1960	Francis
Glen-moriston	36.0	No.1	18.0	11.0	375	Eng. Electric	1958	Francis
		No.2	18.0	11.0	375	Eng. Electric	1958	Francis
Gorton	0.11	No.1	0.11	0.415	612	Eng. Electric	1969	Turgo
Grudie Bridge	24.0	No.1	12.0	11.0	500	Bruce Peebles	1950	Francis
		No.2	12.0	11.0	500	Bruce Peebles	1950	Francis
Inverawe	25.0	No.1	25.0	11.0	167	Eng. Electric	1963	Kaplan
Invergarry	20.0	No.1	20.0	11.0	250	Eng. Electric	1956	Kaplan
Kerry Falls	1.25	No.1	0.25	0.415	333	Bruce Peebles	1951	Turgo
		No.2	0.5	0.415	1000	Bruce Peebles	1953	Francis
		No.3	0.5	0.415	1000	Bruce Peebles	1953	Francis
Kilmel-fort	2.082	No.1	2.0	11.0	750	Bruce Peebles	1956	Francis
		No.2	0.082	0.415	1020	Bruce Peebles	1956	propeller
Kilmorack	20.0	No.1	10.0	11.0	188	Bruce Peebles	1962	Kaplan
		No.2	10.0	11.0	188	Bruce Peebles	1962	Kaplan
Lairg	3.5	No.1	3.5	3.3	167	Bruce Peebles	1959	Kaplan
Lednock	3.0	No.1	3.0	3.3	504	Bruce Peebles	1961	Francis
Livishie	15.0	No.1	15.0	11.0	750	AEI	1962	Francis
Lochay	45.0	No.1	22.5	11.0	500	Eng. Electric	1958	Francis
		No.2	22.5	11.0	500	Eng. Electric	1958	Francis
		No.3	2.0	3.3	435	Eng. Electric	1959	Pelton
Loch Dubh	1.2	No.1	0.6	0.415	750	Bruce Peebles	1954	Pelton
		No.2	0.6	0.415	750	Bruce Peebles	1954	Pelton
Loch Ericht	2.2	No.1	2.2	3.3	504	Bruce Peebles	1962	Francis
Loch Gair	6.0	No.1	6.0	11.0	500	AEI	1961	Francis
Loyne Tunnel	0.55	No.1	0.55	0.415	434	Bruce Peebles	1959	Kaplan
Lubreoch	4.0	No.1	4.0	3.3	334	Bruce Peebles	1961	Kaplan
Luichart	34.0	No.1	17.0	11.0	250	Eng. Electric	1954	Francis
		No.2	17.0	11.0	250	Eng. Electric	1954	Francis
Lussa	2.4	No.1	1.2	11.0	1000	Eng. Electric	1954	Francis
		No.2	1.2	11.0	1000	Eng. Electric	1954	Francis
Morar	0.75	No.1	0.375	0.415	333	Bruce Peebles	1948	Kaplan
		No.2	0.375	0.415	333	Bruce Peebles	1948	Kaplan
Mossford	24.0	No.1	12.0	11.0	500	Bruce Peebles	1957	Francis
		No.2	12.0	11.0	500	Bruce Peebles	1957	Francis
Mucomir	1.75	No.1	1.75	3.3	150	Harland	1962	Kaplan
		No.2	0.2	0.415	1012	Bruce Peebles	1962	propeller
Mullardoch	2.4	No.1	2.4	3.3	755	Bruce Peebles	1955	Francis
Nant	15.0	No.1	15.0	11.0	600	Harland	1963	Francis

Table 2 (contd.)
Scottish & Southern Energy plc - Hydro-Power Stations

Station	Station max Output	Unit	Generator				Year	Turbine type
			Output MW	Voltage kV	Speed rpm	Manufacturer		
Nostie	1.3	No.1	0.625	0.415	750	Bruce Peebles	1950	Turgo
Bridge		No.2	0.625	0.415	750	Bruce Peebles	1950	Turgo
Orrin	18.0	No.1	18.0	11.0	600	Bruce Peebles	1959	Francis
Pitlochry	15.0	No.1	7.5	11.0	167	Metro Vickers	1950	Kaplan
		No.2	7.5	11.0	167	Metro Vickers	1950	Kaplan
Quoich	22.0	No.1	22.0	11.0	300	Eng. Electric	1955	Francis
Rannoch	42.0	No.1	16.0	11.0	500	BTH	1930	Francis
		No.2	16.0	11.0	500	BTH	1930	Francis
		No.3	16.0	11.0	500	BTH	1930	Francis
Shin	24.0	No.1	12.0	11.0	375	Bruce Peebles	1959	Francis
		No.2	12.0	11.0	375	Bruce Peebles	1959	Francis
Sloy	152.5	No.1	40.0	11.0	429	Eng. Electric	1951	Francis
		No.2	40.0	11.0	429	Eng. Electric	1951	Francis
		No.3	40.0	11.0	429	Eng. Electric	1951	Francis
		No.4	32.5	11.0	429	Eng. Electric	1951	Francis
		No.5	0.45	-	-	Eng. Electric	1951	-
Sron Mor	5.0	No.1	5.0	11.0	303	Eng. Electric	1957	Francis
St Fillans	21.0	No.1	21.0	11.0	600	Bruce Peebles	1957	Francis
Storr	2.4	No.1	0.8	3.3	1000	Harland	1956	Francis
Lochs		No.2	0.8	3.3	1000	Harland	1956	Francis
		No.3	0.8	3.3	1000	Bruce Peebles	1956	Francis
Striven	8.0	No.1	4.0	3.3	600	Harland	1956	Francis
		No.2	4.0	3.3	600	Harland	1956	Francis
Tobermory	0.28	No.1	0.08	0.415	-	Bruce Peebles	1954	Francis
		No.2	0.2	0.415	-	Bruce Peebles	1954	Francis
Torr	15.0	No.1	7.5	11.0	167	Metro Vickers	1955	Kaplan
Achilty		No.2	7.5	11.0	167	Metro Vickers	1955	Kaplan
Tummel	34.0	No.1	17.0	11.0	300	BTH	1933	Francis
Bridge		No.2	17.0	11.0	300	BTH	1933	Francis
Vaich	0.32	No.1	0.32	0.415	508	Bruce Peebles	1958	Francis

Table 3
Scottish & Southern Energy plc
Dam and River Flow Compensation Sets (hydro)

Station	Station max Output	Unit	Generator			Manufacturer	Year	Turbine type
			Output MW	Voltage kV	Speed rpm			
Awe Barrage	0.886	No.1	0.443	0.55	386	Alstholm	1963	Bulb
		No.2	0.443	0.55	386	Alstholm	1963	Bulb
Bean-nachran	0.16	No.1	0.16	0.415	610	Bruce Peebles	1963	Kaplan
Cluanie	0.3	No.1	0.3	0.415	507	Bruce Peebles	1955	Francis
Clunie	0.15	No.1	0.145	0.415	508	Bruce Peebles	1951	Francis
		No.2	0.325	0.415	760	Bruce Peebles	1959	Francis
Duchally	0.45	No.1	0.125	0.415	610	Bruce Peebles	1959	Turgo
Dundreggan	0.16	No.1	0.16	0.415	1020	Bruce Peebles	1956	Propeller
Gaur	0.4	-	-	-	-	-	-	-
Invergarry	0.315	No.1	0.285	0.415	760	Bruce Peebles	1957	Francis
		No.2	0.03	0.415	760	Bruce Peebles	1957	Francis
Lochay Fish Pass	0.04	No.1	0.04	0.415	1020	Bruce Peebles	1958	Francis
Lochay Comp.*	2.054	No.1	2.054	-	-	-	-	-
Luichart	0.085	No.1	0.085	0.415	765	Bruce Peebles	1955	Francis
Meig	0.076	No.1	0.076	0.415	765	Bruce Peebles	1959	Francis
Misgeoch	0.35	No.1	0.35	0.415	760	AEI	1963	Francis
Mucomir	0.2	-	-	-	-	-	-	-
Orrin	0.22	No.1	0.056	0.415	1525	Bruce Peebles	1959	Francis
		No.1	0.2	0.415	760	Bruce Peebles	1959	Francis
Pitlochry	0.05	No.1	0.05	0.415	780	Bruce Peebles	1950	Francis
Quoich	0.35	No.1	0.35	0.415	762	Bruce Peebles	1957	Francis
Shin/ Diversion	0.1	No.1	0.1	0.415	434	Bruce Peebles	1959	Bulb
Stronuich	0.18	No.1	0.18	0.415	610	Bruce Peebles	1958	Kaplan
Tralaig	0.083	No.1	0.083	0.415	510	Bruce Peebles	1956	Kaplan
Trinafour	0.55	No.1	0.55	0.415	434	Bruce Peebles	1959	Turgo

* Comp= compensation

Table 4
Scottish & Southern Energy plc
Thermal Power Stations

Station	Year	Type	DNC/ MW	Generator				Year Decom
				Sets	Output MW	Voltage kV	Speed rpm	
Carolina Port	1965	Oil	-	2	129	13.8	3000	-
Peterhead	1981	Dual Gas/ Oil	1550	2	660	23.5	3000	
	1989	Gas Turbine		2	115	13.8	3000	

Diesel Stations

Lerwick	66.0 MW
Kirkwall	34.3 MW
Stornoway	26.2 MW
Loch Carnan	11.8 MW
Tiree	1.6 MW
Bowmore	6.2 MW
Barra	1.0 MW
Mobile Fleet	6.25 MW

Other details not included
since these sets are up-rated
or replaced relatively frequently

Table 5
Nuclear Power Stations in Scotland

Station (Operator)	Year*	Type	DNC/ MW **	Generator				Year Decom
				Sets	Output MW	Voltage kV	Speed rpm	
Chapelcross (BNF)	1959	Magnox	188	8	30.0	11.0	3000	2009
Dounreay (UKAEA)	1962(1)	Fast Reactor	15	1	15.0	11.0	3000	1977
Hunterston 'A' (Magnox)	1964	Magnox	300	6	60.0	11.8	3000	1991
Dounreay (UKAEA)	1975	Fast Reactor	250	1	300.0	11.0	3000	1994
Hunterston 'B' (B.E.)	1976	AGR	1190	2	660.0	23.0	3000	2011
Torness (B.E.)	1987	AGR	1250	2	676.0	23.0	3000	2023

*   year first set commissioned;
**   DNC = Declared Net Capacity;
(1)   reactor critical in 1959 and achieved full design output in 1962

(ii) Development of the Electricity Grid Transmission System in Scotland

by Fred Breingan CEng, MIEE
and Iain Alexander McKenzie BSc, CEng, MIEE

Prior to the Electricity Supply Act of 1926 the provision of electricity supply in Britain was in the control of individual local authorities and private power companies. Each had a monopoly of the supply of electricity in its particular area. There was no standardisation of the voltage or frequency of the supply. Some authorities generated DC others AC, voltages varied from 2.2kV to 11kV and frequencies ranged from 25Hz to 100Hz. Most power stations operated independently, and, as each had to cover all the energy needs of its area, each required enough spare plant to maintain the supply during plant overhauls or breakdowns. As a consequence, there was some 70% more installed plant in the country than was actually necessary to meet the maximum demand at any one time.

The Weir Report of 1925

Nationally, such a haphazard system was unacceptable and wasteful and, in 1925, the Government appointed a Committee under Lord Weir *to review the National Problem of the supply of Electrical Energy*. The Weir Committee reported the same year, and recommended the concentration of electrical power generation to a limited number of large and efficient power stations, all of which would be interconnected by a high voltage **Grid** network. Authorities owning the power stations would sell their entire output to an Electricity Board operating the network, and in turn, they and other undertakings (suppliers) would buy electrical energy back from the Board according to requirements. The Weir Committee's recommendations were accepted, and the Electricity Supply Act 1926 became law.

In 1927, the **Central Electricity Board (CEB)** was created and embarked on the task of selecting those efficient stations which would form the back-bone of a Grid system interconnected by means of a transmission network operating at **132 kV, 3 phase, 50 Hz**. The selected stations would continue to be operated by their owners but, on the instruction of the new CEB, non-selected power stations would close down.

The First National Control

Initially the whole system was run as a number of separate systems, each with its own Control Centre. Interconnectors between centres were closed only when emergency assistance from one to another was required. When the first National Control was set up in 1938, they closed up the whole network and ran it as an integrated system in the face of 'expert opinion' who claimed that it was impossible to run so many generators in parallel; there were no problems. The Grid has operated fully integrated ever since.

In Central and South Scotland, the Central Electricity Board was faced with the task of linking up all the main power stations within the central belt. This involved interconnecting stations as far apart as Greenock in the west and Portobello in the east. In addition, it was charged with collecting the surplus output from the new hydro-electric station owned by the Grampian Electricity Supply Company at Rannoch (48MW) and at Tummel Bridge (34MW).

The scheme network so designed took the form of a figure of eight with east and west loops from Dalmarnock Power Station at the Centre. A spur, taken from the east loop at Bonnybridge, was routed through Fife to Abernethy via the power stations at Dunfermline and Kirkcaldy. In addition to the benefits of interconnecting the power stations, the scheme had the advantage of providing power supplies to places which had no local generating plant. Thus, Saltcoats and Abernethy had the distinction of being the first grid supply points to receive power from the grid for local consumer loads.

During the late 1920s, purchases of land and acquisitions of wayleave consents allowed the construction of new substations and the erection of overhead line interconnections to proceed at speed. The pace at which the network was built was due in no small measure to the degree of standardisation of the equipment used for its design and construction.

The UK plant position in 1937/38 was that 94% of generating sets were still smaller than 30MW. A 105-MW set had been built and was operating in Battersea Power Station in London from as early as 1935, so choice of set size was not constrained by an inability to build larger sets. By 1939, national reserve capacity requirements had been reduced to less than 30% which was enough to justify the £30 million spent on building the Grid and the further investment by companies in new plant to conform to the frequency standard of 50Hz. As far as the consumer was concerned, a **55% reduction in the cost of electricity** over the period was a tangible benefit. Average thermal efficiency increased from

15.54% in 1930 to 20.69% in 1938. The best sets at this time were achieving 28% thermal efficiency.

World War II revealed a further advantage of the Grid. It allowed considerable flexibility in the siting of plant and major loads. The Grid became a valuable energy transport network which allowed existing strategic installations to be relocated and new ones to be supplied quickly.

An example of this in Scotland occurred on 6 May, 1941: Greenock (Dellingburn) Power Station was substantially destroyed by enemy bombing. Supplies to Greenock were restored from the Grid within a week. This was achieved using a spare transformer positioned temporarily on railway sleepers beside the access road and reconnecting 11-kV cables to the power station busbars. Dellingburn Grid substation adjacent to the former power station, referred to in this incident, was only finally decommissioned in 1999.

The pylons and conductors

Interconnection between substations was achieved by stringing stranded steel-core aluminium conductors between steel lattice pylons. Such pylons functioned as suspension or end-strain towers and were designed to carry single- or double-circuits. Conductors were suspended or held in tension by means of porcelain insulators and metal fittings attached to tower arms. Special towers or gantry type structures were designed to cater for differing and difficult types of end strain termination. The most distinctive towers were the 300 feet high and carried the Port Dundas-Greenock and Yoker-Paisley circuits across the River Clyde at Renfrew Ferry.

Current-carrying phase conductors consisted of 7 strands of steel surrounded by 30 strands of aluminium, while the top earth wire had 7 strands of steel covered by 12 strands of aluminium.

Substations

The standard substations with two overhead line terminations and two step-up transformers had three circuit breakers. Yoker, Greenock, Paisley, Clydesmill, Motherwell, Dunfermline and Kirkcaldy were three-switch substations. The three-switch layout could be readily modified to a four-switch mesh configuration and where three overhead lines and two step-up transformers were involved, a five-switch layout was developed. Bonnybridge, for example, was a five-switch substation and in time, Portobello and Kilmarnock would be similarly modified.

Dalmarnock with four feeder overhead line terminations and two step-up transformers was designed with two sets of bus-bars. 132-kV circuit breakers could be used to section off two halves of the main busbars, and couple together both main and reserve busbars.

Circuit Breakers and Transformers

Circuit breakers were of the solenoid-operated large oil volume type: each single-phase tank containing approximately 1500 gallons of insulating oil. Electricity was conducted through multi-shed porcelain bushings to a multi-break contact system housed in an arc control chamber. Thus arc extinction was achieved by the injection of fresh oil into the arc control chamber at the instant of contact separation.

With the exception of the transformers at Dalmarnock, transformer units were generally of 15-MVA or 20-MVA capacity. Dalmarnock, at the centre of the network and the location of greatest local demand, had two 60-MVA units. However, due to transport weight limitations, each transformer was made up of 3 single-phase, 20-MVA units. HV to LV windings were star/delta configuration. Through 15 tapping positions at the neutral end of the HV winding it was possible to achieve voltage variations of plus or minus 10% of the nominal voltage by means of an on-load tap change mechanism which could operate either manually or automatically.

Isolators, interconnectors and the first 132-kV system in Scotland

In all substations, manually-operated interlocked isolators were installed at appropriate positions to permit the removal from service of any item of plant for repair or routine maintenance.

In 1929, the first interconnector between the power stations at Dalmarnock and Bonnybridge was commissioned and, with the 20-MVA transformer at Bonnybridge, became the first 132-kV system in Scotland (and possibly in Britain) to be connected as part of the Grid Network. After the commissioning of any item of plant, the control and security of operation of the plant became the responsibility of a team of control engineers who operated from a control centre at the Central Electricity Board (C.E.B.) Central & South West Scotland Headquarters at Broomhill, Glasgow.

As the various sections of the network were brought into service it became clear that, with an increasing demand for electrical energy, both in the home and at work, extensions to the network would be necessary. The first extension, during the early 1930s was the construction of a line from Portobello to Galashiels. This connected the Grid to the famous **33-kV Berwick Ring**, and brought the latter under control of the Grid Engineers.

Hydro-electric power

At about this time, a group of civil engineers were investigating the possibilities of harnessing the waters of the Rivers Doon, Dee and Deuch Water with the intention of constructing a series of dams and hydro-electric stations to serve Galloway and Stewarty of Kirkcudbright.

The resultant Galloway scheme with five hydro-electric power stations, Carsfad, Kendoon, Earlston, Glenlee and Tongland were commissioned during the years 1935-36. Connection to the Grid System was achieved by the construction of an overhead line from Kilmarnock. This line was subsequently routed from Tongland to Dumfries and further extended to Carlisle. Although the Galloway scheme was originally conceived as a base load system, its connection to the Grid System enabled its combined output of 103MW to be utilised to maximum effectiveness.

The National Grid

In the Borders, a line was built between Galashiels and Wooler in Northumberland so that, by 1938, two cross-border connections between Scotland and England were available. This resulted in a more meaningful understanding to the commonly used expression *National Grid*. The network serviced Scotland well during the 1939-45 War. Although frequently overloaded and stretched to its limits, during the War the only reinforcement of any importance was the construction of a line from Galashiels to Carlisle which provided a valuable east-west link in South Scotland.

To eliminate a possible hazard in the flight paths of aircraft flying from Renfrew (then Glasgow) and Abbotsinch (RN) Airports, a seven-tower section of the Yoker-Paisley line and a twelve-tower section of the Port Dundas-Greenock line were cabled underground. These were the first lengths of 132kV oil-filled cable to be installed in the Central Scotland.

Nationalisation and the Grid to the Supergrid

Very little new generating plant was built during World War II, which resulted in a severe shortage of generating plant at the end of the war in 1945. The labour government of the day decided to nationalise the industry, which they did in 1947. This allowed a concerted effort to be made to build new, large power stations to provide a reliable electricity supply for the post war reconstruction of Britain. There were significant advantages to be gained if the new plant could be built on the coalfields, and the energy transferred as electricity to the fuel deficient areas of the country.

The Electricity Act of 1947 brought the electricity supply industry into public ownership, and created the **British Electricity Authority**. Existing undertakings, some 560 in number nationally, were assimilated into **Area Electricity Boards**. Those Boards were made responsible for the generation and transmission of power. On Vesting Day, 1st April 1948, in Central and South Scotland, management, operation and control of the Grid system remained much the same, except for the change to public ownership. Routine maintenance and fault repair of the System was the responsibility of the Transmission Operation and Maintenance Section, which had five geographically located depots within the region. These depots at Parkhead (Glasgow), Kilmarnock, Portobello, Galashiels and Tongland had sufficient engineering resource of skilled craftsmen and linesmen to carry out routine maintenance and repairs as necessary.

Post-war growth in demand and load-shedding

With the war over, the demand for electricity grew at an enormous rate. This increase was due in the main to the recovery of old and the development of new industries; although, a populace, weary of restrictions and seeking a better standard of living through greater usage of electricity, also contributed to the demand. The existing plant, much of which was of original installation, was in urgent need of replacement. Available generation output could not meet demand, and regular periods of load-shedding to limit usage and maintain system stability, had to be introduced. With an estimated annual growth demand of 10%, the Supply Industry embarked on an immense programme of expansion and reinforcement covering the next 20-25 years.

While it was possible to refurbish and uprate a number of existing power stations such as Portobello, Clydesmill, and Dalmarnock, a new type of high thermal efficiency power station was planned and progressively brought into service: for example, Braehead, Hunterston A, Kincardine and Chapelcross. The generated output from these stations fed directly to the Grid connected by double bus-bar switching stations via integral generator transformers.

The Braehead 132-kV Substation is of particular interest, being the first wholly indoor substation in Scotland: it was built on three levels, with bus-bars on the top and bottom levels and circuit breaker chambers, which housed small volume oil type switchgear, were located between the bus-bars. Outgoing feeder circuits were connected to nearby overhead line terminal towers by 132-kV underground cables.

The Hunterston 132-kV substation is a conventional double bus-bar design, equipped with air-blast current breakers. Due to its direct connection to a Nuclear Power Station and the need to protect the switchgear against faults from atmospheric pollution, the substation was completely enclosed within a roofed barn type building. Through-wall bushings connected the switchgear to the overhead line terminal towers.

At other locations, a number of three-switch substations were replaced by extensible multi-circuit double-bar bus-substations, for example, Clydesmill, and Bonnybridge.

Clydesmill with additional feeder circuits became the northern terminal of an interconnector between Scotland and England. Known as the Harker Line, this twin-conductor double-circuit line operated initially at 132kV, although its tower design and insulation level made it capable of operation at 275kV.

Bonnybridge, also of double bus-bar layout, was extended to receive surplus power from the North of Scotland Hydro-Electric generating stations in Tummel Valley.

132kV high power flow flexibility

To facilitate the interchange of bulk power within the Grid system a number of large 132-kV switching stations were established at strategic locations. These were at Windyhill, Neilston, Currie, and Westfield.

With interconnection to the other new substations a network of high power flow, flexibility and reliability was achieved. Most of the output from Hunterston 'A' was sent to Neilston; the output from Loch Sloy Hydro-Power Station was sent to Windyhill. Thus bulk power from stations in relatively remote locations was connected to the Grid System at switching substations close to the main load centres. These new switching substations were also the source for a large number of bulk supply substations which were situated in areas of high industrial and commercial development. In this way power supplies at transmission voltage were taken to distribution points, which hitherto had been wholly dependant on the distribution network for its source of energy.

Typical 132-kV grid supply substations were at Newarthill, Coatbridge, Cupar, Devonside, Leven, Partick, Kilbowie, Govan, Haggs Road, St Andrews Cross, Broxburn, Bathgate, Telford Road, Gorgie and others.

In 1955 political pressures were again instrumental in the re-shaping of the management structure of the supply industry in South Scotland - **the South of Scotland Electricity Board (SSEB)** was formed. This new Board, combined in one all-purpose unit, the functions previously carried out by the Area Boards and the Scottish Division of the British Electricity Authority. It had responsibility for all aspects of electricity supply within its area - from the power station plant to consumer terminals. With ever-increasing load growth, it became evident that the 132-kV Grid System had reached saturation, and that future development of the Grid would have to be at the nationally accepted higher voltage of 275kV.

The Supergrid - 275kV and 400kV

The 132-kV Grid lacked the capacity for the bulk transmission of power between regions. In 1950 the decision was taken to build a **275-kV Supergrid**, upgradeable to 380kV. In 1960 it was decided that a **400kV Supergrid** should be established, to be achieved initially by upgrading existing 275-kV lines and later by building purpose designed 400-kV lines. One consequence in Scotland was that the four 132-kV lines out of Hunterston, which were 275-kV construction, could be uprated to 400kV when the additional 1200 MWso* from Hunterston 'B' came on stream. This required re-insulation and restringing, but the existing towers and wayleaves could still be used.

During the early 1960s a 275-kV ring was constructed round the main centres of population in the Forth and Clyde Valleys. This Supergrid ring stretched from Windyhill to Lambhill, to Kincardine, to Grangemouth, to Kaimes, Strathaven, Busby, Neilston and back to Windyhill. While new 275-kV substations were established, many were 275-kV extensions to 132-kV substations. The cross-border connection between Clydesmill and Harker was uprated to 275kV and the northern end terminated at the new switching station, at Strathaven.

A spur from this substation provided a 275-kV reinforcement to Ayrshire with bulk supply substations at Kilmarnock, and Ayr.

---

*so = *sent out,* (for example a 660-MW machine, e.g. Longannet or Hunterston "B", delivers 600MW to the Supergrid, the rest feeds all the auxiliaries associated with the machine.)

Substations in the new 275-kV supergrid ring were generally equipped with air-blast circuit breakers which, when operated, gave noise levels of the order of 110dB. In locations where such noise levels were unacceptable large oil volume 275-kV "lenticular" current breakers were installed.

From substations on the outskirts of Edinburgh and Glasgow, 275-kV cables brought power into the city centres. In Edinburgh, Whitehouse Loan and Dewar Place were supplied from Kaimes, while in Glasgow, West George Street and Charlotte Street were supplied Lambhill, Giffnock was fed from Busby.

Ravenscraig Steel Works received a 275-kV cabled supply from a new 275-kV Substation at Wishaw.

System Control

With the rapid development of both the Grid and Supergrid Systems, the System Control Centre at Broomhill in Glasgow became overloaded and outdated. A new Centre at Kirkintilloch was established and control and operation was exercised from this new Centre.

The generation power input to the 275-kV System was further increased by the commissioning of two large power stations: Cockenzie with an output of 1200MW and Longannet with output of 2400MW. Like Hunterston 'A', the substation associated with each power station was enclosed within a building to protect switchgear from possible salt spray or other atmospheric pollution. Circuit breakers were air-blast and the modern configuration of one and a half switches per outgoing circuit was adopted for both substations.

Reinforcing the interconnection capacity

With the output from these highly efficient power stations connected to the System, it was considered prudent to reinforce the interconnection capacity with adjoining Boards. To this end, a 275-kV interconnector between Cockenzie and Stella (N.E. England) was built, and lines from Kincardine and Glenrothes in Fife to Tealing in Angus consolidated additional ties with the North of Scotland Hydro-Electric Board (NSHEB). In anticipation that the Cockenzie-Stella line might eventually be uprated to 400kV, the design and construction of the circuit was arranged to allow for this. In the west, the output from the pumped-storage hydro-station at Cruachan was connected to the 275-kV substation at Windyhill.

By the early 1970s a number of the older power stations were so inefficient that their removal from service was inevitable. To restore the balance, two further power stations were programmed: Hunterston 'B' (Nuclear AGR*) and Inverkip (oil fired). With a combined output of 3000MW connections had to be made at 400kV. From each of the associated 400-kV substations, quadruple-conductor overhead lines transmitted the output to Neilston, Windyhill and Kilmarnock South, where it was transferred to the Supergrid system by 400/275-kV 1000-MVA transformers. A loop from one of the Inverkip circuits to Devol Moor provided a valuable reinforcement to West Renfrewshire and the towns of Greenock, Gourock and Port Glasgow.

A second nuclear AGR power station was commissioned at Torness during the mid-1980s. As with other power stations in coastal areas, both the 400-kV and the adjacent auxiliary 132-kV substations were protected from weather and enclosed in buildings. Modern switchgear in both substations used Sulphur Hexafluoride (SF_6) gas as insulant and arc extinguishing medium. The 1300-MW output was transmitted across the Pentland Hills by two double-circuit 400-kV lines to link up with the Supergrid System at Cockenzie, Stella and a new switching substation at Smeaton.

Privatisation and continuous trading of bulk energy
The interconnection to England and Wales was initially at 132kV, using 275-kV construction. After the mid-1950s, when the South of Scotland Electricity Board (SSEB) (1955) and the Central Electricity Generating Board (CEGB) (1957) were established, the respective systems north and south of the border were planned for zero net transfer, apart from 'economic transfers and emergencies'. This was how the interconnector was used up to 1990, when the industry was privatised. The interconnectors had been upgraded to 275kV as the Scottish system was developed.

Under privatisation the interconnectors started to be used for continuous trading of bulk energy. This activity has become a major component of the Scottish generating companies' business. The Anglo-Scottish interconnector now operates at 400kV, the two parts of the Scottish 400-kV system are connected and interconnector capacity has been doubled to meet the trading duty. The additional capacity is fully utilised for bulk energy export. A further increase in the capacity of the

_____
* AGR = Advanced Gas-cooled Reactor

Anglo-Scottish interconnection is planned. The duty expected of the transmission system has thus escalated.

In 1988, after 50 years of public authority control, the Supply Industry was returned to private ownership: **ScottishPower** was formed. The decline in traditional heavy industries of shipbuilding, iron and steel manufacture, coal mining and the like, led to a reduction in the total demand on the system. With modern high performance power stations operating ideally at maximum output, the economic need to enhance the export capability was recognised, and the original interconnector between Clydesmill/ Strathaven/ Harker circuits were replaced by a new 400-kV double-circuit line. This effectively doubled the cross-border transfer capacity. While further increases in Anglo-Scottish interconnections are being considered, a part overhead line, part under sea cable 275-kV connection between Coylton and Northern Ireland is being planned.

Since first commissioned in 1920 the Grid and its successor the Supergrid has increased five-fold, both in the number of primary substations and in circuit miles. Almost all of the initially installed substation plant has been replaced but a number of the original 132-kV circuits are still in service. These old circuits become most valuable assets when set against amenity and environmental bodies, who vigorously oppose further development of new overhead line circuits, in the belief that they disfigure the countryside. On a straight circuit-for-circuit replacement basis valid arguments by these groups disappear.

Over the years, the Transmission System had proved to be a most reliable source of electrical energy to the inhabitants of Scotland, and has contributed substantially to the prosperity of the inhabitants.

(iii) Electricity Supply in Dumfries and Galloway
by R D Cowan CEng, MIEE

The very fact that when the electricity supply network of Dumfries and Galloway was developed it needed 4,600 miles of overhead line, enough to stretch across the Atlantic, London to New York and halfway back, to supply its 76,000 customers, tells us not only of the enormous benefits to the rural population but that that it is not typical. This electrification was made possible by four generations of high calibre, dedicated and versatile Electricity Supply Engineers.

Of course, this was the home of many of Scotland's most famous men - the king of Scotland Robert the Bruce (born 1274 in Lochmaben), Ayrshire born Robert Burns (Scotland's bard), Kirkpatrick MacMillan (of bicycle fame), Edinburgh born James Clerk Maxwell (known world-wide for his equations on electrodynamics), Thomas Carlyle (the literary genius), Sir John Richardson (the Arctic explorer and naturalist), to name but a few.

The most important resources in any Electricity Supply Unit are the employees and the distribution system. They have a major effect on how good (or bad) a service is given to the customer. Most employees in Dumfries and Galloway were prepared to go above and beyond the call of duty.

Engine Room - Crichton Royal Institution - 1895 *Courtesy of CRI archives*

Overhead Lines

The first overhead lines in Dumfries and Galloway were erected during the early 1900s. They were mostly low-voltage lines on wood pole supports. They replaced the short earlier lines which were installed by private estates from their engine houses to their mansion houses. In 1903 overhead lines were erected at Portpatrick to supply street lighting and domestic consumers.

From about 1913 the Burgh of Dumfries had its own hydro-electric generating station on the banks of the River Nith (the building is now the Burns Museum). An overhead line across the Nith linked up the little hydro-electric station with the Maxwelltown and the town supply systems.

In the Stewartry of Kirkcudbright five small undertakings were set up to generate and distribute electricity between 1912 and 1926. Steel poles, some of which are still in use today, were used for low voltage distribution.

The first high voltage line (6.6 kV) in Dumfries and Galloway was probably erected during World War I (1914-18) from the Ministry of Supply's power station at Gretna to the munitions factory at Eastriggs. During the 1920s a 33-kV line was erected between Willowholme power station at Carlisle to Gretna where the voltage was stepped down to 6.6 kV.

After World War II (1939-45) the rapid increase in demand for electrical energy threatened overloading of the 11-kV system of the 1930s. It had to be extended in all three counties: five hundred miles of 33-kV overhead line was erected and twenty-eight 33/11kV primary substations were established to reinforce the existing 11-kV systems.

After nationalisation of the electrical system in 1948 the British Electricity Authority standardised voltages and other specifications for the erection of lines. During the 1950s to the 1970s the old wooden poles, now showing signs of rot, were replaced in an extensive renewal. Larger conductors were used carry higher currents and to give greater mechanical strength thus meeting the ever-increasing demand for electrical energy.

Even when well maintained, overhead lines are vulnerable to gales, snow and icing and the effects of lightning. The forces of nature are responsible for the vast majority of the problems whilst

those encountered from equipment failure (switchgear, transformers and underground cables) are minimal. However, the engineers realised that many faults on the high-voltage overhead systems (particularly the 11-kV systems) were of a transient nature and that the performance of the system could be greatly improved if the supply to consumers could be restored immediately after a transient fault. Extensive development in collaboration with the manufacturers was carried out on all the then available types of pole-mounting and ground-mounting automatic reclosing switchgear. This development work was carried out during the 1950s and the early 1960s and was led by the Area Engineer **Stewart Money** assisted by Technical Engineers **Robert D Cowan, Stewart Craig, Charles Jack, John McKeown** and several others.

In the 1970s the original main lines of the 1930s still performed well; a large percentage had steel-cored aluminium conductors and were over forty years old. However, conductor breakages of steel conductors on spur lines were giving cause for concern. A major renewal of 800 miles of spurs was completed during the 1980s in Kirkcudbrightshire, Dumfriesshire and Wigtownshire where cadmium copper conductors were simply not strong enough to withstand the gales in the Machars and Rhins peninsulas.

During the 1980s and until the present day a programme of replacing and rebuilding the high-voltage overhead line system is ongoing, many of these lines being over fifty years old. At the same time, many of the low-voltage overhead line systems in towns such as Stranraer, Dalbeattie, Annan, Langholm, Castle Douglas, Sanquhar and others will be placed underground.

These overhead lines have completely transformed domestic living; the paraffin lamps and gas lighting were replaced by the more convenient and efficient electric light, heating, washing, cleaning, cooking, food freezing and in-house entertainment all of which depend on electricity, gave us more and richer leisure time. Between the years 1930 and 1948 the number of consumers increased from 4600 to almost 35,000, today there are 76,000 consumers; the consumption of electrical energy increased from 9 million units (kWh) to 95 million in the same period and today it has reached over 800 million units.

On farms the change has been even more dramatic - before electricity arrived, one man could only milk about 10 cows. Farms with large herds had to employ quite a number of people for milking. With the coming of the electric milking machine one man could milk a large herd on his own. At the same time electricity can be used for heating, sterilising equipment and any motive power requirements. The same sort of revolution has been carried through in factories, workshops, hospitals, office and shops. Outside the home and workplace streets are well lit with traffic signals to control and to ease traffic flow.

What will the future bring? In 1990 the electricity supply industry was privatised. The industry being taken over was no lame duck, it was well organised, efficient and its staff were well motivated. The tariffs were amongst the cheapest in Europe and many members of the general public were of the opinion that we were going back to the dark days before nationalisation in 1948. This opinion is much too simple. In 1948, over 500 relatively small undertakings were taken into public ownership and welded into supply units. Since then, the scale of developments and integration of systems is such, that this will continue in privatisation. As demand for more electrical power reaches saturation, huge load increases of the 1950s and 1960s are unlikely. However, with good management and staff well motivated, there is no reason why progress in places like Dumfries and Galloway and elsewhere should not continue.

The electricity supply industry of Dumfries and Galloway developed from small beginnings at the start of the century and today its product, electrical energy, is used in every home, farm factory, shop, school and other premises. The community has experienced many benefits - from paraffin lamps and the gas light to the convenience and efficiency of electric light; from the flat iron heated on an open fire to the thermostatically controlled electric iron; from the carpet beater to the vacuum cleaner; from cooking on a smoky open fire to the electric cooker; from the pantry to the refrigerator; from the 'wireless set' powered by the old rechargeable accumulator to the 'hi-fi' and the CD player; from the weekly washing in a crude coal-fired boiler with the zinc scrubbing board and the hand-wringer to the automatic electric washing machine; from the zinc bath in front of an open fire to the electric shower; from houses without heating to central heating with off-peak supplies - life has changed beyond recognition with added richness to our leisure time. Changes on the farm have been just as dramatic - from hand milking when one man or woman milked a few cows to electric milking machinery which can deal with a whole herd in a few minutes; from the cold, dark barn to the well lit and heated cow shed. In factories, workshops, hospitals, offices and shops, motive power, automation and computers improved speed and efficiency to previously unimagined heights, all of whch have been brought about by the ingenuity and inventiveness of engineers.

A chronology of the developments in Dumfries and Galloway over the last 100 years is given below and gives a clear indication of the many benefits which have been brought to the people of this area.

Chronology of Electricity Supply Developments in Dumfries and Galloway, 1899-1999

Late 1800s
Private generating plants (mainly for lighting) installed in a limited number of estates, works, shops, hospitals.

1894
Crichton Royal Institution (Psychiatric Hospital) built a power station and installed three steam-driven engines and DC generators to provide supply to their various premises. Consulting Engineer was **Professor Bottomley**, a nephew of **Lord Kelvin**. This plant ran until late 1930s. The Crichton was one of the first mental hospitals in the U.K. to use electric shock treatment for relieving depression.

1899
Dumfries Town Council granted a Provisional Order to supply electricity within the Burgh (not taken up until 1906).

1903/04
Portpatrick Electric Supply Co. Ltd., Wigtownshire granted a Provisional Order to supply Portpatrick and within a two mile radius of village. Works commissioned in 1904. Leading light Mr Charles Lindsay Orr-Ewing, MP for Ayr Burgh. Company went into liquidation in 1922.

1906/07
Dumfries Town Council accept an offer by India Rubber Gutta-percha and Telegraph Co. Ltd., of London to take over responsibilities granted to them in the Provisional Order of 1899 to generate, distribute and supply electricity within the Burgh. The Council included in the Contract an option to purchase the works at specified dates up to 42 years. Consumers started being connected in 1907.

In 1909 a separate Company was formed - Dumfries Electricity Supply Co. Ltd. In 1913 this Company obtained a Provisional Order to supply Maxwelltown on the other side of the River Nith. In 1923 Dumfries Town Council exercised their option to purchase the undertaking from the Dumfries Electricity Supply Co. Ltd.

1912/26

Small undertakings started in Twynholm Village (1912), St. John's Town of Dalry (1919), Castle Douglas (1923), Dalbeattie (1924), Gretna (1925) and Gatehouse of Fleet (1926).

1914/18

Ministry of Supply build a Power Station at Rigg near Gretna and provide high and low-voltage distribution to supply their munitions complex at Longtown, Gretna, Eastriggs, Dornock and Workers' houses. Factory manufacturered Cordite and ceased at the end of the 1914/18 War. The Power Station had steam turbines with a total capacity of 10.5 MW. The underground and overhead distribution was 6.6 kV. The distribution transformers from 100 to 1000 kVA were duplicated in every substation.

1914/18

Ministry of Supply build a small hydro-electric station (400 hp) near Tongland in Kirkcudbrightshire to supply factory carrying out war work (Galloway Engineering Co Ltd). At the end of the war, the factory was taken over by Arrol Johnson who for a time built the "Galloway" car there (a small car costing about £500).

1926

Electricity Supply Act proposing the erection of a National Grid to operate at 132kV to link power stations with larger generation units and make a reduction in spare plant (reduced from 80% to 15%). Work started in 1929 and the first scheme in Central Scotland was completed in 1931. The Grid reached Dumfries about 1934.

1929

Galloway Water Power Act, passed by Parliament giving the Galloway Water Power Company the right to develop the water power from Loch Doon, Clatteringshaws, River Dee etc, to operate generators in Power Stations at Kendoon, Carsfad, Earlstoun, Glenlee and Tongland, all in the Stewartry of Kirkcudbright. Scheme was completed in 1935. Combined capacity of stations 107 MW. The scheme is still working and generating 'cheap' units for ScottishPower. As early as 1923 Major Wellwood Maxwell, convenor of Kirkcudbright County Council and Captain Scott Elliot discussed whether the water power resources could be harnessed. They contacted Colonel McLellan, a native of Dalbeattie, and a partner in the firm of Merz and McLellan, the well-known Consulting Engineers. The matter was taken to conclusion when Sir Alexander Gibb and Partners carried out a feasibility study.

1929

Dumfries County Council, Stewartry of Kirkcudbright County Council and the Wigtownshire Electricity Co. Ltd., all granted Provisional Orders to supply electricity within their boundaries. By 1935 all three had established high- and low-voltage underground and overhead networks to supply their predominantly rural customers. The three companies took bulk supplies from the new National Grid. However, in Dumfriesshire, while awaiting the new Grid, the supply to a good part of their newly-built system came from Carlisle power station in England. The small undertakings, which started up between 1912 and 1926 and generated direct current, were taken over by the new company. Dumfries Burgh, which started in 1906, continued as a separate unit until 1948.

1948

1 April - Electricity Supply Industry in U.K. comes under public ownership. Dumfries and Galloway became a sub-area of the South West Scotland Electricity Board with five operational districts. Mr. **John Pickles** (later Sir John Pickles), County Electrical Engineer in Dumfriesshire became the first Chairman of the South West Scotland Board. His deputy in Dumfriesshire, **HW Wills**, became the first Manager of the new Dumfries and Galloway Sub-area (Pickles and Wills published their pioneering work on single-phase rural distribution in 1946 (7)). **SH Money**, the County Electrical Engineer in the Stewartry of Kirkcudbright, became the first Sub-Area Engineer.

1955

South West Scotland and South East Scotland Electricity Boards combine to form the **South of Scotland Electricity Board (SSEB).** The responsibilities for transmission and generation within the new board were transferred from the British Electricity Authority. The Board became an all-purpose Board similar to the North of Scotland Hydro-Electric Board. Dumfries and Galloway remained an Area of the new Board and the operational districts were reduced from five to four.

1969

Dumfries and Galloway Area becomes a single District of Central and South West Scotland Area of the South of Scotland Electricity Board.

1990

Electricity Supply Industry in Scotland is privatised. South of Scotland Board re-named **ScottishPower.**

References

1. The South of Scotland Electricity (Scottish Power) - Records and Historical Material.
2. The Electricity Council - Electricity Supply in UK - A Chronology 1982 and 1985 Editions.
3. Dumfries and Galloway Council - Archives - Royal Burgh of Dumfries.
4. Dumfries and Galloway Health Board Archives of Crichton Royal Institution.
5. The Ewart Library, Dumfries.
6. *A History of the Development of Electricity Supply in the Dumfries and Galloway Region of South West Scotland* by Bob Cowan CEng, MIEE
7. *Rural Electrification used in single-phase Distribution Systems* by J Pickles and HW Wills, Publ. JIEE, part II, Vol. 93, pp.501-515, Dec.1946.

Chapter 5

A Century of Installation Engineering
by Jack Davidson CEng, FIEE

Installation Engineering was the new title for The Institution of Electrical Engineers Professional Group P5 coined by **Ken Shaw** when he chaired the Group in 1983. It was previously known as *Non-industrial Installations and Electrical Building Services* and many of those engaged in this field felt that it was much more than just a change of name. There was a considerable opinion that it had been a 'Cinderella' Group, dealing as it did with wiring, and according to the name, not much else - it certainly lacked the appeal of large-scale generation, high voltage transmission and the economic and technical expertise of supply distribution.

This is perhaps surprising since the Institution was formed in 1871 as *The Society of Telegraph Engineers* and broadened in 1880 to *The Society of Telegraph Engineers and Electricians* which became **The Institution of Electrical Engineers** in 1888.

The one aspect of installation engineering which has commanded constant interest has been the provision and updating of the safety standards for electrical installations. *The IEE Wiring Regulations* since 1882 have passed through sixteen editions, with numerous amendments, supplements and revisions until 1992 when they became a British Standard - **BS7671**. This was a truly national standard and, although not statutory, formed the basis of several pieces of legislation. Although the 'Regulations' can, and have, been the subject of a good many full length volumes, the following is an outline of the development of electrical installations, particularly in Scotland, over the past hundred years.

Electrical Installations in Scotland
In 1886/7 arc lights were installed in the construction yard of the first Tay rail bridge (1 p.5), and a year or two later there were other installations in Pullar's dyeworks in Perth, followed by St Enoch's Station in Glasgow. Although Sir William Armstrong's 6-kW hydro-electric installation at 'Cragside' in Northumberland in 1880 is generally accepted as the first of its kind (3 p.126), Scotland was not far behind. In 1885 there was a public supply in Greenock powered by a 40-hp Gunther water-turbine driving two dynamos (3 p.133).

There was underground distribution to one of the sugar refineries for about ninety Swan incandescent lamps, while another ninety were installed in place of the existing gas street lighting lanterns. Oddly enough, the system only ran for two years with apparent success, but the cost of lamp replacements proved prohibitive. This was only a temporary setback however, and by 1900 Greenock had a steam-powered public supply.

In 1890 a public supply was provided in the village of Fort Augustus, where one 18-kW dynamo was driven by a water turbine, and another by an oil engine, at St. Benedict's Abbey (1 p.18). This was a 130-volt dc supply with a 72-cell battery and was in operation until at least 1936 when there were thirty-six consumers with a maximum demand of 18kW (13, p.438). Large and small hydro-electric plants were installed: Milngavie in 1894, Fort William in 1896 (4 p.28) and that year the British Aluminium Company began smelting at Foyers on Loch Ness (1 p.20), initially, with 2500 kW which was doubled in capacity in 1905 and operated until 1967 when the company accepted a supply from the National Grid. By 1909 the company's Fort William refinery was generating 12MW (4 p.37).

Hydro-power for country house lighting arrived even earlier: Carsaig in Mull in 1890 and Scatwell at Muir of Ord in 1900 with a 4.5-hp turbine on a 276-foot head of water (5 p.136).

By 1900 electrical contracting had become well established:

Not all of these early private plants were small; in 1902 Johnson & Phillips/Gilbert Gilkes installed a 142.5-hp turbine with a 550-foot head of water at the Spa in Strathpeffer, followed by another of the same size in the following year (5 pps.141-2). The plant list of Messrs Gilbert Gilkes & Gordon Ltd contains dozens of such items, large and small, but contrary to what might be expected, there were many more in England than there were in Scotland. For every one of these generators there was an associated installation, so that one hundred years ago, electrical contracting had become well established.

Municipal Supplies

The enormous growth of domestic, commercial and industrial installations in the cities and agricultural lighting and power supplies extended to the neighbouring countryside. Dundee and Glasgow had power supplies in 1893, Aberdeen in 1894, Edinburgh in 1895 and Ayr in 1896 (6 pps.413-4)

Battery Charging Systems

Of course, not every Scottish country estate and castle had a loch or a river to provide hydro-power and from the earliest days engine-driven battery charging systems had been installed. At Fort Augustus and at Taymouth Castle, near Aberfeldy, a combination of turbine and engine was used to cope with water shortages and to cover breakdowns (1 p.18). The earliest engines were single-cylinder, horizontal, slow running machines made by such as Tangye, Blackstone and Allen of Aberdeen. They were fuelled by paraffin, vapourising oil and occasionally by producer gas, necessitating a miniature gasworks beside the engine house as at Hallyburton House in Angus.

DC Switchboard c1920s

These installations were usually looked after (or neglected) by the estate handyman and were of considerable size, with engines and dynamos up to 50 hp or so. The battery room contained the open-topped, glass-cased lead-acid cells, a switchboard of marble or slate with fine brass-cased instruments, a reverse-power cutout complete with mercury cup contacts, a field regulator, open-wire fuses and end-cell switches for load voltage adjustments. The electrical contractors maintained both the electrical and mechanical components, checking and topping-up lubricating oil, fuel and cooling water.

Push-button starting had not yet arrived: a cast-iron bulb on the cylinder head or a removable metal block was heated using a large vertical blowlamp. The metal block was hastily bolted back on the cylinder head and the flywheel, perhaps six feet in diameter, was heaved round to just the right spot on the compression stroke of the engine followed by another heave on the unguarded flat leather driving belt, hoping for a start first time.

About 1930, higher speed, multi-cylinder petrol generating sets arrived, commonly American Kohler and Onan, which seemed to have been designed to ensure maximum difficulty in access for maintenance. British sets such as Lister, Austinlite and Boulton & Paul (Electrolite) were an improvement and, after the 1939-45 war, smaller 600/1000-rpm 3- or 6-kVA diesel sets were developed by Lister, Petter, Dale and Shanks of Arbroath. These machines started automatically when a minimum load, usually a 40-watt lamp, was switched on and remained running until the last light was switched off. Low loads sometimes caused injector problems with diesel engines and water heaters were connected to ensure a reasonable load.

These small sets, of 240 volts and 50 Hz were the delight of farmers' wives who could now use a wide range of household appliances. The farmers too were impressed with the convenience of instant and adequate lighting throughout the steading on cold and dark winter mornings. The use of milking machines and other agricultural appliances made life much easier.

As the networks of public rural supplies were extended throughout the country the need for private generating sets diminished but many are still held in reserve against the possibility of mains failure in remote areas. There is also a revival of fairly large scale hydro generation in the megawatt range by landowners who have the satisfaction of producing energy from a renewable source and gaining extra income.

230/460-volt DC Switchboard 1925

The change from 110 volts dc to 240 volts ac in private plants was, to some extent, matched by the changeover from dc to ac in the public supply, usually at the same voltage but sometimes at a higher voltage; for example: Dundee changed from 200/400-volt dc to 200/346-volt ac only later changing again to 240/415 volts. Many thousands of household appliances had to be converted or replaced; the cost to the power companies was considerable and exacerbated by the quantities of dangerous antiques which were produced from attics, cellars and sheds!

The IEE and the Electrical Contractors' Association
While 1900 saw the founding of IEE Scotland, by coincidence, it also saw the formation of the Electrical Contractors' Association of Scotland (now 'SELECT'). In the previous year, 1899, the Cable Manufacturers' Association was formed (1 p.21), and the following year, 1901, saw the start, in England, of the Electrical Contractors' Association; the electrical contracting industry was beginning to be organised nationally. Legislation was coming 'thick and fast' too: the first Board of Trade Regulations for electrical installations were issued in 1896 - fourteen years after the first IEE Wiring Regulations. Then came the Power Bills - legislation on the large scale generation and high voltage transmission of energy - and Acts of Parliament relating to private power companies, as distinct from municipalities. The Electric Lighting (Clauses) Act of 1899 laid down many general principles for the provision of public supplies (1 p.20).

The year 1908 saw the introduction of the *Electricity (Factories Act) Special Regulations* which with the 1944 *Amendments* lasted until Health & Safety legislation took over in 1989 - a remarkable example of well drafted and far-seeing technical regulation.

The 1937 Electricity Supply Regulations prohibited 'undertakers' (electricity suppliers) from fitting fuses in any earthed supply conductor. The *10th Edition* of the *IEE Wiring Regulations* already had this requirement by September 1934 for the neutral and mid-wire of 3-phase ac supplies as well as three-wire dc supplies but not for single-phase ac supplies or one-sided connections to a three-wire dc supply (8 p.13). The latter was incorporated in the *11th Edition* of the *IEE Wiring Regulations* in June 1939 (9 p.16) but it was not until the 1950s that single phase and neutral (sp&n) switch and fusegear became accepted practice, in spite of the fact that this equipment was available before the war (as in the GEC catalogue of 1935). It was a matter of price - a 15-ampere, double-pole switch fuse cost 4/8d (23p) whereas the sp&n version cost 5/- (25p). Another price difference was in the five-way, 15-ampere, teak-cased fuseboard with solid back to comply with IEE Regulations, priced at £1/1/4 (£1.07), whereas the comparable sp&n board cost 19/- (95p). Other deviations included the use of 'betweens' or 'strapping wires' for two-way switches which were always wired in black; two 15-ampere switched sockets were wired in a 7/.029-circuit instead of the permitted one, and three 5-ampere switched sockets were often found in a 3/.029-circuit with a 10-ampere fuse. The cost of electrical energy was about 8d (3.3p) per kilowatt-hour equating to about 4 hours pay for a first-year apprentice in 1939.

Design and Development

To return to the main subject of consideration - the design and development of electrical installations. A good starting point is an IEE Paper by **W.E. Chamen** read at The Institute of Engineers & Shipbuilders in Glasgow on 23rd January 1900, and titled *The Electric Wiring of Buildings* (10). It is a remarkable summary of the practices at that time. The discussion on this paper took place on 20th February, and continued on 20th March; clearly, it was an epic event. Much of the discussion was reported verbatim with some pithy comments which indicated the depth of feeling of both the speaker and his audience.

Dorman Smith Switchboard Assembly Shop, 1954

The paper starts with a brief but disparaging comment about wood casing and capping. This early means of protection against mechanical damage afforded little protection against damp or wet conditions -

perhaps an indication of the state of some of the buildings at that time. It took a joiner to erect it and a wireman 'for laying and jointing the wires' (10). It was not highly recommended one hundred years ago, but there are still a few bits of it to be seen in old buildings. Then followed lead-covered cable systems - originally 'lead tubes into which india-rubber covered wires are drawn'. This developed into lead sheathed cable with a paper- or fibre-insulated core, and was followed by two-core cables (identified red and black) and finally, a concentric version where the outer conductor was not insulated from the sheath. Such an arrangement, then as now, was not legally acceptable for installations connected to a public supply. Mr Chamen fought shy of debating whether or not the Board of Trade regulation about mid-wire earthing should be retained.

Great emphasis was laid, throughout Chamen's Paper on the importance of earthing lead sheaths to a water pipe 'preferably at some point in the lower part of the building near its entrance' (10 p.138). There was a warning too, about the use of lead covered cable joint boxes having mechanical clamps for the sheath rather than sweated connections. Next, he described 'conduit systems' which ranged from 'iron gas barrel with screwed joints' and cast iron joint boxes, 'to unwelded sheet-iron tubes or skelps' (the word *skelps* was not understood, since its Scottish dialect means slap !) with cast iron boxes fitted with slip sockets (10 p.139).

Then came welded iron tubes with an insulating lining, boxes and other accessories being similarly lined but with what, is not stated. The insulating lining was intended to prevent internal condensation. Chamen also criticised open-seam tubing with slip joints in outdoor situations, and the use of gas barrel fitted into untapped entries in boxes, sometimes with two locknuts, more often with one, and sometimes with none at all! He then proceeds to advocate the design and adoption of a system which would be moisture-resistant and in which the conductors would not be subject to mechanical damage or to abrasion by rough edges within the tube (10 p.144). What he proposed was quite new but totally impracticable: it consisted of 15/20ft. lengths of wrought iron pipe containing two insulated conductors, the pipe being then 'filled up solid', presumably with bitumen or wax, but no material is specified. It was admitted that jointing would be 'an almost unsurpassable difficulty' which might be eased if the form was changed to concentric with the iron tube serving as the return conductor. Since only dc was involved, induction losses and consequent heating would not have been a problem. It is not stated whether the pre-formed lengths of tube and conductor could be bent or offset, or if manufactured bends, with their attendant jointing would be needed.

Various suggestions were given on how the tubes might be jointed using long screwed sockets (couplings), split sleeves or glands secured with grub screws, or 'a sleeve without an internal thread, but external tapered threads and saw cuts at each end with nuts to screw down to make it tightly grip the tube ends which it encloses'. There is no indication of how the central conductor would be connected and insulated. The idea is somewhat similar to an underground system produced by the Callender Bitumen Company about 1885 (1 p.8), where six foot lengths of cast iron troughing with spigot and socket joints were bolted together and sealed with bitumen. The single core cables, which could be hv or 1v were supported every two feet by slotted wooden spacers. The stranded, tinned, copper conductors were insulated with vulcanised bitumen and then taped. After the cables were installed, the troughs were filled with pure bitumen, and the troughing was finally sealed with either an inch of concrete or cast iron cover plates. Then followed a description of the original 'tree' distribution system, where cables are run from the meter position to the top of the building, branches for each floor being teed off via fuses, and perhaps reduced in size again as the extremities of the building were reached. So the principle of fusing where cable cross-section is reduced has been known and practised for a hundred years (10 p.145).

This arrangement meant, of course, that pairs of fuses were to be found in all sorts of corners, and possibly inside ceiling roses where 3/.22 (alias 3/.029, alias 0.002sq.in, now 1.5sq.mm) 'hard wiring' was connected to 14/36, (14/.0076, 0.0006sq.in, now 0.5sq.mm) flexible cord, where a single fuse sufficed. Often found beside lighting switches with plain or fluted brass covers, were porcelain 'pot' fuses, looking like ceiling roses, but with four vent holes rather than a central flex entry, but still with a porcelain screw-on cover. These were often missing or broken, with the burn and smoke marks of blown fuses (possibly lead rather than copper) much in evidence. A copper fuse wire to carry 3 amperes was 0.006" dia., or 38 SWG, and the chance of successfully securing it beneath the screws and (sometimes) washers of pot fuses without stretching or breaking it was small indeed, while a 'Standard Alloy' fuse, 63% tin and 37% lead to BS88, would be 0.024" diameter, or 23 SWG and much easier to handle, if somewhat more spectacular in operation. (8 p. 141)

The distribution board installation developed from the tree system. Fuses were now grouped together in polished teak, glass-fronted cases with porcelain fuse bases and bridges. The early versions of fuse bridges were of course, rewirable, with open wires passing almost exactly where the bridge would be gripped to remove it from the board. This, apart from the possibility of burnt fingers, may have been acceptable for 100-volt supplies, but not for 250 volts; this led to the Home Office fuse carrier, which enclosed the wire and protected the fingers from contact with live parts.

Cartridge fuses arrived in the mid-1930s fulfilling a much needed improvement in the safety of high current circuits, and ever higher prospective fault currents. There were rewirable fuses at least up to 500A and since the 10th Edition of the IEE Wiring Regulations (1934) required a single strand of 14 SWG (0.08" diameter) for a 100-A fuse; there was much molten and vaporised copper in evidence when one of these large fuses blew. Alloy fuses mentioned earlier, were only used up to 5A, 21SWG, 0.032" diameter. Industrially, fuseboards were developing from the open and unprotected marble or slate panels to heavy cast iron cases with hinged metal covers. The use of distribution boards in place of the tree system gave rise to the bunching of cables at fuseboards, and Mr Chamen had great reservations about this:

> .....it is clear, therefore, that if bunching is to be allowed at all, it must be limited. A convenient and fairly safe limit may be set at two wires only, when of opposite polarity and in iron or other similar suitable metal tubing, and four wires only when of the same polarity either in metal tubing or wood casing. In each instance the circuits not to carry more than three amperes each at 250 volt. (10 p.146)

Mr Chamen was a cautious individual, and once again, of course, he was concerned only with dc supplies.

A final quote deserves to be made from his remarkable paper:

> It is usually the labour which costs the greater part of the money in fitting up an installation, but if things could be standardised, so as to reduce the amount of time necessary to spend in consumers' houses (to their great annoyance), it might still be possible to carry out the work at an even less cost, though the materials might be a little more expensive.
> (1 p.144).

To prepare a circular wood block on which to mount a lighting switch, it was necessary to drill and countersink two fixing holes, make two lead holes for the switch fixing screws and cut the notch in the pattress or block to accommodate the surface cable, standardisation and availability of ready-to-use items was clearly needed. To continue with the same example however, was not possible when a simple surface switch might be one-way, with two cable entries, two-way with three, or intermediate with four connections; the action could be under- or over-slung, and the notching of the block was an individual site requirement. The GEC catalogue of 1896 lists, for the first time, wood blocks on which to mount accessories, thus signifying the withdrawal of the carpenter from electrical installation work (16 p.40)

Today, we have surface or flush boxes with knock-out cable entries to which all kinds of accessories may be fitted. Similarly, with wiring cables, the vulcanised india-rubber, taped and braided, (vir) cables, which were used from the beginning of the century until about the 1960s, had to be carefully prepared by removing the rubber insulation for the required length, then trimming back the tape and braid for one-and-a-half inches, otherwise poor insulation readings would result; apprentices were well warned of the consequences should this happen on their work! Nowadays, one quick operation of a wire-stripping tool is all that it takes.

With larger cables, sweated lugs were the means of termination at transformers and switchgear. For really big lugs, it could take the best part of half a day to fit a set using a paraffin blowlamp. This was lit with an oily rag (the methylated spirits recommended by their makers did not appear in contractors' stores). The lugs and the solder pot took time to heat and solder needed topping-up as it cooled. Once filled, cooling off began and was sometimes hastened by a wet rag, but not too wet or too often, or cracking of the joint would result. Then followed the removal of burnt insulation, asbestos wrapping having provided some protection, then final taping with Empire tape and yellow varnished cotton to build up the insulation to the original thickness, overlapping the shank of the cable socket. Today, the lug is applied with a hydraulic crimper in a very short time, and the job is done. The use of power tools on site is a great time saver. The old method of fixing to stone and concrete using Rawlplug jumpers and star drills has been superseded by percussion, tungsten tipped drills. Heavy fixings which needed ragbolts cemented in, or long bolts laboriously leaded in, either poured from a ladle or hammered in with lead wool, are long gone, and there are much better and quicker fixes. Chasing or raggling of brick walls was another job for apprentices; all walls seemed to be of brick. Breeze blocks were not yet to be seen, but of course there were masonry walls, constructed of whinstone boulders, which were almost impossible to chisel and required wood plugs or 'dooks' driven into the gaps or joints between the stones - and they rarely occurred where they were wanted. Today, power driven chisels, and cartridge fired fixings are used to make the job much easier.

The electrical installation labour system

The mention of apprentices leads to a consideration of how the electrical installation industry labour system evolved. In the beginning, there was no specific organisation; joiners installed the casing and capping since this was a basic woodworking exercise, while a new trade of 'wireman' completed the work. The first men simply improvised; they 'made it up as they went along' since there could be no-one to train them. The name 'electrician' had been in use long before 1880 to refer to those who studied electrical science (for example, Sir William Thomson, later Lord Kelvin); this explains the use of the word 'electrician' in the title of the original (amended) name of the Institution. It is of interest that those entering the trade as recently as 1937 were indentured as 'apprentice electrical engineers', not as 'electricians'. The grade of journeyman electrician was established later, and now we have in addition, 'approved electricians' and 'technician electricians'. Apprentices are 'registered' (with the Electrical Contractors' Associations) rather than indentured (2 p.52) and they no longer have to undertake to be 'faithful and obedient' to their Master, not to do any electrical work on their own account and not to change their employer without the Master's written permission; all on pain of forfeiture of the 'One Pound Indenture Fee', a fairly negligible sum today, but three full weeks' pay for a first year apprentice in 1939 when the working week was 48 hours. Having satisfactorily served five years, an apprentice would be granted his *Certificate of Discharge*, but he was unlikely to receive journeyman's pay while remaining with the same employer. An indeterminate period as an 'improver' would follow his apprenticeship. Improvers were phased out in 1972, and apprenticeships were reduced to four years in 1978.

The Electrical Contractors' Association of Scotland

Until 1900, while there were very many electrical contractors, there was no trade association until twenty-five Glasgow contractors met to discuss common problems. They founded the Electrical Contractors' Association of Glasgow. An Edinburgh branch was formed in April 1904 and six months later the Association amalgamated with the Electrical Contractors' Association of England (11 p.294). A Dundee branch was formed in 1907 and another in Aberdeen in 1909. It was now possible to set up the **Electrical Contractors' Association of Scotland** which was formed in November 1911; it is now known as *SELECT*. In 1901, **Thomas Wright** of Messrs Anderson & Munro was elected Chairman, and **William McWhirter**, a Member of the IEE, was Vice-Chairman, who, during the discussion on Chamen's Paper the year before, regretted Chamen's reference to poor workmanship and suggested it was caused by engineers and masters who had not yet adopted the apprenticeship system in use for many years by other trades (10 p. 161). Then as now, few electrical contractors were IEE members, but Messrs Osborne & Hunter Ltd, formed in 1898, had three Associate Members: **John Hunter AMIEE, Hugh Osborne AMIEE** and **John Black AMIEE**; Hugh Osborne attained full membership (equivalent to Fellowship today) in 1920.

The Inspection of Electrical Installations
Since safety and good workmanship are essential in electrical installation work, it was clearly necessary that the public should have some way of selecting a good contractor. The first body formed for this purpose was the *National Register of Electrical Installation Contractors* (NREIC) which was constituted in 1924 with twenty-six Board Members (11 p.295). There were seven contractors, five supply authority representatives, two consulting engineers, six from the IEE, one Illuminating Engineer, one from the Central Electricity Board, and four from BEAMA and EWF plus a chairman. For a body supposed to represent the interests of the public, it was a curious mixture and, perhaps not surprisingly, it had little effect. In its first six years, although it listed 1300 firms, only four had been struck off for bad workmanship, there were no powers of inspection, only complaints were dealt with, but it was still in existence in 1935. A new body, the *National Inspection Council for Electrical Installation Contractors* (NICEIC) was formed in 1956 and, as the name implies, it did have a policy of inspection of members' work. In addition, *The Electrical Contractors' Associations* carry out inspections and represent 550 firms and 8,000 operatives in Scotland, with 2,200 firms and about 22,000 operatives in England.

Authors who taught Electrical safety and Practice

In 1908 **Sydney F Walker** of Bath wrote *Electric Wiring & Fitting for Plumbers and Gasfitters;* the IEE purchased a copy for their library in February 1908. Mr Walker was a member of several Institutions: MIEE, MIME, MInstME, AMICE. He was not a plumber by trade, but in the preface he declared the purpose of his book to be:

> *to enable skilled workers such as plumbers and gasfitters to carry out the work [of the wiring of buildings] ... and to avoid the disastrous mistakes that have sometimes been made by men employed on wiring contracts in the past.* (12, preface)

The book contains 160 pages of good sound advice on the practices of his day. There were, however, some peculiar suggestions that plumbers and gasfitters who carry out electrical work should test the insulating and protective qualities of the enamel on their conduit. This involved bending the conduit to a right-angle, straightening it in a vice and then examining it, inside and out, for evidence of cracking or flaking. There were also other recommended tests such as: prolonged immersion of the conduit in tap water, rainwater, 40:1 water and sulphuric acid, and an unspecified concentration of hydrochloric acid and finally, burial of the conduit in a wet sample of the plaster which was to be used on the project. One wonders if anyone ever carried out such tests and with what results.

However, Mr Walker really had no need for such doubts and precautions. In 1901 **LM Waterhouse AMICE, AMIEE**, a graduate of Heriot-Watt College, who was also a Member of the International Society of Electricians, had published his: *Conduit Wiring & Erection.* It was he who invented the *Simplex* conduit system, laying the excellent foundations for the methods and materials used today. It was a wonderfully detailed system with all the variations necessary. There were eight sizes of conduit from 1/2" to 2" diameter of which all but 1" and 7/8" are still in use, in either imperial sizes or metric equivalents. There was light gauge, either close joint or brazed seam, for use with 'slip joint' (unthreaded) accessories which were available enamelled or galvanised. This was little used in Scotland, although widely so in England. It is still to be found in lift installations, which are usually wired by the lift installers rather than by electrical contractors. There was heavy gauge enamelled or galvanised brazed seam conduit suitable for screwing; solid drawn conduit was to come later. Even in 1901 there was a range of more than 400 accessories, although with eight sizes of conduit, this only meant that about fifty items for each size were available; nevertheless, it is an excellent system which still serves us well.

Lead Pipes, Conduits, VIR, Lead-covered cables and Pyrotenax
An important difference in the early erection method and that of more recent times was the wiring of the conduit as it was erected, known as 'threading' rather than 'drawing in'. It was considered to produce a much more economical job, but the *8th Edition* of the *Wiring Regulations* in 1924 required conduits to be complete before wiring was installed (14 p.52).

From the original lead pipes and afterwards steel conduits, other materials have been used at different times for different reasons. A copper conduit system was installed in the Bank of England and in the new Houses of Parliament to ensure an 'everlasting' installation. These were screwed copper conduits, although lighter gauge conduits with sweated fittings were also available (15 p.120). Aluminium conduit made a brief appearance just after the 1939-45 War when steel was practically unobtainable. It had to be treated differently to steel since, without copious lubrication, the softer metal threads were easily torn by the dies and when formed on a bending machine, particularly if a bend was pulled too quickly, the cross section of the tube was seriously reduced and therefore weakened on the inside of the bend. Prevention of corrosion was another problem when the recommended aluminium accessories were not available and malleable iron was pressed into use. The scarcity of steel conduit during the War led to a revival of a much older wiring system - vulcanised india-rubber (v.i.r.) cables in porcelain cleats. This was used in vast quantities in Army and Air Force camps and other establishments where it could be erected quickly and cheaply and, if not subject to abuse, was quite serviceable. It was also used in factories, particularly old timber roofed mills and warehouses which were converted to wartime production.

There have been so many wiring systems which have come and gone, some for general purposes, such as lead-covered flat cable, tough rubber-sheathed single- and multi-core, aluminium sheathed mineral insulated cable. When the price of copper soared other copper sheathed cable such as *Stannos* and *Kopperclad* was used, but of these there only remains copper sheathed mineral insulated cable which originated in France in 1934, and manufactured by *Pyrotenax* in the UK from 1937.

The introduction of steel trunking is hard to date - probably about 1930 (although **Key Engineering** made a semi-circular steel trunking in 1908) (16 pps .213-4). This was followed, a good many years later, by plastics, both for trunking and conduit. Bus-bar trunking has been in existence since before the War; **Marryat & Place** evolved their rising main system in 1937 (14 p.206), but **English Electric Co**, were making overhead busbars, much as we know them today, for the automobile industry in 1935 (16 p.209). Underfloor ducting came a little earlier, **GEC** were marketing a system in 1932 (16 p.218), and a British Standard emerged in 1938.

Domestic Electrical Installations

The 13-ampere fused-plug and socket was first proposed in June 1942 by an IEE committee dealing with post-war building policies. **RA Ure** of Edinburgh, a Scottish electrical contractor, ensured that the requirements of the Scottish Building Regulations were taken into account. The IEE's report was submitted to the Minister of Works, Lord Portal of Laverstock, and its proposals were published in the HMSO Report *Post-War Building Studies* No.11, 1944. This 96-page booklet proposed ring circuits each with a 30-amp fuse to be wired with 7/.029in cable supplying up to twenty socket outlets.

The committee wrote to every UK 'electrical undertaker' (supplier) for opinions on the 13-amp plug and socket as well as on lighting, power, telephone, sound broadcast, television, bells, clocks, fire and burglar alarms etc. Conduit and vir was recommended but the possible post-war scarcity of rubber led to pvc insulation as a substitute. The proposal to use skirting trunking to accommodate telephone, radio and television cables (18 p.23) in domestic premises was rarely used but was more commonly used in commercial premises. In farm buildings tough rubber sheathed cable with a vulcanised-on cotton braiding and overall compounding (ie the Callender Farm Wiring System of 1937) were used with an excellent range of moulded accessories with compression gland cable entries developed by BICC (16 p.93).

The committee considered only 'new-build' installations and ignored mineral insulated cable which was widely used in post-war housing. Plaster depth boxes were developed to dispense with glands and nuts and, to reduce site erection time, the 'harness' wiring system for a whole house was introduced in a ready assembled kit with joint boxes completed, cable ends bared and labelled ready for connection to sockets, switches, cooker outlets and pendants (20 p.61). PVC insulated and sheathed cables (which originated in Germany in 1937 under the trade name 'Minpolim') are widely used today.

The search for a universal plug and socket

The wide variety of plugs and sockets used throughout the UK included the two-pin GEC and Crompton type, the three-pin interlocking Simplex type and several different guages of pin size, type and spacing were available. Standardisation for round-pin plugs occurred in 1927 and for the three-pin plug in 1934. Even after the 13-amp plug and socket arrived in 1947 round pin plugs continued to be widely used. In 1966 the International Electrotechnical Commission discussed a 'Worldwide Plug and Socket System' (21 p.15) and after seventeen meetings during the next ten years no final solution emerged, possibly because of the astronomical costs involved and the reluctance of so many nations to abandon their own designs.

The development of lamps

The great American inventor **Thomas Alva Edison** (1847-1931) was the first to patent the electric lamp in 1875. However, a relatively unknown Dundee born Scotsman, **James Bowman Lindsay** (1799-1862) demonstrated his electric light bulb in the year 1835, some forty years before Edison. He neglected to patent it but he predicted the street lighting of cities. Evidence of this claim was published in the *Dundee Advertiser* of his day:

> *Mr Lindsay, a teacher, formerly lecturer to the Watt Institute*
> *[Edinburgh], succeeded, on the evening of Sunday 25 July,*
> *in obtaining a constant electric light. The light in beauty*
> *surpasses all others.*

An aspect of electrical installations which has affected all users since the earliest days is that of the light source itself. Firstly, arc lamps, already referred to, were only suitable for outdoor applications and large enclosed spaces such as railway stations where adequate mounting height was available. Domestic lighting of 100 years ago was well established in the form of carbon filament lamps (**Messrs Edison and Swan** had separately developed their carbon filaments in the 1880s). A price list of 1896 shows a remarkable range: from 5 to 100 cp (candle power) at voltages of 3 volts to 400 volts; the price ranged between 5/- (25p) to 10/6 (52p) each. Lamps which were silvered on one side or on top to provide a reflector could be obtained for another shilling (5p) per lamp (17 p.84).

From 1901 metal filament lamps were available: first, tantalum then tungsten in 1906. The disappearance of carbon filaments led to the change from vacuum lamps to gas-filled lamps for all but the smaller sizes. Coiled coil filaments were available in 1913 and the British GEC catalogue of 1935 refers to them as a new innovation in which a 40-watt coiled-filament lamp gave 20% more light than the single coil filament.

Mercury vapour lamps were introduced by Cooper Hewitt in the USA in 1900 (1 p.22). They had to be tilted manually to strike the arc then returned to their normal vertical position. By 1932 high pressure mercury lamps were used with a degree of colour correction using phosphors (1 p.34). At this time low pressure sodium lamps were introduced for street lighting. In 1935 fluorescent tubes were available in America in 'daylight', white and five other colours (1 p.35); they became available in the UK from about 1939. Smaller fluorescent lamps were manufactured from about 1980; for example, the Philips 'SL' in 1980 and the Thorn '2D' in 1981 (1 p.109). They were the 'economy lamps' of the future but they were five times more expensive than their tungsten equivalent, however, they lasted five times longer giving the same light output for a quarter of the wattage.

This chapter covering a Century of Installation Engineering has described several innovations but inevitably there are omissions some of which are: the introduction of paper-insulated cables, which began with a patent by **GH Nisbet** - the 'BIW System' of 1894; the oil-filled circuit breaker invented in 1882 by **GW Partridge**; the air-blast circuit-breaker which arrived in 1926; the development of domestic switchgear from cast-iron, slotted entry double-pole switch fuses to tidy consumer units. It is hoped that the foregoing will perhaps encourage the reader to look a little further into the history of an industry which has of necessity been one of constant change, improvement and innovation.

References

1. *Electricity Supply in the United Kingdom*. The Electricity Council, 3rd Edition. 1982. ISBN 0 85188 087 8

2. *Electrical Contractors' Association Yearbook* 1935-36

3. *Hydro Electricity for Public Supply in Britain,* 1881-1894 Professor DG Tucker. Industrial Archaelogoy Review, Vol.I, Issue No.2. 1977.

4. *The First Half Century of Hydro Electricity* by Professor DG Tucker.

5. *Gilbert Gilkes & Gordon Plant List (1900-1986)*

6. *Electric Wiring, Fittings, Switches and Lamps* by W Perrin Maycock. 1899.

7. *Electrical Contracting* by H Mayers Purdie. 1926.

8. *10th Edition IEE Wiring Regulations*. 1934.

9. *11th Edition IEE Wiring Regulations*. 1939.

10. *The Electric Wiring of Buildings* by WE Chamen, IEE paper, 23rd January 1900

11. *Electrical Contracting* by HR Taunton. 1933

12. *Electric Wiring & Fitting for Plumbers and Gasfitters* by Sydney F. Walker MIEE, MIME, MInst.M.E. AMICE,.1906.

13. *Conduit Wiring & Erection* by L.M. Waterhouse, AMICE, AMIEE. 1901 (reprinted 1932)

14. *8th Edition IEE Wiring Regulations*. 1924.

15. *Copper Pipeline Services in Buildings*. Copper Development Association. 1963.

16. *The History of Electrical Wiring* by J Mellanby. 1957.

17. *Precautions to be Adopted on Installing the Electric Light* by K Hedges. 1886.

Chapter 6

A History of Telecommunications in Scotland
by EurIng John Lough BSc(Eng), CEng, FIEE

"Mr Watson, come here, I want to see you." Nine small and seemingly innocuous words spoken by **Alexander Graham Bell** to his assistant Thomas Watson - nine small words which were to spark a revolution in communications and set the world talking.

They formed the first articulate sentence ever spoken on a telephone and were transmitted over 100ft of wire in Boston, Massachusetts, on 10th March 1876.

Today the telephone, e-mail and the Internet are an integral part of everyday life in Scotland and it's all thanks to the inventive Scotsman who was born at 16 South Charlotte Street, Edinburgh, on 3rd March 1847.

Alexander Graham Bell
Courtesy of British Telecom

Like Archimede's bath and Newton's apple, Bell's discovery was an historic harbinger to a future not even their great minds could foresee. A future which has seen the metamorphosis of British Telecom (BT) from a UK telephone company to a global communications company focussed on being the best worldwide communications group.

BT now operates in more than 70 countries. And together with US giant AT&T it is creating a $10 billion global venture to serve multinational customers, individuals and businesses around the world; a market currently estimated to be worth $40 billion.

Despite this, BT has never forgotten where its roots lie and in the run up to the new Scottish Parliament, it formed BT Scotland specifically to look after its two million Scottish customers and ensure that they are at the forefront of the fastest-moving and most exciting industry on the planet.

Billions of pounds have been spent in Scotland, creating a state-of-the-art infrastructure which reaches out from major cities and areas of dense population to hamlets in the remotest Hebridean islands.

This is an investment which has shattered the distance barriers which could so easily have left Scotland stranded on the periphery of Europe, far from the growing overseas markets which are a feature of today's trading. And new technology has brought huge savings to Scots - since BT was privatised in 1984, the cost of calling has more than halved. BT Scotland now employs 12,000 people across Scotland and has established a call centre industry, creating thousands of new jobs in Glasgow, Dundee, Alness and Thurso.

Today the 'phone is no longer an instrument used just to talk to someone - it is the access to a superhighway which is about to deliver a technological and social revolution vital to the future of Scotland.

New companies now compete for telecommunications customers - Mercury Atlantic, Scottish, and in the bigger cities the cable companies compete with BT for land based services whilst Vodaphone, One2one and Orange offer their services in direct competition to BT Cellnet's mobile services within Scotland.

In a world featuring super-fast Internet, interactive TV and video on demand customers can choose from recorded television programmes, videos and music, shopping on demand, a range of educational programming, home banking and community links.

Every home, every school and every business in Scotland will feel the benefits of the information revolution and the way we work, learn and relax will be transformed.

Scotland intends to be at the forefront of that revolution, helping to shape the lives of the Scottish people in the exciting years that lie ahead.

How did we get here and what has actually happened in the 123 years since Bell uttered those nine small words and managed to transmit them 100ft down the line to his assistant Mr Watson?

Firstly, we must return to Bell's early years in Scotland. Having completed his education at the Universities of Edinburgh and London, he emigrated with his family to Canada, following the loss of his two brothers from tuberculosis.

Later, he moved to Boston as a teacher of the deaf, and his studies into the artificial reproduction of vowel sounds using electricity and magnetism ultimately to led to the development of the telephone.

1876

Six months after Bell spoke his historic nine words, Sir William Thompson (President of the IEE in 1874 and to be so again in 1907 after becoming Lord Kelvin, and who regularly lectured at Glasgow University) exhibited Bell's telephone to the British Association for the Advancement of Science in Glasgow, describing it as "the greatest by far of all the marvels of the electric telegraph."

1877

Bell and his financial backers formed the Bell Telephone Company in the US and a year later he demonstrated the telephone to Queen Victoria on the Isle of Wight, with calls to London, Cowes and Southampton. They were the first long distance calls in the UK.

1879

Britain's first public telephone exchange opened at 36 Coleman Street, London, and was followed by the first two in Scotland in Glasgow and Edinburgh.

'Gallows Telephone' produced by Alexander Graham Bell.
Courtesy of British Telecom

1885

Glasgow and Edinburgh were connected by telephone for the first time and Scotland's top two cities discovered that *it's good to talk!* The National Telephone Co. provides the longest telephone line in the UK to link the east and west. Two years later, Edinburgh had 421 telephone subscribers, but the Glasgow patois was to the fore, with 1321 subscribers on-line.

1889

Almond B. Strowger, a funeral parlour proprietor of Kansas City, patented an automatic telephone system having apparently discovered that his local telephone operator was diverting his business calls to another undertaker who just happened to be her husband!

Although his amazing experiments involved the use of brass collar studs and matches, his switching system proved extremely popular and by 1922 would be adopted as the standard for all automatic telephone exchanges in the UK. The Strowger remained a vital part of the UK network until as late as 1995, when the last one was decommissioned at Crawford in Midlothian and time-based charging was introduced.

1892

North greets south as a telephone link was established between Glasgow and London; Dundee linked up with Glasgow and Edinburgh. Aberdeen got in on the act the following year.

1895

In the early days, telephone service in the UK was provided by the General Post Office, a Government department, in competition with private sector companies. The Post Office trunk system opened and trunk lines linked Glasgow to London, Belfast and Dublin for the first time, while Edinburgh linked up with London. The Glasgow-Ireland was linked by means of a submarine cable running from Portpatrick to Co. Down.

1896

The Post Office took over the private sector trunk service paying £459,114 3s 7d for 29,000 miles of cable in 33 trunk lines, the telephone dial was invented and Marconi demonstrated his "telegraphy without wires." Aberdeen now linked with London.

1901

Municipal telephony was provided by Corporation of Glasgow, covering an area of 140 square miles from Clydebank to Kilsyth. The council ran the city's telephones for the next five years, before selling to the Post Office for £305,000.

1916

The 'buddies got on the blower' as Scotland's first automatic exchange opened in Paisley with capacity for 1600 subscribers. It was the first by a long way and it was not until 1924 that the opening of Dundee Central sparked off the general advancement of automatic telephones in Scotland. It meant that people on the same exchange could call each other without calling the operator.

Meanwhile, manual exchanges opened up all over Scotland and in rural areas switchboards were frequently installed in shops or private houses. Many exchanges closed at night and in others, someone slept by the switchboard and was woken by a bell when a call came through. In manual exchanges, operators connected calls by plugging cords into rows of sockets on the front of switchboards. Small electric bulbs or indicators with moving flaps were used to show that someone was calling. As the size of switchboard increased with the demand for service, operators had to be a certain minimum height to be able to reach all the sockets.

1925

The London to Glasgow trunk telephone cable with repeaters was completed to form the backbone of the British trunk network and kiosks were fitted with A and B buttons for the first time.

1927

Trans-Atlantic telephone service was established using long wave radio transmission. The original tariff was £15 for three minutes, reducing to £9 the following year.

1931

The first voice frequency telegraphy system with 12 carrier channels was installed between London and Dundee. Using voice frequency dialling, operators at zone centres were able to dial directly to subscribers in distant zone centres, avoiding the costs and delays involved with incoming operators.

1936

The 'Speaking Clock' speaks for the first time and the famous Jubilee Kiosk, the traditional red 'phone box, was designed by Sir Giles Gilbert Scott to commemorate the Silver Jubilee of the coronation of King George V.

1938

The 999 emergency service was established in Scotland and it handled 13,000 calls in its first month - a far cry from today when 250,000 calls a month are handled by two state-of-the-art call centres in Glasgow and Inverness. The service was introduced in London the year before following a fire in which five people died. It experienced its first success within a few days but it wasn't a life-saving operation - a burglar was caught red-handed thanks to police arriving at the scene within five minutes.

1943

Colossus, the world's first programmable electronic computer, was designed by a Post Office research branch team headed by Tommy Flowers (a member of the IEE who is to become a Fellow in 1945), helping to hasten the end of the Second World War. So secret was this work that Churchill ordered the complete destruction of Colossus at the end of the war.

1954

An Anglo-Norwegian submarine telephone cable was laid between Aberdeen and Bergen by the Post Office cable ship *Monarch* - the longest submarine cable in the world at a length of 300 nautical miles. A year later the last Post Office inland Morse telegraph circuit between Barra and South Uist in the Western Isles was recovered.

1956

The first trans-Atlantic telephone cable was laid between Oban and Newfoundland, a distance of 2240 miles.

1958

The telephone network took a giant leap forward with the introduction of STD - Subscriber Trunk Dialling. Callers were at last able to make trunk calls automatically without having to use an operator. The service was launched by HM Queen Elizabeth who dialled a call on 5th December from Bristol Central Telephone Exchange to the Lord Provost of Edinburgh. It travelled a distance of 300 miles, the limit for a subscriber trunk call at the time.

1960

Automatic calling arrived in Scotland as Dundee became the city of jute, jam, journalism and STD.

1962

A sky-high era in telecommunications began with the spectacular launch from Cape Canaveral of Telstar, the first broadband communications satellite. The day after the launch, it was used to transmit the first high-definition television pictures across the Atlantic.

1963

International STD (later called IDD) to Europe arrived in Edinburgh and Glasgow and Scotland connected its 500,000th telephone line. The original speaking clock, introduced in 1936, was replaced by new clocks using a revolving magnetic drum.

1966

All Figure Numbering was introduced for the first time, initially in Glasgow and Edinburgh, and the old system of using different letters and numbers to identify exchanges was abandoned.

1968

Scotland's first electronic exchange opened at Bishopton, Renfrewshire, providong modern phones for modern times. The *Trimphone* make its debut and is still fondly remembered today for its entirely new and lightweight design, boasting many novel features. Despite the conventional bell being replaced with a tone caller with adjustable volume, the phrase "give me a bell" remains to this day.

1971

Trans-Atlantic dialling was extended and six UK cities, including Glasgow and Edinburgh, were able to dial direct to the whole of mainland USA by dialling 0101 followed by the USA area code and local number.

1973

Telephone growth in Scotland gathered momentum as the one millionth customer is signed up.

1976

'Hello girls' were consigned to history when the last manual exchange in the UK closed its doors at Portree, on the Isle of Skye. The UK telephone system became fully automatic. Trans-horizon radio, using tropospheric scatter, was inaugurated to provide telephone links between North Sea oil platforms and the mainland, and the Scottish Radiophone service was introduced.

Scottish customers were able to punch numbers instead of dialling them, thanks to the latest phone, the Keyphone. Its most striking and innovative feature was a keyboard replacing the familiar dial, making it easier to dial long STD numbers.

1978

Thirty foot snow drifts in the Highlands as the worst storms for many years occurred one Friday night in February, three trains were "lost" overnight, all roads were closed, much of the area was without electricity and there was no TV for over a week. Telecommunications were particularly hard hit but the opportunity was taken to install underground plant to storm-proof the service for the future.

1979

Scotland notched up yet another UK milestone as customers in Glenkindie in Aberdeenshire became the first subscribers to be connected directly to a digital exchange. The STD system was completed, allowing direct dialling between all UK subscribers, and radiopaging made its Scottish debut.

1980

Post Office Telecoms became *British Telecom*, the trading identity "Telecom Scotland" was introduced and the Prestel Viewdata came to Scotland. Scotland achieved a world No. 1 listing when the first, purpose-designed optical fibre submarine cable was laid in Loch Fyne.

1981

British Telecom severed its links with the Post Office, to become a totally separate public corporation on 1st October. Among its first achievements were the introduction of the first cashless, card operated payphone and phones for sale rather than rental. Radiopaging was extended to give a virtually nationwide service.

1982

Mercury entered the fray and the Government announceed its intention to sell up to 51% of British Telecom to the public, the first example of the privatisation of a public utility. Kenneth Baker, Ministry for Industry and Information Technology, introduced the Telecommunications Bill, saying: "The Bill creates freedom from Treasury and ministerial control. It also gives freedom to BT to grow, to operate overseas and to make acquisitions. . . the market is growing so quickly that BT can expand only by becoming a free, independent company."

The inland telegram service in Scotland was superseded by telemessages, with overnight delivery, and British Telecom published the first national directory of facsimile users' numbers.

1983

British Telecom's first cordless phone brought more customer freedom to Scotland. The Hawk used a radio to link the mobile extension set with the customer's telephone line at distance of up to 600ft.

Display Page, the first British Telecom radiopager with a digital message display, bleeped for the first time. A 10-digit liquid crystal display on the new pager displayed the caller's phone number or message.

1984

The Telecommunications Bill, delayed the previous year because of the General Election, received Royal Assent on 12th April, and 50.2% of the new company was offered for sale to the public and employees in November.

In the advertising world, the singing and dancing Buzby, which captured the imagination of the public for the past five years, was finally given the 'bird'.

In the second major snow storm within 10 years the Highlands were again in trouble; no electricity service north of Perth at one time and many villages without electricity for over a week. And this over the *Hogmanay* holiday! Telecommunications was not so badly affected as in 1978 but even more storm-proof plant was used to replace damaged trunk routes. 238 telephone exchanges were without a power supply but only 18 suffer loss of service.

1985

Cellnet, the British Telecom and Securicor joint venture cellular radio service was born, replacing the existing radiophone service. Integrated Digital Access, British Telecom's first ISDN-type service, made its first appearance and the first steps to improve the much-maligned payphone service in Scotland began, with the launch of a UK-wide £160m investment programme which will transform the service.

1986

Computerisation of directory enquiries was completed, replacing the existing microfiche system, and response times to callers' enquiries became even faster. DIY telephone extensions were permitted for the first time and British Telecom kits were on sale in its Scottish shops. Glasgow Central became the first exchange in Greater Glasgow to go digital.

1987

A star was born and Beattie took the nation by storm. Maureen Lipman's Jewish granny starred in 32 TV commercials and contributed the word "ology" to the English language. An £87m programme to provide itemised billing for all customers was announced, and British Telecom's research laboratories at Martlesham demonstrated the world's first instantaneous translation of speech by a computer.

1988

The forerunner of Chargecard hit the streets of Scotland in the shape of the British Telecom credit card. With a secret PIN and a unique account number, customers now made calls from any telephone and had the cost added to their next home or office telephone bill.

1989

The Highlands and Islands Initiative, a £20 million joint venture between BT and Highlands and Islands Development Board was announced and will bring an advanced digital network to 80% of businesses in the North of Scotland, years before similar rural areas in Europe and many city centres. HIDB estimated that over the years the initiative has created more than 1200 jobs.

Automatic Voice Response was introduced into the directory enquiries service to give a faster response to customers. Actress Julie Berry's voice was digitally recorded speaking all British Telecom's 6000 exchange names, plus the full set of numbers and number combinations. While the AVR equipment was passing the number to the enquiring caller, the operator was already talking to the next customer.

ISDN 2, a new advanced service capable of carrying voice, data and pictures at high speed, came on the market.

1990

Another UK milestone was completed in Scotland, as BT's long distance network went totally digital with the closure of the electro-mechanical exchange at Thurso. This completed the trunk lines modernisation programme, begun back in 1985, and the UK became the first country in the world to have a fully-digital trunk network.

1991

On 2nd April British Telecom was laid to rest, re-emerging blinking into the sunshine as BT, trading as British Telecommunications plc to become a company ready to face the competitive challenges of the 1990s following a huge programme of change called Sovereign, to reflect the company's commitment to meeting customer needs - "The customer is King."

The new BT was launched with a new corporate identity suitable for a quality company in a highly-competitive world marketplace. And the changes paved the way to give BT the foundation to achieve its vision - to become the most successful telecommunications group in the world.

1992

The world-leading BT Commitment was launched with compensation for missed appointments and customers whose service was not restored by the end of the next working day after the fault is reported. A network of malicious calls bureaux was set up throughout the country, with Scottish callers being handled sympathetically by specially-trained staff at a bureau in Dundee.

The Dundee centre dealt with around 1000 calls a week from worried BT customers. More than half were dealt with through advice and help but some had to change their number and others had traces put on their lines to catch the 'phone pests. The good news today is that more and more people are being caught, cautioned and convicted of making malicious calls.

BT clocked up a world first in the Highlands and Islands as a dozen directory enquiry operators working in and around Inverness began a year working from home in a unique teleworking experiment. The operators were linked to the exchange by videophone, which they used to chat to supervisors, and the commuting time saved cut their working day by up to two hours.

A payphone at Cockburnspath in East Lothian became the first in the UK to be powered by solar panels. The village of Sandhaven near Fraserburgh went one better when its payphone became the first in the UK to be lit by wind and solar power.

1994

Peak rate charging was abolished, long distance charges were cut and BT received the world's largest quality registration. BT began trials of Interactive TV services. Caller Display and Call Return services were launched after successful trials in Moray, Perthshire and Edinburgh, and Scottish customers now knew who's calling before answering the 'phone.

A&B buttons, which were introduced in 1925 and survived many kiosk changes, finally bowed out with the decommissioning of the last unit on the remote Shetland island of Papa Stour. BT launched the UK's biggest ever marketing campaign with top actor Bob Hoskins telling us: "It's good to talk."

1995

BT became the first major national telephone operator anywhere in the world to change its entire network over to per second pricing by abolishing unit-based charging for all its customers. A new era of split-second timing and pricing made it easier for customers to see the cost of calls, which have been cut by more than £1 billion since December 1993.

The new era was ushered in at Crawford in Lanarkshire on June 23 when BT switched off the last of its old mechanical exchanges and replaced it with state-of-the-art computerised technology. Crawford Primary School nine-year-olds Lyn Anderson and Adam Fordyce switched on the new digital exchange seconds after engineers sliced through cables to cut off the old unit and silence the familiar clicking and whirring sounds of calls being connected. Strowger is no more!

BT's initiative has been made possible by its £20 billion investment in the UK phone network over the past 11 years - enough to build two Channel Tunnels. More than £2 billion has been invested in Scotland, where current investment is running at £500,000 every working day.

In 1984 BT inherited a network of more than 6700 exchanges - 1185 in Scotland - many of which were based on electro-mechanical technology developed 100 years ago. All have been replaced by modern exchanges and a network of computerised billing centres which can charge calls with the precision required for per second pricing.

Scottish customers begin to come to terms with the extra digit "1" which has been added to dialling codes to meet burgeoning demand for new numbers.

1996

Scotland started to surf with the launch of BT Internet and BT clicked open its own world wide website, bt.com, following development work by staff in Edinburgh and Aberdeen.

1998

BT Scotland was officially launched on 20th June before 500 invited guests in a marquee in the grounds of Holyrood Palace, just yards from the future location of the Scottish Parliament. It is the first company to be given permission for an event in the Palace grounds and the site is particularly significant, because BT Scotland has been formed in response to the creation of the new Parliament. In an editorial on the setting up of BT Scotland, the Edinburgh Evening News commented: "Such a tremendous boost from BT can do the new Parliament's early standing nothing but good."

BT Scotland unveiled a five-year investment programme in which it will invest in its Scottish network at the rate of £200 every single minute of every single day including:

- £100 million to improve data links around the country to meet increasing demand for data communications and Internet services;
- £20 million to upgrade Cellnet coverage in Scotland, in addition to £20m already committed to upgrades in the Highlands and Islands;
- £5million to bring enhanced services to 220 digital exchanges in the Borders, Dumfries and Galloway and Tayside, on top of £8m upgrading 200 exchanges in the Highlands and Islands;
- £400 million on additional network capacity and new technology.

A £59 million exchange modernisation programme in Glasgow is completed when the last 5700 customers in the city become fully digital. The upgrading programme, which kicked off in 1986, has allowed over 460,000 customers throughout the Glasgow area to benefit from clearer lines and faster call connections.

AT&T and BT announce a $10bn global venture to serve all the communications needs of multinational business customers and carriers, and BT takes the wraps off a free e-mail address service for all to mark the Millennium.

1999

BT Scotland becomes the first Official Sponsor of Hampden, Scotland's National Stadium, in a £5 million commercial partnership which will run until at least 2008. The new South Stand is named The BT Scotland Stand.

Cellnet and Vodaphone work closely with Highlands and Islands Enterprise on a European Funded project to extend the reach of mobile services in the Highlands which is due completion in March 2000. 90% of A and B roads will be served from new masts in some of the most inaccessible areas such as Rannoch Moor, Skye and Lewis. Masts are shared by different operators to minimise environmental impact under the eagle eye of HIE and Scottish Natural Heritage who ensure they blend into the countryside with low visual impact.

Mountain rescue services already reap the benefit of these new services which have been the key to the success of several rescues.

HIE provides European funds to BT and Scottish Telecom; BT upgrade remote exchanges to complete ISDN provision whilst Scottish Telecom install high capacity links to Orkney, Shetland, and the Western Isles. The University of the Highlands and Islands will use these new facilities.

The Information Technology revolution arrives in Scotland with many new jobs created by the use of advanced telecommunications, enabling work to be delivered to the workers, no matter where they are. Call Centres are in use all over Scotland, and even in the remote areas over 2,000 new jobs are created in centres as far apart as Thurso, the Isle of Bute, Stornoway, Kinlochleven and Nairn.

Crofting communities enhance their employment with a wide range of activities - high level technical support to engineers, internet help for home users, home banking, mobile phone support, cinema and train bookings, marketing campaigns, year 2000 compliance monitoring, handling London parking tickets, PC after-sales help, helpdesk for computers in schools, and technical support for IT networks in various nation-wide companies - UK and international services made possible by digital telecommunications.

BT Scotland invests £120m, underlining its commitment to Scotland, by opening two new flagship offices in Glasgow and Edinburgh and upgrading properties in Aberdeen, Dundee and Inverness.

The Glasgow building is named after **Alexander Bain**, father of the modern fax machine, who was born on a croft at Watten, Caithness, in 1810. His inventions in telegraphy in the mid-1800s led to him being credited with the first facsimile transmission.

The Edinburgh office commemorates the work of another celebrated Scottish inventor - the man who started it all, **Alexander Graham Bell.**

We began this potted history of telecommunications with the nine little words first spoken on the telephone by Bell, and it is fitting that we end it as IEE Scotland pays tribute to the man whose inventiveness and foresight was the catalyst that created the fastest-moving and most exciting industry in the world today.

Chapter 7
Broadcasting in Scotland
by Alan Smith BA, CEng, FIEE

The Pioneers

Telegraphy by wire was the jumping off point for most modern communications systems and it may be surprising to learn that as early as 1753 Scotsman **Charles Morrison** wrote to the *Scots Magazine* suggesting a method for the first practical telegraph. Although there were many workers in the field, the race to implement a practical scheme was won by **Samuel Morse** (1791-1872) some ninety years later. The Morse Code was based on the frequency of alphabetical letter occurrence in written text and it remained in use for official purposes until 1998. Although not normally used in broadcasting the BBC used Morse code to transmit a daily news bulletin to French Resistance during the second World War.

James Bowman Lindsay (1799-1862), a Dundee inventor, demonstrated a form of wireless telegraphy by sending messages through water across the River Tay in 1854. *The Dundee Advertiser* printed the comment: 'The experiment removes all doubt of the practicability of Mr. Lindsay's invention and there is every reason to think that it will soon connect continent with continent.' (*Daily Mail,* Wed. August 4ᵗʰ 1999*)*

Radio and Television Broadcasting can be traced back to the work of the 'greatest experimentalist ever', **Michael Faraday** (1791-1867) and the Scottish physicist, **James Clerk Maxwell** (1831-1879) - the 'father of modern physics'. Faraday made discoveries in electromagnetism in 1831 and Maxwell, born in Edinburgh in the year of these discoveries, built on Faraday's work. He produced a brilliant mathematical solution of electromagnetism that predicted electromagnetic waves. In 1887 the German physicist **Heinrich Hertz** (1857-1894) realised Maxwell's predictions in his discovery of the existence of electromagnetic waves in a series of experiments.

Edinburgh born **Alexander Graham Bell** (1847-1922) followed in his father's footsteps in teaching the deaf. Bell emigrated to Canada for health reasons in 1870 and subsequently to the United States in 1871. In 1874, while working on a harmonic telegraph, he discovered the principles of the telephone and was granted a patent for it in 1876.

The names of these pioneers are commemorated by the **bel**, the logarithmic unit of power ratio (usually given in decibels), the **farad**, the unit of capacitance (usually given in microfarads), the **maxwell**, the cgs unit of magnetic flux (1 maxwell = 10^{-8} webers), and the **hertz**, the unit of frequency.

Michael Faraday is commemorated by the Institution of Electrical Engineers award of the Faraday Medal and the annual Faraday Lecture; in addition, his portrait appeared on the Bank of England twenty pound note until mid 1999. James Clerk Maxwell is commemorated by the Clerk Maxwell premium awarded by the SET Division of the IEE.

Guglielmo Marchese Marconi, (1874-1937), the Italian electrical engineer and Nobel laureate, is credited as the inventor of the first practical radio-signalling system. He patented his system in Great Britain and formed *Marconi's Wireless Telegraph Company Ltd.,* in London (1897). In the same year he set up a link to Rathlin Island, which is off the coast of Nothern Ireland at Ballycastle. The link was used by the Lloyds Station at Torr Head, east of Ballycastle. A memorial to Marconi stands in the harbour area at Ballycastle and is inscribed:

MARCONI MEMORIAL

unveiled by John McAffee, Chairman of Ballycastle District Council on 16th July 1973
to recall the historic occasion in 1898 when Marchese Marconi
and his assistant George Kemp established wireless communication with Rathlin
to report to Lloyds station at Torr Head on ships passing along
the north side of the island.

In 1899 he established communication across the English Channel between England and France and, in 1901, across the Atlantic Ocean between Poldhu, Cornwall and Saint John's, Newfoundland, Canada. The Marconi system was quickly brought into service by the British and Italian navies, and within a few years the transatlantic wireless telegraph was in service for public and military use.

Naval interest in wireless telegraphy is understandable with the need to communicate with ships at sea. *The Admiralty*

Handbook of Wireless Telegraphy was a standard textbook on the subject during the first half of the present century. **Admiral Lord Louis Mountbatten** was a naval communications officer in the earlier part of the century and was a founder member and a patron of the British Institution of Radio Engineers which became the **Institution of Electronic and Radio Engineers** (IERE). He is commemorated by the Mountbatten Memorial Lecture. The IERE amalgamated with the IEE in 1987.

In 1904 **Sir John Ambrose Fleming** (1849 -1945) invented the diode thermionic valve with two electrodes, the anode and the cathode. In 1906 **Lee De Forest** inserted a third electrode, the grid, and created the triode. Broadcasting was about to appear.

In a sense communicating with ships at sea is a form of broadcasting. On Christmas Eve 1906 a Canadian, **Reginald Fessenden**, broadcast music and speech from The Electric Signal Company's Wireless Telegraphy (W/T) station in Massachusetts. This first broadcast was picked up by ships in the Atlantic and used amplitude modulation.

Communications systems were further developed during the 1914-18 World War I and in the peace that followed there was a need to find an outlet for the production capacity and the new workforce which was too valuable to lose. There were also a lot of amateur radio enthusiasts and experimenters some of whom had been trained in the forces and were familiar with the surplus equipment especially the radio receivers which required some expertise in operation.

In 1912, while still in college **Edwin H. Armstrong** (1890 - 1954) invented the regenerative (positive feedback) circuit and, in 1918, the 'superhetrodyne' receiver. He also invented frequency modulation which he developed during 1925 to 1933.

In 1919 the Marconi station in Montreal, Canada was licensed as XWA/CFCF and began transmitting regularly.

Frank Conrad of Westinghouse, Pittsburgh began transmitting from his garage, sending out 'programmes' of gramophone records; this was very popular.

Harry Davis, Conrad's manager asked him to build a more powerful transmitter in time to announce the outcome of the next US presidential election. Conrad completed his assignment and on 2nd November 1920, station KDKA in Pittsburgh, Pennsylvania, broadcast the announcement that **Warren G. Harding** had been elected president. About 1000 people heard this first news broadcast.

The Radio Corporation of America was formed from the Marconi company in the USA in 1919 and by 1922 radio was big business. The President of RCA was **David Sarnoff**, a former employee of Marconi.

Frequency Bands

Once broadcasting got under way the amateur radio enthusiasts (Hams) were no longer allowed to use the LF/MF bands and were allocated frequencies in the HF or short wave band. These frequencies were thought to be unusable for anything other than short distance communications. Soon however, it was discovered that the 'Hams' were able to communicate over long distances with low power transmitters.

Before this, in 1902, **Oliver Heaviside** (1850-1925) a self taught electrical engineer postulated the existence of a reflecting layer in the atmosphere. He also devised a new form of mathematics, Heaviside's Operational Calculus, that solved line transmission problems and led to the development of loaded lines for long distance telephony.

Researchers in the radio field began to study radio propagation at different frequencies and discovered Heaviside's reflecting layer, the ionosphere. They used transmitter and receiver aerial systems pointing upwards and transmitted RF pulses measuring the delay in reception of the reflected pulse. As the frequency was raised the existence of different layers in the ionosphere was detected, the E- layer (named the Heaviside layer) and F-layer (named the Appleton layer). The latter was discovered by **Sir Edward Appleton** (1892-1964), Nobel laureate and Principal of Edinburgh University. It was also found that the F-layer split into two layers, F_1 and F_2, during the day but collapsed into one layer during the night. The absorbing day time D-layer was also discovered. At the highest frequencies the signals passed through all layers and were not reflected.

Low frequency transmissions are bent round the earth contained by the E-layer and the Earth surface, rather like a waveguide. They can travel long distances given sufficient power. Transmissions on other frequency bands have two distinct components: a ground or direct wave, which gives a service in an area around the transmitter, and a sky wave. The medium frequency sky wave was found to be absorbed by the D-layer during daylight hours but in the evening was refracted by the E-layer and could be received in other countries.

An interesting experiment on the effect of the D-layer was carried out during the total eclipse of the sun which occurred at 11.10 am on 11th August 1999. Listeners were asked to tune to a Spanish MF station which can be received in the UK at night but not during the day. The effect of the eclipse on the D-layer may give some information on radio propagation. On the day there were some reports of reception of the Spanish station during the eclipse.

High frequency or short wave transmissions are not absorbed by the D-layer but have a limited ground wave and a very efficient sky wave. Variations in the height of the refracting ionospheric layers and multi-path reception causes fading of the signal.

The radio frequencies used in UK broadcasting are divided into bands:

LF Low frequency AM radio transmission	(160 - 225 kHz)
MF Medium frequency AM radio transmission	(525 - 1605 kHz)
HF High frequency AM radio transmission	* (3 - 30 MHz)
Band 1 VHF405 line television channels 1 to 5	(41 - 68 MHz)
Band 2 VHF FM radio transmission	(88 - 97.6 MHz)
Band 3 VHF405 line television channels 6 to 13	**(174 - 216 MHz)
Band 4 UHF 625 line television channels 21 to 34	(470 - 582 MHz)
Band 5 UHF 625 line television channels 39 to 68	(614 - 854 MHz)
Band S SHF Satellite broadcasting band	(2.0 - 3.0 GHz)
Band C SHF Satellite broadcasting band	(3.0 - 8.0 GHz)
Band Ku SHF Satellite broadcasting band	(10.0 -15.0 GHz)
Band Ka SHF Satellite broadcasting band	(17.0 - 22.0 GHz)

Modulation

There are three distinct types of modulation used in broadcasting:
(i)   Amplitude Modulation using Double Side Band (DSB) or Vestigial Side Band (VSB)
(ii) Frequency Modulation
(iii) Pulse Code Modulation

Amplitude Modulation

This is achieved by varying the peak amplitude of the radio frequency carrier from its normal 'steady state' level by the modulating signal. The modulated levels can vary from 0 to 100% (twice the normal steady state level). Modulation levels greater than 100% lead to severe distortion and in practice the maximum level is 90%. Side frequencies or sidebands of frequencies, above and below the RF carrier, are produced by the modulation frequencies.

---

*   High frequency transmissions are, by their nature international, and use portions of the spectrum in wavelength bands e.g. the 49-, 41-, 31-, 25-, 19- metre bands

**   Transmission of 405 line television ceased and these bands have been released for other purposes

By international agreement LF and MF transmitters have a channel separation of 9 kHz. This means that the maximum useable audio frequency is about 4.5 kHz; frequencies above this may interfere with the adjacent channel. As a result the audio lines from studio centres, to other studio centres and to transmitters, provided by Post Office Telephones (now British Telecom) were only required to have a response of 6.5 kHz. When high fidelity ('Hi-Fi') record players appeared on the scene the contrast was marked.

The first broadcast television service used DSB amplitude modulation and a frequency of 45 MHz which avoided refraction from the ionosphere. The sidebands were about 3.5 MHz and it used 405-line interlaced scanning with 50-Hz frame scanning.

Television closed down at the outbreak of the second world war and the engineers and factories concentrated on the war effort. Radar systems were developed quickly and it is no coincidence that the IF strips of the vast majority of radars used 45 MHz.

After the war, television recommenced and surplus radio and radar equipment came on the market. Many home built television receivers made use of 45-MHz IF strips and green trace electrostatic oscilloscope cathode ray tubes which gave a black and green picture instead of the normal black and white; in a way, this echoes the beginning of radio broadcasting.

Later television transmitters used VSB modulation. In VSB the low frequency video signals are transmitted in a DSB mode but the higher frequencies are transmitted only in the upper sideband. This reduces the space required for the television channel.

Frequency Modulation (FM)

FM transmitters use an audio signal with higher frequencies giving higher quality. The modulating signal bandwidth required for compatible stereo transmission is about 53 kHz and the sidebands required are much greater than this.

The sound channel in television uses Frequency Modulation (FM) as does the VHF radio channels. In FM the frequency of the RF carrier is varied by the audio signal. The shift or deviation in frequency depends on the amplitude (loudness) of the audio signal and the rate of variation depends on the frequency of the audio signal. The amplitude of the RF carrier remains constant.

This is a more complex form of modulation and it is difficult to define 100% modulation. Instead, a figure for maximum deviation is set and in the UK the maximum deviation is 75 kHz.

Radio stereo transmission on VHF FM channels is done in such a way as to be compatible with mono or non-stereo reception. This system is not used to provide stereo sound for television programmes.

Because of the wide frequency spectrum required by the system used in radio a completely different approach is used by television. The mono channel is transmitted using a mono FM transmitter and the stereo signal is provided by a second sound transmitter, modulated by a NICAM (Near Instantaneous Companded Audio Multiplex) signal which is a type of pulse code modulation.

Radio Broadcasting

The Marconi Company started broadcasting in 1920 from Writtle near Chelmsford and from 2LO in London.

The **British Broadcasting Company** was formed on 18th October 1922 at a meeting held at the Institution of Electrical Engineers. The first BBCo broadcast took place on 14th November 1922. The first General Manager of the BBCo was a Scotsman, **John CW Reith** (1889 -1971) born in Stonehaven, who was appointed on 14th December 1922. He became the first **Director General** of the **British Broadcasting Corporation**, serving from 1927 to 1938. He was knighted on 1st January 1927 and elevated to the peerage as 1st Baron Reith of Stonehaven in 1940. He was appointed Chairman of the Commonwealth Telecommunications Board from 1940 to 1942. Reith was a son of the manse and had enormous influence on the character and ethics of the BBC. He is commemorated by an annual series of radio lectures with the title of *The Reith Lectures*.

The British Broadcasting Company in Scotland

The British Broadcasting Company began to open stations in Scotland in 1923. The first at Glasgow (5SC) opened on the 6th March. The studio was initially at 202 Bath Street but moved to 21 Blythswood Square on 7th November 1924, and in 1930 to 268 West George Street. This studio was connected by Post Office line to the transmitter which was located at Port Dundas Power Station. **JMA Cameron** was *The Engineer*, this curious title may have been the reason for the title of 'Scottish Engineer' being applied to the BBC's **Regional Engineer, Scotland** many years later. Cameron was the Northern Area Maintenance Engineer and the Engineer-in-Charge, Glasgow was **VAM Bulow**. The two men were to become Superintendent Engineer (North) and Assistant Superintendent Engineer (North) respectively by 1924.

The Glasgow studio mounted an outside broadcast of an opera from *The Coliseum* shortly after it was commissioned and, in April 1924, pioneered schools broadcasting. In October 1924 came the first election address, this was made by the then Prime Minister **Ramsay MacDonald** at a political meeting in Glasgow.

There were now a number of stations in the UK and a simultaneous broadcast of news by all stations took place on 29th August

15 Belmont Street, Aberdeen

1923. This broadcast required the use of Post Office Telephone lines to interconnect the stations; this was to play a big part in the future.

The second Scottish studio was built in Aberdeen (2BD) and was located at 15 Belmont Street and opened on the 10th October 1923; the Engineer-in-Charge was **CG Harding**. The transmitter was sited at the Aberdeen Steam Laundry Company's premises at 40 Claremont Street. Aberdeen made the first Gaelic broadcast which is a little surprising given that there is a much larger Gaelic speaking community in Glasgow. The pipes and drums of the Gordon Highlanders, a famous local regiment, featured in the first and many subsequent programmes. The first Listeners' Club in the UK was formed in Aberdeen. The club organised many events which resulted in broadcasts.

The next Scottish station to open, on 1st May 1924, was Edinburgh (2EH). It was a relay station but it had a studio, initially at 79 George Street moving to 87 George Street. The transmitter was sited at The Quadrangle, University Buildings, Teviot Place and the first Engineer-in-Charge was **JA Beverage**. A second relay station, Dundee (2DE), was opened on 12th November 1924 with a studio at 1 Lochee Road. The transmitter was at the Caldrum Jute Works, St Salvador Street and the first Engineer in Charge was **AC Cameron**. This completed the complement of stations that the British Broadcasting Company was allowed to open in Scotland.

The British Broadcasting Corporation

John Reith became the driving force behind the creation of Public Service broadcasting and on 31st December 1926 the BBCo was dissolved. On 1st January 1927, the British Broadcasting Corporation came into being by Royal Charter. Reith received a knighthood on the same day for his services to broadcasting.

The Chief Engineer of the Company, **PP Eckersley,** became the Chief Engineer of the Corporation. He had already put forward a plan in 1924/25 whereby as many listeners as possible could have access to two channels i.e. the local transmitter on Medium Wave and a UK channel on Long Wave. He was far-sighted as the scheme was to be revived by BBC Radio 4 in 1978 using VHF/FM in place of the Medium Wave transmitters.

The Daventry (5XX) which transmitted on Long Wave with a wavelength of 1600 metres (187.5 kHz) was the first Long Wave station designed for broadcasting. It opened on 27th July 1925 and was estimated to serve 80% of the UK population. A second transmitter (5GB) was installed at Daventry operating on Medium Wave 491.6m (610 kHz) opening on 21st August 1927. This format proved the feasibility of Eckersley's proposal for a similar configuration at five sites in the UK. These were destined to be at Brookmans Park near London, Moorside Edge near Huddersfield, Westerglen near Falkirk, Washford Cross in the West Country of England and Droitwich near Birmingham. The scheme was completed with the opening of the Midlands Regional transmitter on 17th February 1935. As each new regional programme transmitter came into service the old transmitters were closed.

Broadcasting House, Edinburgh opened on 29th November 1930 and became the Scottish Region Headquarters in readiness for the changes that were about to take place.

Scottish Regional and UK transmitters at Westerglen came into service on 12th June 1932, serving the central belt of Scotland and as far as Dundee, using 376.4m (797 kHz) and 288.5m (1040 kHz) respectively. The Glasgow, Edinburgh, and Dundee transmitters were closed down. The Aberdeen transmitter became a relay on 214.3m (1400 kHz). Westerglen was to be used in experiments to improve transmitter design, as there were now three transmitter sites using the same frequency for UK programmes: Brookman's Park, Moorside Edge, and Westerglen; this required synchronisation of the transmitters. An improved system was supplied at the time and in 1938 Westerglen received one of the first quartz crystal drives.

The aerial system was used to test the viability of using one aerial for two high power transmitters. The success of these tests had a great effect on the future transmitting stations. It is interesting to note that in the late 1970s transmitter engineers installing transmitters at Westerglen were faced with the task of feeding five transmitters into one aerial.

After completion of the regional transmitter plan there were still some areas of poor coverage in the Highlands and remote areas of Scotland. A 100-kW Scottish regional programme transmitter was built at Burghead using the same frequency as the Westerglen transmitter. Extensive tests were carried out to determine the coverage and the 'mush' area. This was controlled by synchronising the transmitters and adjusting the output power. The station opened on 12th October 1936. Since this was before the introduction of crystal-controlled oscillator drives, a new system of tuning fork drives was used. The slave drive was controlled by a 1498.05-Hz tone derived from the master drive and fed over a line from Westerglen to Burghead.

Unfortunately Aberdeen was now in the mush area and the service area of the local low power (0.3 kW, 500 m, 600 kHz) transmitter was unsatisfactory. Redmoss was chosen as the transmitter site. Visitors to Aberdeen from the south have a clear view of the 250-ft station mast which in turn has a very good view of the city and surrounding area. The station opened with a higher power (5 kW, 233.5m, 1285 kHz) on the 9th September 1938 replacing the existing transmitter.

Broadcasting House, Glasgow opened on the 18th November 1938, occupying the building of the former Queen Margaret College in Queen Margaret Drive. At the time this was the largest centre apart from Broadcasting House, London which opened in 1932. The extended building housed 10 studios, 2 echo rooms, a control room, library and offices; Studio 1, the Music Studio, could accommodate a large orchestra.

Broadcasting House Aberdeen opened on 9th December 1938 occupying a large house, with garden to match, in Beechgrove Terrace. A portion of the garden was to become the set and site of the popular television programme, *The Beechgrove Garden*. The site has now moved to an out-of-town location but the programme has kept the name.

Television

There may have been a viable Beechgrove garden in 1900 but television was very much in the experimental stage. Devices such as the Nipkow Disc (a disc with holes arranged in a spiral pattern) and the cathode ray tube were invented in the 1880s. Facsimile transmission of photographs by wire and wireless was in use in the 1920s.

The first person to develop a practical television system that coped with subject movement was **John Logie Baird** (1888-1946). Baird was born in Helensburgh. He was educated at the Glasgow and West of Scotland Technical College, now Strathclyde University; Lord Reith of the BBC, a contemporary of Baird, was also an engineering student there. Logie Baird is commemorated at Strathclyde in the *John Logie Baird Institute of Vision Technology* which was opened on 10th November 1999 by the inventor's son, Professor Malcolm Baird.

Baird used a Nipkow disc, with 30 holes, rotating at 12.5Hz to scan the picture. A beam of light was projected through the holes on to the darkened scene and the reflected light, picked up by a light sensitive cell, amplified and transmitted it to a receiver with a similar Nipkow disc synchronised to the transmitter disc. The pictures, even though chosen to best advantage, were very crude. The bandwidth required was 15 kHz and could be accommodated by the existing broadcasting transmitters. The BBC was persuaded to allow test transmissions. These took place, originating from Baird's studio in August 1929, using the medium wave 2LO in Oxford Street. Since there was only one transmitter these were 'silent pictures'.

2LO closed down on 21st October 1929 when the first Brookmans Park transmitter came into service. The second Brookmans Park transmitter came into service in March 1930. This gave an opportunity for experimental programmes in sound and vision from Brookmans Park on 30th March 1930 and these continued until June 1932.

Broadcasting House in Portland Place, London was officially opened on 1st May 1930 and the BBC arranged to take over the originisation of the experimental transmissions of the Baird system. The first of these programmes from Broadcasting House took place on 22nd August 1932. From now on the BBC began to see that television was on the way and staff were recruited and deployed to work in the field. **Douglas C Birkinshaw** a future Superintendent Engineer, Television, co-author of a text book on television, and **TH Bridgewater** a future Chief Engineer Television were in this first group of staff.

Meanwhile others were at work, **VK Zworkykin** (1889-1982) director of the Electronic Research Laboratory of the Radio Corporation of America (RCA) working on electronic methods of picture scanning developed the iconoscope camera tube in 1933. EMI in the UK had set up a team under the Director of Research, **Isaac Schoenberg**. In 1933 he informed the BBC that he had a viable plan for the development of a high definition television system based on the *Emitron* camera. The BBC was impressed with this work.

The Postmaster General, set up a committee in 1934 under the chairmanship of **Lord Selsdon**. The committee reported on 14th January 1934 in favour of a high definition television service but could not decide on the system to be adopted and recommended a competition between Baird and EMI.

The two systems were brought up to a working standard, the Baird system was based on 240 lines, 25 pictures per second and EMI on 405 lines, 25 pictures per second with interlaced scanning. The competition was launched on 2nd November 1936 with the official opening of the service from Alexandra Palace. The Baird system was used one week and the EMI system in the next. The Television Advisory Committee, set up in the wake of the Selsdon Committee, monitored the two systems and at the end of January 1937 recommended the **EMI system**. This became the system in use as from 8th February 1937.

Following the general project pattern the system was used on some local outside broadcasts but there was a very important event due soon - the **Coronation of King George VI** took place on 12th May 1936. The first outside broadcast vehicle was constructed for this event. This housed the existing studio vision and sound control equipment and used three cameras. EMI had the foresight to design a balanced pair cable, suitable for video which could be used for distances up to about eight miles. The Post Office (now British Telecom) pulled the cable into ducts from Hyde Park Corner to Alexandra Palace. The programme went well and it is interesting to note that **TH Bridgewater,** the Engineering Manager, also looked after the programme production. Many new techniques were developed in this initial period which were used until the television service closed down at 12.00 on 1st September just before war was declared. The last words were from Mickey Mouse who said, "I tink I go home!"

A Television Advisory Committee was appointed, under the chairmanship of **Lord Hankey** in September 1943 'to consider the reinstatement and development of the television service'. It reported on 8th March 1945 that the BBC should retain control of the television service and restart it after the war ended.

Television restarted on 7th June 1946 having been off the air for 6 years and 9 months. The presenter, **Jasmine Bligh** opened with *Remember me?,* and the programme included the Mickey Mouse cartoon which had the last words before the war. The first post-war Outside Broadcast (OB) was *The Victory Parade* on 8th June 1946 and it was estimated that this transmission could be received by 25% of the UK population; only 75% to go!

Planning for extension of the television service had been underway for some time. The next phase included four further vestigial side band 405-line television transmitters in Band I, these were:

Sutton Coldfield, near Birmingham, on Channel 4 opened on 17th December 1949. Estimated increase in coverage: 9 Million; total coverage 43% approx.

Holm Moss, in the Pennines, on Channel 2, serving Lancashire and Yorkshire opened on 12th October 1951. Estimated increase in coverage: 11 Million; total coverage: 64% approx.

Kirk o' Shotts, near Glasgow and Edinburgh, on Channel 3, opened on low power temporary transmitters on 14th March 1952 and on high power transmitters on 17th August 1952. Estimated increase in coverage: 4.1 million; total coverage 72% approx.

Wenvoe, near Cardiff, on Channel 5, serving south Wales and West of England, opened on 15th August 1952 on temporary transmitters and on high power transmitters on 20th December 1952. Estimated increase in coverage: 4.3 million; total coverage 81% approx..

The next phase of transmitter construction included:

Redmoss, Aberdeen, serving Aberdeen on Channel 4, opened on low power temporary transmitters on 14th December 1954.

Divis, Belfast serving Northern Ireland and part of South West Scotland on Channel 1 opened 21st July 1955 replacing a low-power transmitter at Glencairn, Belfast.

Meldrum, Core Hill, Aberdeenshire on Channel 4 opened on 12th October 1955, serving North East Scotland replacing Redmoss; total coverage at the end of 1955: 93.5%.

Three more new broadcasting trials were opened in 1955. On 2nd May the first VHF/FM radio station, using Band II, was opened, on 22nd September **Independent Television** started, and on 10th October the BBC began colour television test transmissions using the American NTSC system on 405-line transmitters.

At first, the ITV transmitters used different transmitter sites which required receiver aerials pointing in different directions for the Band I and II transmitters but in due course co-sited transmitters became common.

The first VHF/FM transmitters in Scotland were installed at **Meldrum** and opened on 29th March 1956 and 1957 saw the opening of **Rosmarkie** on the Black Isle, the launch of the first *Sputnik* and the opening of VHF/FM services from Kirk o' Shotts. From then on television and VHF/FM spread steadily northwards, eastwards, westwards and even southwards to the Borders.

Colour television on BBC2 started on 1st July 1967 and was extended to BBC1 in November 1969. Again, the work on individual transmitters took some time. **Craigkelly,** a satellite of **Blackhill** the main central Scotland transmitter site, was converted to colour in August 1971.

Studio Centres and Outside Broadcasts

As the television transmitter chain grew so did the studio centres. In Scotland, the main centre is Broadcasting House, Glasgow, which at one time had been Queen Margaret College, a medical school. The first, rather small studio was built in the college morgue. Nearby there was a television continuity area where the presentation staff could switch between the network and local programmes, give service information and so on. An Outside Broadcast Unit was formed and worked out of various temporary premises until purpose-built premises were provided by East Kilbride Development Corporation in the late 1950s. The unit used venues which were suitable for studio type programmes such as *The White Heather Club.*

A common format at the weekend was:

> Thursday, set up for an outside broadcast of football.
> Friday, move on to a church. Set up and record *Songs of Praise*
> Saturday, back to football ground to transmit or record football.
> Sunday, back to the church for *Morning Service* and possibly a recording of another *Songs of Praise.*

Memorable programmes include the launch of the cruise liner *Queen Elizabeth II, The Commonwealth Games* from Edinburgh in 1974 and 1986, *The Open* from various Scottish golf courses, the climb of

BT Radio Link with
solid state equipment

The Old Man of Hoy in Orkney and there were many others. Outside Broadcasts are connected to studio centres by cable, by radio link or by a mixture of both. The radio link equipment is usually a microwave link and since, the late 1980s, often a satellite link.

Studio A, a much larger studio, was added in the mid-1960s and was used for Drama productions. Some were produced for Scottish consumption but many others were for BBC1 or BBC2. Examples were: *Dr Finlay's Casebook*, with **Bill Simpson** as *Dr. Finlay* and **Andrew Cruikshank** as *Dr. Cameron*, a dramatisation of AJ Cronin's work, *Para Handy, Private Shultz* and many other plays and serials. The small studio, Studio B, was used for news, sport and current affairs programmes such as *Reporting Scotland*. Well known television presenters and reporters of the time included **Mary Marquis** and **Archie MacPherson,** who also did football commentaries.

BBC2 started in 1964 on a 625-line standard, BBC1 continued on 405 lines. The studios and Mobile Control Rooms (MCRs) were modified to allow switched operation between the two standards. A standards converter was developed to convert 625-line programmes to 405-line and, at this stage, London TV studios went over to permanent 625 working. The converter then fed the BBC1 network distribution system. The MCRs of Scottish studios continued to switch standards: 405-line for local and 625 for network productions. Eventually, standards converters were installed at the main transmitter stations and when Kirk o' Shotts was converted on 13th December 1969 the Scottish studios and MCRs went over to 625-line working permanently.

The installation of BBC1 625-colour transmitters proceeded. After this network had been completed and operating for a number of years, 405-line transmissions on Band 1 and 3 ceased and the bands were released for non-broadcasting purposes.

Radio Clyde, the first Independent Local Radio Station in Scotland started to broadcast at the end of 1973. It was followed by **Radio Forth** in 1975, **Radio Tay** in 1980 and **North Sound** 1981. More ILR stations followed and there are twenty ILR stations in Scotland. **Heartland FM**, covering Pitlochry and Aberfeldy, was featured in a television series in 1999.

The BBC followed a different path: **BBC Radio Scotland** opened on 23rd November 1978. This was preceded by the MF/LF changeover whereby Radio 4 UK took over the Low Frequency allocated to the BBC, and Radio Scotland took over the Radio 4 transmitters in Scotland.

Four Community Radio Stations opened Radio's Orkney, Shetland, Solway and Tweed on VHF/FM. A fifth station, **Radio nan Eillean**, opened in 1984. These stations normally broadcast Radio Scotland but 'opt-out' at certain times of the day.

Direct Broadcasting by Satellite

In 1945 radio broadcasting was beginning to get back to normal after the war, in fact regional broadcasting had just recommenced. The October issue of *Wireless Word* carried an article by **Arthur C Clark**, who was later to write the classic science fiction novel, and fast approaching, *2001*. The article outlined the possibility of satellites in geostationary orbit. A satellite in an equatorial orbit 36,000 kilometres from Earth will rotate at the same speed as Earth and appear to be stationary. Clark calculated that 3 satellites would give complete communications cover.

In 1957 the USSR launched the first satellite, Sputnik I, but it was too low and its orbit was not equatorial. Nevertheless it radiated tones intended to be picked up by radio amateurs, a salute to their work in radio transmission over the years.

The US followed later in 1962 with **Telstar**, immortalised in the 'pop' charts by the tune of the same name. This carried the first live television from the USA

Early Bird was the first geostationary satellite and on 2nd May 1965 it carried a television programme *Out of This World*.

Many television organisations, including BBC Scotland, regularly use satellites for programme contributions. In 1989 the BBC acquired its own satellite up-link transmitter and, later, a down-link receiver was installed at Broadcasting House Glasgow. In effect the Satellite forms what is known as the 'mid point' of a '2-hop' link; the frequencies used in each hop are different and are usually in the Ku microwave band (10-15 GHz).

In Direct Broadcasting by Satellite, a transmitter in the satellite takes on the role of the transmitter in terrestrial broadcasting. There are a number of transmitters in a satellite covering different zones and countries. The service area, or 'footprint', is controlled by aerial positioning, polarisation, and power output.

Sky TV started broadcasting in February 1989 and British Satellite broadcasting began transmitting just over a year later. In November the companies merged to form **BSkyB**.

The number of Scottish viewers of satellite transmissions has been increasing steadily. Interest in **digital television** is increased with special offers of free decoders using either terrestrial or satellite transmitters.

Eventually digital television will replace analogue television in much the same way as 625-line television replaced 405-line television. This may happen as early as 2006 but may be as late as 2010. The terrestrial television transmitters have been sold: the IBA transmitters to the NTL company and the BBC Transmitters to Castle Transmission Services. The rest of the BBC's resources are now in the hands of BBC Resources, a BBC owned company.

This century has seen the growth of broadcasting from the clickitty-clack of the wired telegraph to digital colour television with surround sound. In the next century of broadcasting there are sure to be many changes, perhaps interactive 3D or even holographic television is just round the corner!

Dates of Broadcasting Events

1906
R.A. Fessenden transmitted an amplitude modulated signal, using an 80-kHz alternator as an oscillator, from Brent Rock Massachusetts.

1920
Britain's first radio broadcast from Marconi, Chelmsford.

1922
18 Oct British Broadcasting Company Ltd formed (designated here by BBCo to distinguish it from the BBC which was formed in 1928).
14 Oct First daily transmission from 2LO, Marconi House.
15 Oct First broadcasts from Birmingham (5IT) and Manchester (2ZY).
14 Dec JCW Reith appointed General Manager of BBCo.

1923
8 Jan First outside broadcast.
13 Feb Cardiff (5WA) opened.
6 Mar Glasgow (5SC) opened.
Mar First Scottish outside broadcast, an opera from the Coliseum, Glasgow.
1 May Savoy Hill Studios opened (now part of the IEE headquarters building).
29 Aug First Simultaneous Broadcast of news from all stations.
10 Oct Aberdeen (2BD) opened.
2 Dec First broadcast in Gaelic from Aberdeen.

1924
5 Feb First Greenwich Time signal.
5 Apr 2LO moved to roof of Selfridges.
1 May Edinburgh (2EH) opened.

27 Jul Daventry transmitter 5XX opened on 1600 metres (Long Wave)

13 Oct First election address, Prime Minister Ramsay McDonald at a meeting in Glasgow.

12 Nov Dundee (2DE) opened, Baird transmits first successful television pictures.

1925

18/19 Mar International conference at 2 Savoy Place, London that resulted in the creation of IBU.

1926

14 Nov Implementation of the wavelength changes agreed under the Geneva Plan begins. Aberdeen, Dundee, Edinburgh and Glasgow. transmitter wavelengths changed by 12 Dec.

31 Dec BBCo Ltd dissolved.

1927

1 Jan British Broadcasting Corporation established by Royal Charter.

1929

20 Aug First BBC transmission of 30 line experimental television using Baird's studio via Savoy Hill and 2LO medium wave transmitter at Selfridges.

21 Oct Brookman's Park transmitter opened and takes over transmission of 2LO from Selfridges transmitter.

1930

29 Nov Broadcasting House, Edinburgh opened.

1932

12 Mar First broadcast from Broadcasting House, London.

1 May Broadcasting House became BBC HQ.

14 May The end of Savoy Hill.

12 June Westerglen Transmitting Station, near Falkirk, opened.

22 Aug First experimental television programme broadcast from Broadcasting House.

1934

7 Oct Droitwich high power long wave station (1500metres) replaces Daventry (5XX).

1935

Scottish Symphony Orchestra formed.

11 Sept Last 30-line Baird television experimental programme.

1936

12 Oct Burghhead, North East Scotland transmitter opens.

2 Nov Official inauguration of world's first high definition television service from Alexandra Palace.

1937

12 May Coronation of King George V1 and Queen Elizabeth. First use of television outside broadcast van.

1938

18 Nov Broadcasting House, Queen Margaret Drive, Glasgow opens
9 Sep Redmoss Transmitter, Aberdeen opens.
9 Dec Broadcasting House, Beechgrove Terrace, Aberdeen opens.

1939

1Sept Television Service closed down and Home Service replaced other services.

1943

30 Apr BBC commences daily news bulletin in morse code to French Resistance.

1945

29 Jul Regional broadcasts renewed and Light Programme began.
Oct *Wireless World* publishes an article by Arthur C Clarke on geostationary orbits who sets out a plan for communications satellites.

1946

7 Jun Television Service resumed on 405 lines 1950.

1950

30 Sept First television broadcast from the air.

1952

14 Mar Kirk o'Shotts television transmitter opened serving.
Edinburgh Glasgow and surrounding areas.

1953

1 Jan Broadcast Council for Scotland set up 1954.
1 May Glencairn low power temporary television opens serving Belfast opens.
2 Jun Coronation of Queen Elizabeth II.
2 Jul Divis television transmitter opens serving Northern Ireland and parts of South-West Scotland.

1954

14 Dec Redmoss temporary television transmitter station opens serving Aberdeen and NE Scotland.

1955

2 May First VHF transmitting stations opened.
22 Sept Start of ITV.
10 Oct Colour television test transmissions began on 405 lines.
12 Oct Meldrum TV station replaces Redmoss for television in NE Scotland.

1956

29 Mar Meldrum VHF/FM transmitter opened - first in Scotland.

1957

16 Aug Rosemarkie on Black Isle opens.
4 Oct *Sputnik-1* launched with two radio transmitters on board. Signals picked up by BBC were also intended to be picked up by amateur radio enthusiasts.

30 Nov Kirk o'Shotts VHF FM station opens 1958.

1958

5 May Experimental 625 line television transmissions began.

7 May *White Heather Club* televised for first time.

1 Oct Ampex video tape recording used for first time.

12 Oct Rosemarkie VHF FM transmitter station opens.

4 Nov Coronation of Pope John XXIII televised via *Eurovision.*

15 Dec Thrumster temporary TV transmitter station opens.

22 Dec Orkney temporary TV transmitter and VHF FM Transmitter for Radio 4 (Scotland) opens.

1959

19 Dec BBC electronic field store convertor used for the first time.

22 Dec Orkney VHF/FM transmitter station completed.

1960

1 Mar Thrumster television station completed.

27 Mar First transmission of colour television between Paris and London demonstrated at the **Institution of Electrical Engineers**, Savoy Place, London.

2 May Orkney television transmitter completed.

29 Jun Opening of Television Centre, London.

1962

11 Jul First live television from USA by *Telstar* satellite.

16 Aug *Dr Finlay's Casebook* televised

28 Aug Experimental stereo radio transmission began

1964

20 Apr BBC2 opened on 625-line transmission

15 Dec *Culloden* televised

1965

26 Apr Melvaig BBC1 and VHF FM single service operational

2 May *Out of this World* using Early Bird geo-stationary satellite.

31 Dec 'Pirate' radio station Radio Scotland opens on board converted lightship *Comet.*

1966

28 Mar Melvaig VHF FM transmitter station completed.

9 Jul Blackhill BBC2 television station completed.

1967

1 Jul BBC2 regular colour television transmissions using the PAL (Phase Alternating Line) System begin.

29 Jul Durris BBC2 transmitter station completed.

13 Jul 'Pirate' radio station Radio Scotland on board the *Comet* closed down.

14 Aug Marine Offences Act comes into force to deal with pirate stations round the UK coast.

31 Aug BBC field-store converter used for first time for transatlantic colour television.

1969

28 Jul Angus BBC2 station operational.

27 Oct Craigkelly BBC2 station operational.

15 Nov Colour extended to BBC1 and ITV.

1970

11 Jul Rosemarkie BBC2 colour transmissions begin.

1971

10 Jan Open University programmes begin.

7 Aug Craigkelly BBC1 colour transmissions begin.

1973

31 Dec ILR Radio Clyde opens.

1974

Apr BBC engineers won *Queens Award to Industry* for sound-in-sync system.

23 Sep Regular CEEFAX service started.

1975

1 Jan ILR Radio Forth (Edinburgh) opens.

1978

23 Nov BBC Radio Scotland becomes operational. MF/LF change-over. Radio 2 transfers to Medium Frequency band and Radio 4 UK takes over Radio 2 's Low Frequency slot with a slight change in frequency. This allows reception of Radio 4 UK in Scotland and makes possible the BBC Radio Scotland take-over of Radio 4 Scotland transmitters.

Four community radio stations are set up, Radio Orkney (Kirkwall), Radio Shetland (Lerwick) Radio Solway (Dumfries), Radio Tweed (Selkirk). These stations, plus Radio Aberdeen and Radio Highland all opt out from Radio Scotland's VHF/FM transmission at set times.

1979

2 Sept First program with CEEFAX subtitling broadcast.

1980

17 Oct ILR Radio Tay AM & Tay FM (Dundee) opens 1981.

27 Jul North Sound One (FM) & Two (AM) (Aberdeen) opens.

16 Oct West Sound AM & FM (Ayr) opens.

1981

27 Jul ILR NorthSound One (FM) and Two (AM) (Aberdeen) opens.

16 Oct ILR West Sound AM and FM (Ayr) opens.

1982

23 Feb ILR Moray Firth Radio (Inverness) opens.

2 Mar Permission for satellite television granted.

1983

May ILR South West Sound (Dumfries) opens.

1984

BBC Radio nan Eillean (Stornoway) opens to coincide with the National Mod in Stornoway. This station works with Radio Highland to provides a Gaelic language service. Channel 4 opens.

1986

Televising of the Commonwealth Games from Edinburgh.

1987

26 Nov ILR SIBC (Lerwick) opens.

1988

20 Sept Radio Data System (RDS) officially launched. Volvo is the first car to be sold with RDS.

1989

5 Feb Satellite television begins from Sky TV.

1990

22 Jan ILR Radio Borders (Galashiels) opens.
5 Feb Time signal from Greenwich heard for last time.
Apr British Satellite Broadcasting, BSB, begins transmitting.
4 Jun ILR Central FM (Falkirk) opens.
Nov BSB merges with Sky TV to form BSkyB. Independent Television Commission replaces IBA and Cable Authority.

1991

1 Jan The Radio Authority begins official duties.
31 Aug Start of BBC TV NICAM stereo sound services.

1992

1 Sept ILR 96.3 QFM (Paisley).
7 Sep IR Classic FM (National Radio Channel) opens.

1993

30 Apr IR Virgin 1215 (National Radio Channel) opens 1994.
16 Oct ILR Scot FM (Leith) opens.

1995

14 Feb IR Talk Radio (National Radio Channel) opens.

1997

Feb The BBC's 738 transmitter sites sold to Castle Transmission Services for £244 million. The proceeds to be invested in digital production technology. The sale includes an agreement that Castle will transmit the BBC's Analogue TV and five national radio services for ten years. IBA Transmitters have already been sold to NTL.

1998

30 Mar Channel 5 Television opens.
1 Oct Digital Satellite Television opens.
5 Oct ILR Kingdom FM (St Andrew's) opens.
15 Nov Digital Terrestrial Television opens.

1999

1 Jul Televised opening by HM Queen Elizabeth of the first Scottish Parliament in 292 years.

11 Aug D-Layer ionospheric propagation experiment based on solar eclipse.

Sep Chris Smith, Culture Secretary, stated that digital television would take over from analogue television between 2006 and 2010.

References

1. *The BBC : The first fifty years* by Briggs, Asa. Pub. Oxford University Press 1985.
2. *The BBC: 70 years of broadcasting* by Cairns, John. Pub. BBC 1992
3. BBC Engineering 1922-1972 by Pawley, Edward. Pub. BBC Publications.
4. *The Setmakers: A History of the Radio and Television Industry* by Geddes, Keith. Pub. BREMA 1991.
5. *DK Chronicle of the 20th Century* Pub Dorling Kindersley 1995.
6. *Encarta 96* Pub, Microsoft 1995.
7. *Radio Authority Pocket Book*, June 1998.

Chapter 8

The Scottish Coal Industry - electricity wins coal

by JD Wightman BSc, CEng, FIEE

Nationalisation

When the coal industry was nationalised in 1947, there were 187 collieries in Scotland producing approximately 22 megatonnes (Mt) of coal per year. Today, with the dramatic decline in deep mining, only the Longannet complex exists. Its annual output of 2 Mt is conveyed direct into the Longannet 2400-MW Power Station.

With the anticipated increase in demand at nationalisation, the Scottish Divisional Board embarked on an ambitious programme of reconstruction of existing collieries and a number of new sinkings to provide an output of 30 Mt/annum.

In 1953 there were 39 collieries at various stages of reconstruction and 7 new collieries being sunk in Fife, Kincardine,Lothians and Ayrshire.

The programme was not without its problems mainly because of geological difficultues which was made worse with increased water during and after shaft sinking. More recently the development of North sea oil, gas and cheap imports necessitated a revision of the programme.

Coal is now exclusively won by electricity

Just before nationalisation the industry was moving from a highly labour intensive operation using compressed air as the main means of power, to the extensive use of electricity (DC firstly) for all activities. Coal is now exclusively won by electricity, using highly sophisticated cutting and tunneling machines complete with onboard computers.

Scottish Mining Machinery and Plant Manufacturers led the world in mining technology for many years with firms like Anderson & Boyes, Mavor & Coulson, Belmos, Wallacetown, Nelbest, Bruce Peebles, Bonar Long, Hariand Engineering, Scottish Cables, Ferranti etc.

Privatisation

With privatisation of the industry in 1994/95, only Longannet remained operating as a stand alone unit from the rest of the UK.

Regulations controlling the use of electricity in mines were first introduced in 1905 and have, over the years, been revised and extended with the inclusion of the latest electricity at work regulation in 1989.

Wherever coal is mined underground methane gas is liberated and can cause an explosive methane/air mixture. This, if ignited by an electrical source, would result in a methane gas explosion which could then trigger a coal dust explosion.

The electricity regulations require that electrical power must be removed from that part of the mine if methane gas exceeds 1.25% by volume. However, the regulation allows exemption to this rule to permit communications and certain safety monitoring equipment to be maintained even in heavy concentrations of methane. In this case the equipment must be *intrinsically safe* that is, the equipment must be tested and certified that in the event of open sparking in either normal or faulty conditions, insufficient energy would be released to ignite the most easily ignitable methane concentration.

The regulation places on the manager of the colliery the responsibility to state where gas may be present in areas of a mine in sufficient quantity to be a potential hazard. In these nominated areas only approved equipment, such as switchgear, transformers, motors and cable couplers are Certified Flameproof (FLP) or Intrinsically Safe (IS) for Group 1 (methane) gas, can be used.

The use of aluminum underground is banned as under the correct conditions a frictional spark from it can cause an ignition.

Electricity Supplies

Prior to nationalisation, a number of collieries generated their own electricity, in certain DC installations: Bowhill-Fife, Cardowan-Stepps and Gartsherrie Iron Works, supplied their 11-kV network to collieries as far as Kilsyth; some also supplied the local community. In the transition from DC to AC mercury arc rectifiers were used.

With the increase in mechanisation and resulting rise in electrical demand, generation was discontinued and supplies were taken from the Electricity Boards. To comply with National Coal Board instructions, two separate supplies from separate parts of the network are required to minimise complete failure of supply to a colliery. The supply to collieries is given priority by the Electricity Boards because of the risk to life that could arise from its failure. It is necessary to restore electricity to mine winders, ventilating fans and pumps quickly if men are trapped underground and to ensure the colliery is not lost.

Generally supplies would be taken from the 33-kV primary sub-station on the perimeter of the colliery or from the 11-kV network. Each single feeder must be capable of handling the colliery demand of 7 MVA to 20 MVA and the high fluctuating loads of a modern colliery with a normal utilisation factor of about 50%.

Surface Distribution

The main colliery switchboard would normally be supplied at 11 kV with a minimum of two feeders. Distribution to the electric winders, ventilating fans and, in certain cases, coal preparation plants would be at the supply voltage, by duplicate feeder or ring main. The greatest proportion of the load at a colliery is the induction motor, which, in the majority of cases, leads to a poor power factor, this is corrected by means of capacitors on the main 11-kV switchboard.

The introduction of vacuum circuit breakers in recent years, replacing oil- and air-break switchgear, has greatly reduced switchboard maintenance.

For many years the underground distribution voltage has been 3.3 kV but with the continued rise in coal face loads it has been necessary to install 6.6-kV feeders and even in certain instances 11-kV feeders.

Undergound Distribution

A minimum of two underground distribution feeders must always be installed, one in each shaft or mine drift to provide security of supply.

The cables are PVC insulated and double wire-armoured with PVC sheath and single wire-armoured if neutral point reactors and instantaneous short circuit protection is used. These shaft cables would normally be cleated at intervals in the shaft, but single suspension is not uncommon where the cable is reinforced at the point of suspension to carry its entire weight.

The supply distribution from the shaft bottom is routed radially to the faces and transformed by 1-MVA air-cooled flameproof transformers (originally oil-transformers were used) to the coal face operating voltage. For many years coal face equipment operated at 550 volts, but due to the steady increase in coal face mechanisation with larger motor drives, the operating voltage has been standardised at 1100 volts. In a number of cases this has been increased to 3.3 kV.

At the coal face substation, electrical supplies are required for the coal cutting drum shearer, the armoured face conveyer, the stage loader conveyer and hydraulic power packs for roof supports. A total installed

2-MVA face is now common. A separate substation supply is required for the roadway cutting machine, its attendant conveyor system and auxiliary fans. Substations located along the cable route provide 6.6-kV or 1100-volt supplies to conveyors, haulages, pumps and auxiliary fans.

At the surface the three-phase supply is earthed and maintained at a 2-ohm resistance value. Earthing resistors are normally included. Modern practice, however, is to limit the earth fault current in 3.3-kV systems to 150 amps and in 6.6-kV systems to 100 amps, using neutral point reactors. All outgoing feeders are protected by overload, instantaneous short circuit and earth fault protection.

Greatly improved short circuit protection is now provided near the coal face, referred to as *phase short circuit protection*. This type of protection was developed to prevent the through current necessary to start high-rated coal face motors in excess of 400 kW with up to six times full load current at 0.2 power factor and yet trip on short circuit at twice full load current at 0.8 power factor.

The earth leakage current near the coal face is restricted to 750 mA. Earth leakage and earth leakage lockout protection are used, the latter making it impossible to switch on to an earth fault.

Shaft Winders
Prior to nationalisation, the majority of colliery winding engines were powered by steam which was replaced by electrical supplies for AC motors using dynamic braking and "Ward Leonard" systems. This gave easier speed control with improved efficiency. Later thyristor-controlled large DC machines were introduced.

All winding engines originally were single-rope ground mounted using a steel structure with exposed pulley wheels. During the reconstruction years, a move was made to build tower mounted friction winders with two or four ropes over a grooved drum with suspended cages or skips or a combination of either with a counterweight.

As this winding movement is totally dependent on friction to raise or lower the load, rope 'slip' or 'creep' occurs but is automatically corrected on completion of the winding cycle. The inclusion of "Closed Loop" power and speed controls ensure operator error is not possible. With this type of protection, automation of skip winding was introduced ensuring that maximum output could be maintained continuously.

Ventilation

An essential requirement of mining is the need to provide adequate ventilation. This is achieved by a centrifugal or axial flow fan situated at the surface of the return shaft and driven by a slip ring induction motor through a gear box. Changes in air flow are achieved by gear changes and alteration to fan blade angle where possible.

In recent years the 1000-kW variable speed AC motor has been used. This can provide speed variation from half to full speed without the need to undertake gear alterations. This has enabled speed reduction to be made at weekends or when the colliery is not working with the benefit of reduced consumption.

Underground Transport

The transportation of coal from the coal face to the shaft bottom and of men and materials to and from the coal face, has always required serious consideration to meet the demands of maximising output

Rope haulages are used extensively, the smaller units below 100 kW are driven by flameproof (FLP) induction motors fitted with traction couplings, while the larger units use FLP thyristor converter control.

Diesel and battery locomotives were used where the roadways are reasonably level. The battery locomotive is normally powered by a 100-cell, 200-V, 550-Ah lead-acid battery fitted with battery leakage monitoring. Great care is taken in battery charging stations to ensure that adequate ventilation exists to clear the discharge of hydrogen when batteries are on charge.

The important development however has been the introduction of high-capacity belt conveyors designed to clear high tonnage coal face outputs. These main trunk belts are fitted with two or three 300-kW direct-on-line FLP motors, supplied at 3.3 kV or 6.6 kv and controlled by FLP vacuum starters. Extensive protection is fitted for their remote start from the surface control room via a computer-based transmisssion system.

Continuous monitoring of the air environment as well as belt slip, blocked chute, belt alignment and slipping belt is essential; the latter is particularly important because these belts are also used for manriding.

A further advance in high capacity conveying has been the development of the cable belt conveyor for long distance conveying as in the four-mile long Longannet mine complex. Conventional conveyor belting is limited to distance used because of tensile strength. In the cable belt, the belt is supported on wire ropes. The twin ropes act as a haulage and are driven by two 800-kW NS variable speed drive motors, controlled from the surface control room.

Coal Face Layout

While the principle of establishing a coal face between the main air intake and return roadway will never change, coal face equipment has changed and 'retreat mining' is now the order of the day.

At nationalisation mining was labour intensive with the coal face electrical demand barely exceeding 100 kW at 550 V. Development of the Shearer drum coal cutter and the multi-motor armoured face conveyor, enables large tonnages to be cut and conveyed from the face. As a result the electrical demand is now in excess of 1000 kW at 1100 V or 3.3 kV.

In each of the roadways to the face, a 6.6-kV cable from the shaft bottom substation is installed terminating in a flameproof vacuum circuit breaker fitted with over-current, earth fault and short circuit protection. This circuit-breaker connects one or two 1000-kW, FLP transformers (mounted on a pantechnicon) by a pliable armoured cable. This allows the transformer together with a number of 1100-V, FLP contactor panels (gate-end boxes) controlling the face Shearer drum loader, multi-motor armoured face conveyor and stage loader motor, connected by individually screened cables to retreat with the face without isolating the supply.

Attached to the bank of gate-end boxes in the intake roadway is a flameproof intrinsically safe signalling and communication unit. Connected to this unit and spaced at intervals along the armoured face conveyor and stage loader, are signalling and communication units each equipped with emergency stop and lock-out key, alternate units incorporate loudspeaker and microphone. Through these units audible warning is given prior to the movement of the face conveyor. The system is also connected to the surface control room providing instant and direct communication to any part of the coal face.

Power Loaders

For a number of years after nationalisation, coal continued to be won by the established method of using explosives after undercutting the seam. This was loaded by hand into a (hutch) tub or on to a conveyor along the length of the face.

Development of different types of coal cutting machines culminated in the Shearer Drum Loader in the early fifties. This revolutionised the method of coal cutting. The principle of fitting a 3-ft diameter drum with rows of picks and mounted on a modified coal cutter machine provided an excellent cutting tool when rotated. This design was quickly introduced throughout the coal field.

The 'Shearer' with its powered cutting drum and hydraulically driven haulage sprocket, engages a toothed rack on the armoured face conveyor. The conveyor structure is designed to support the Shearer.

Further developments of the Shearer from the initial 150-kW drive, saw the fitting of a ranging arm to arc the drum and cater for varying seam thicknesses. In addition, a trailing drum was fitted for thicker seams. These changes have resulted in a continued rise in drive motor rating up to 500 kW.

All-Electric 1700-kW Shearer - Long-Airdox, Motherwell,
(this shearer set a new record of 738,000 tonnes/month in Australia)

The all-electric Shearer with two electrically driven cutting drums, two thyristor controlled controlled haulage motors and on-board power pack for height control has been developed and is now in use at Longannet; the manufacturer, Long-Airdox, Motherwell has now developed a 1700-kW all-electric Shearer loader for Australia.

The flexible trailing cable used to supply the Shearer from its gate-end box starter, is made up of individually power screened cores to ensure the sensitive earth fault protection will operate before a short circuit can develop. Additional cores allow monitoring of the machine condition to take place. Arrangements also exist to transmit this information to the surface control room for action where necessary. Each machine has an operator and, with radio control available, the operator can control the Shearer from distances of 20 m.

Automatic steering is also fitted to monitor the seam condition and ensure the Shearer drum only cuts the level of coal to provide quality product. With greater dependence on reliability of performance to ensure continuous operation and maximum output. figures of 93% reliability are being achieved.

Heading machines

The introduction of heavy duty roadway cutter loaders in the 1980s, enabled underground roadways to be quickly and safely driven. These machines are fitted with two 100-kW, FLP motors to operate the hydraulic power pack for traction and the cutting head. Gathering facilities enable the cut stone to be removed by a take away conveyor.

Certification of Electrical Equipment

All electrical equipment designed and developed for use in areas underground where methane could be present, requires to be certified flameproof for Group 1 Gases (methane) initially covered by BS227 and BS4683.

Following a joint agreement with the European countries, such equipment today is required to comply with the European Standard issued by the *European Committee for Electrotechnical Standardisation* (CENELEC) for acceptance by the European Economic Community (EEC) without further testing.

Approved FLP Equipment

Before the development of the FLP transformer, the oil-filled transformer fitted with an FLP circuit-breaker was used but required to be located a minimum of 300 yards from the coal face in the intake only. These transformers were rated at 250 kVA.

With the rapid increase in face loadings and the necessity to position the transformer closer to the coal face, the FLP air-cooled transformer was developed at ratings up to 1000 kVA with 1100 V secondary.

The incoming 3.3-kV or 6.6-kV circuit-breakers are fitted with sulphur hexafluoride (SF_6) units. A flameproof m.v. chamber mounted on the opposite end of the transformer houses the over-current, sensitive earth-leakage and short-circuit protection which will trip the hv circuit breaker on fault.

All FLP motors are controlled by flameproof contactor panels (gate-end boxes), the upper chamber is fitted with an interlock and reversing isolator and the lower chamber houses the vacuum contactor together with sensitive earth leakage, overcurrent and short-circuit static protection. The gate-end box is connected to the FLP motor by a five-core trailing cable, with three individually screened power cores, earth and pilot for remote control. Each end of the cable is fitted with a FLP plug and socket, providing flameproof termination and allowing damaged cables to be quickly disconnected and replaced.

The Coal Mines Safety and Health Regulations require certain underground areas to be illuminated. This is carried out with FLP, 120-V, 240-V or Intrinsically Safe lighting fittings. In addition each person going underground, must carry his own cap lamp which he collects and returns to the surface lamp station to be charged.

The present face lighting was developed in 1973. Today the 8-watt fluorescent tubes, positioned along the face, are fed from an intrinsically safe mains transformer high frequency supply.

The Longannet Complex

In 1962 the South of Scotland Electricity Board, announced the intention to build a second Power Station on the north bank of the Firth of Forth; it was to be three times the size of the existing coal-fired Kincardine Power Station.

To meet the coal requirements of this new Power Station, called Longannet (2400 MW), an estimated 20,000 tonnes/day of coal would be required. The upper Hirst coal was already being mined at Bogside mine and, to provide additional output, two new mines Castlehill and Solsgirth, would be driven; the remainder to come from Westfield opencast and Seafield colliery were proposed. To link these three mines, a five-mile tunnel was planned to enable their combined outputs to be conveyed by cable belt and emerge at the surface for the first time at Longannet Power Station.

One of the most urgent tasks facing the Board apart from the extensive mining work, was how to apply a high degree of centralised control and monitoring, in particular to the conveying system.

For the first time the National Coal Board would make a thorough-going application of automation to colliery processing. All functions from the coal face to the surface would be remotely controlled and, if the blend of coal at each underground bunker lost consistancy, a computer would instruct the production points to restore the required mixture.

Longannet -Castlebridge Access, *Courtesy of Scottish Coal*

Such a method of control had never been used in mining before and necessitated the development of special outstation equipment, to operate in conjunction with the selected Ferranti, Argus 2000 computer. These outstations are signalled to control flameproof motor switchgear. The development, the Mines Inspectorate approval and the manufacture of outstations took many months to achieve. This was breaking new ground in the 1970s, but today it is a the normal standard and uses the *Mine Operating System* (MINOS) computer control.

With production and development of the Solsgirth and Castlehill mines, it became necessary to sink a new shaft in the 1980s at Castlebridge, to reduce travelling time to the Solsgirth and Castlehill coal faces for men and materials. Both mines provide ventilation and pumping for the complex.

To extend the necessary control of conveyers from the coal face to bunkers which feed the Longannet cable belt, a new control centre was set up at Castlebridge; this was in addition to the existing centre at Longannet monitoring and controlling the cable belt.

Today the original concept of production, machine and environmental monitoring is carried out from two control centres. This exceeds that which was possible when the system was first commissioned; the limitation was due to the lack of developed transducers.

The control centre at Castlebridge monitors and controls, conveyers, pumps and fans, and is in communication with all areas underground, with broadcasting capability. It also provides continuous monitoring of: the ventilation condition continuously for CO, CH_4, O_2 and fire detection; the condition of face Shearer Loader and the electrical consumption and maximum demand

The Longannet Control Centre in addition to the above controls loading from the staple bunker to the cable belt and its speed. It also monitors: the ash content of coal from the mine using natural gamma radiation detectors; the ash and moisture of the final product to Longannet Power Station, and provides inmix of clean coal when necessary.

Since nationalisation, the use of electricity in the mines has not only been shadowing new technology but in many cases has led it.

References

1. *The Disappearing Scottish Colliery* by R. S. Halliday 1990
2. *Intrinsic Safety* by J R Hall 1985
3. *Mining Applications* by R. Harthill BSc(Hons), CEng, FIEE, Hon FIMEMME
4. *The Role of the Shearer in a High Production Mine* by K Mackie MBE, IEng, FIMEMME

Chapter 9

The Manufacture of Electrical Equipment

(i) 100 years of Cable Manufacture in Scotland
by John T Henderson BSc, DipRTC, CEng, FIEE

From Golf Balls to Cables

Amazing though it may seem, the manufacture of cables in Scotland started from the humble golf ball during the late 1800s. Gutta percha goods and golf balls ('gutties') were the main products of the **United Rubber and Gutta Percha Company** in Dennistoun, Glasgow. They were shipped to all parts of the world. In 1897 the works of the United Rubber and Gutta Percha Company were taken over by the **Craigpark Company Limited**. The expertise in the use of gutta percha was now used in the manufacture of insulated wires and cables in addition to the gutta percha goods and golf balls. The company built up the cable business by selling to the Corporation of Glasgow and the North British, the Caledonian and the Glasgow & Western Railways.

Rubber insulated cables and multicore paper-insulated cables came into prominence early in the twentieth century, and to meet the growing demands for electricity larger premises were required to enable the range of cables to be extended. A factory in Springburn was purchased and in 1903 the **Craigpark Electric Cable Company** was registered. This company took over the assets and liabilities of the Craigpark Company Limited. At this period the company was fortunate to have the services of **William Thomson, 1st Baron Kelvin (1824-1907)** in a consulting capacity. He was knighted in 1866 for his researches into submarine cables and was made a peer in 1892 for his incomparable work in pure science.

Golf was changing and the "guttie" was replaced with the new rubber core ball which was introduced in 1906. It was at this time that the company started producing rubber core balls and gutta percha sheet for the outer covers for other golf ball makers such as Dunlop. Golf ball and gutta percha production continued until 1938.

War time (1914-18) and post war expansion

During the First World War the company was heavily engaged in war work supplying cables for Government Departments, most notably in the manufacture of field signalling cables.

In the early 1920s the cable business developed rapidly and very large contracts were received for the extension of the London underground system. Trackside cables were very susceptible to sheath damage due to movement and vibration with consequent cable failure. Craigpark Electric Cable Company Limited developed a very successful "treaded" and toughened rubber sheathing to combat this problem. The range of cables was extended in the early 1930s to impregnated paper insulated cables up to 11,000 volts.

In 1937 **Scottish Cables Limited** was formed to help to alleviate the serious unemployment situation in Lanarkshire and a factory was built at Renfrew for the manufacture of impregnated paper insulated lead sheathed cables and rubber insulated cables.

World War II

During the Second World War both companies, Craigpark Electric Cable Company and Scottish Cables Limited, made invaluable contributions to the war effort supplying specialised cables for His Majesty's Services including millions of metres of cellulose finished cables for aircraft and specialised cables for night fighters.

During the Battle of the Atlantic from 1940 (the U-boat war) severe losses to shipping were experienced initially due to the laying of magnetic mines by the German Navy. To counter this weapon Royal Naval ships and merchant ships were protected by the fitting of degaussing (demagnetising) cables and both the Craigpark Electric Cable Company and Scottish Cables Limited were heavily committed in the supply of these cables.

The *Luftwaffe* inflicted crippling damage to the Clydeside shipyards during the devastating Clydebank Blitz of March 1941, but by dint of the dedicated spirit of the cable manufacturing industry the required cables for reconstruction were supplied in record time, thus enabling the yards to get back into production quickly.

Post War work

After the war Scottish Cables commenced production of a wide variety of cables including paper-insulated lead-covered and armoured cables up to 33 kV, rubber insulated house wiring cables, rubber insulated mining cables and welding cables. In addition, cables were supplied to many countries overseas.

Glasgow citizens had justifiable pride in their transport system - the 'trams'. They were reliable and a real saviour in the days of the 'peasoup fogs' which occurred during the first half of the century. The trams were driven by 600-volt dc motors. The electric current was conducted via an overhead wire and a pantograph to the motors and returned through the track and feeder cables. Stray current from the return circuit could leak into the lead sheath of paper-insulated cables causing erosion, eventual penetration of the lead and the eventual failure of the cables. The development by Scottish Cables of *Renex*, a specially formulated rubber/bitumen material, which was applied over the lead sheath of cables used in the city eliminated the problem.

Polyvinyl Chloride (PVC), a thermoplastic, was introduced in the 1950s as an insulating and sheathing material for many designs of house wiring and signalling cables and this material latterly superseded rubber, in many cable constructions.

In 1955 Scotland's first cable company, Craigpark Electric Cable Company, ceased manufacturing and closed and Scottish Cables Limited joined the **British Insulated Callender Cables Limited** (BICC) group of companies in the late 1950s. This is one of the world's largest cable manufacturers and Scottish Cables Limited benefited from its wide exposure to world markets. A second factory was built at Renfrew for the manufacture of plastic cables including polyethylene insulated telephone and control cables for the General Post Office and Electricity Boards.

In the post war years the large electrical companies in England had established graduate training schemes which recruited graduates from Scottish as well as English Universities. These schemes deprived Scottish companies, which lacked suitable training facilities, of a required graduate intake. In 1957 the **Scottish Electrical Training Scheme (SETS),** later renamed the Scottish Engineering Training Scheme, was formed by a number of prominent Scottish companies to train and retain in Scotland graduates of Scottish Universities. Scottish Cables was one of the founder members of the scheme which greatly benefited the industry.

In 1965 the factory of **Enfield-Standard Power Cables (Scotland) Limited** was opened by Lord Cameron of Lochiel. The factory was situated in Cambuslang and manufactured a range of low-voltage and medium-voltage PVC insulated and sheathed cables, concentric cables, and paper-insulated lead covered cables for voltages up to 33 kV. The factory also carried out development of new designs of distribution cables for the Electricity Boards. Cross-linked polyethylene insulated cables were also introduced at this time.

A third factory was built at the Scottish Cables site at Renfrew in the late 1960s for the manufacture of oil-filled paper-insulated lead-sheathed and aluminium sheathed cables up to 132 kV. In addition to its production units at Renfrew, Scottish Cables had a Construction Unit for the installation of cables in power stations and major transmission and distribution systems. Production factories were also established in South Africa and Malaysia and the company had interests in Australia and several other overseas countries.

As the last quarter of the century approached cable companies were investing in new factories and plant to capitalise on improved materials, manufacturing techniques and cable designs. This involved the transfer of products from the Scottish Cables factory at Renfrew to newly-built and equipped sister factories in England and production finally stopped at Renfrew in 1976.

A similar fate befell Enfield-Standard Power Cables Limited and production ceased at Cambuslang in the late 1980s. However a different field of cable technology was emerging at this time. Industrial technology had advanced rapidly and the performance requirements of cables became increasingly more demanding.

Cabling plant at Brand-Rex, Glenrothes, *Courtesy of BICC Brand-Rex*

Brand-Rex was started in Glenrothes in 1972 and established itself as a leader in the design and manufacture of cable and cable systems for specialised applications. A wide variety of insulation and sheathing materials has been developed and are available for cable systems which require good fire performance, resistance to water, oil, solvents etc, as well as having good electrical and physical properties. Brand-Rex designs and supplies a world-wide market with specialised cables for aerospace, defence, rail and mass transport, marine and off-shore and automotive industries. Brand-Rex merged with BICC plc in 1989.

The computer age necessitates ever increasing performances from cable systems and equipment and Brand-Rex at Glenrothes is in the forefront of design and manufacture for the coming millennium.

(ii) A Short History of Bruce Peebles & Co Ltd
by Stanley W Milne MBE, CEng, MIEE

The Formation of the Company

The origins of Bruce Peebles date back to 1866 when Mr David Bruce Peebles, at the age of 40, founded the firm of "David Bruce Peebles & Company" at Fountainbridge Edinburgh, to manufacture Gas Appliances.

David Bruce Peebles FRSE was born in Dundee in 1826 and apprenticed there with the general engineering company of Umpherston & Kerr. He then worked with and gained valuable experience with several companies including The Great Western Locomotive Company at Swindon, The Locomotive Works at Amiens in France, John Fairburn & Company in Leeds and Fullerton and Company in Edinburgh.

He became a partner with Fullerton and Company and for the next nine years he was engaged in the manufacture of gas meters and other gas equipment. At this point, in 1866, he left Fullertons to set up his own company, *David Bruce Peebles & Company* at Fountainbridge Edinburgh where, for the next 10 years, he established a similar business in the gas industry.

The move to Tay Works, Leith

The expansion of work at the Fountainbridge factory was such that a move to larger premises became necessary. In 1876 he bought two-and-a half acres of land on the estate of Hill-house Field, at Bonnington in Leith, (now laid out in streets and situated at the corner of West Bowling Green Street and South Fort Street). He built a factory there which he named Tay Works, and closed down the works at Fountainbridge.

The company then entered an era of experimentation and development on gas meters and gas governors of various kinds for station and district applications. An outstanding development, patented in 1875, was a mains governor operated by a pilot governor. This was a big advance in its day, especially where high gas pressures were involved. Another invention of David Bruce Peebles was that of the needle governor gas burner which removed the "hiss" from the jets of the domestic lighting burners then in current use. The Company also undertook installation contracts for street gas lighting and in the early 1890s the company began to make electric arc lamps, then a dominant form of outdoor lighting for major street areas.

In the early 1890s the company started to manufacture gas engines and in doing so became involved in the development of various systems of engine ignition. (1)

David Peebles had a great interest in electricity and in 1894 he attended a lecture, given by **Sebastian Ziani de Ferranti** to the Edinburgh Royal Society of Arts on the future development of electricity. The evening before the lecture David Peebles met the speaker at a dinner party at the home of a Dr Taylor in Edinburgh. He replied to Dr Taylor's invitation to this party in some amusing verse:

Dr. Dr. Taylor,
Your kind invitation I freely accept;
It is always a pleasure to meet you;
When Saturday comes I'll be with you that's sure
And at seven and a half I shall greet you

Had you asked me to meet a very dear friend,
Say a cousin our uncle or auntie;
The pleasure I'd have would not equal by half
What 'twill be, when I meet with Ferranti.
We shall drink to his health, and rejoice that the land
Which gave us such poets as Dante,
Can also alternately change her bit plan and yield such a man as Ferranti.
D. Bruce Peebles.

And upon being asked for a copy of the verses he added a charming postscript:

You asked me for a copy of the above -
I comply with your wish, and now that I've met
Both Mr. & Mrs. Ferranti,
He pleasant and frank, a man we all liked,
She beautiful, charming and canty.

We all wish them well, may they flourish and thrive,
And their goods and their gear ne'er be scanty;
So I thank you good friend, for great pleasure I had
Meeting Mr. & Mrs. Ferranti.
D. Bruce Peebles (2)

Two of David Peebles sons, **W Carmichael Peebles** and **Arthur C Peebles** trained as engineers, the former in the USA (3) and the latter in Chemnitz Saxony. Arthur then joined Ferranti as a student apprentice and worked there with **RS Portheim** and **MT Pickstone**. On lst January 1898, the two sons, along with Mr Portheim and Mr Pickstone set up an electrical department at the Tay Works and, in collaboration with **Professor Blyth** of Glasgow University, designed and built dynamos and electric motors (4). The demand for dynamos for electric lighting and power installations built up rapidly as shown in Company records of the late 1890s as follows:

'Over 50,000 electrical horse power of dynamos are at the present moment running in the various lighting and tramway power stations in the United Kingdom and the Colonies.' (5)

Extra space at the Tay Works became necessary and neighbouring buildings near Anderson Place Bridge were utilised for armature winding. (6)

The Move to East Pilton

When David Bruce Peebles FRSE died, at the age of 73, in December 1899, his trustees took over the administration of the Company for the next three years. In the *Reminiscences of an Old Boy,* a journeyman of 1901, George Happer, recalled:

> *Our hours of work were nine and a half hours on each of five days and five and a half hours on Saturday, making fifty-three hours a week. The wage was 7d. per hour. There were no tea breaks and no smoking.*

In 1902 a reorganisation took place to form a Limited Liability Company with name of 'Bruce Peebles & Company Limited'.The first Board of Directors included W Carmichael Peebles, Arthur C Peebles, RS Portheim, and MT Pickstone. They adopted as a trade mark, the initials *PPP*, and immediately set about the task of building a new factory for the manufacture of much larger machines and to take over the load from the Electrical Department at the Tay Works. This new factory was built on a 10-acre 'green field' site at East Pilton, Edinburgh. It was fully equipped and went into production in 1904 at a cost of £93,000. (The Gas Department remained at the Tay Works and in 1908 separated under the name of 'Peebles & Company').

The first real venture of the Company into the making of large rotating electric machines was through a trading agreement with the Hungarian manufacturer, Ganz & Company of Budapest for the use of their designs in connection with Ilgner flywheel motor generators, traction motors, large generators and motors. For a short time, labour was brought from the Continent to East Pilton to train local labour in the methods employed in the making of these large machines.

The Directors of the Company at this time became aware of a new German invention, by Bragstad and La Cour, called the 'Cascade Converter' subsequently called a 'Motor Converter' and promptly, in 1903, secured the Sole Patent Rights to manufacture this machine in the United Kingdom and the Dominions. At the same time the Company secured the services of **JL La Cour**, one of the joint inventors, who came to East Pilton as Chief Designer. There was an immediate demand for this machine as it provided a very efficient means of converting a high ac voltage supply to a low dc voltage for many town distribution and tramway schemes then being built. A steady flow of orders resulted (7). One of the many advantages of this type of converter was that it was able to accept ac input voltages up to 11,000 volts without the necessity of having a step down transformer. It also had a low noise level which made it attractive for substations in residential areas. The success of this machine contributed greatly to the fortunes of the company for many years. (The first orders for 'Peebles La Cour' motor converters came from the West Ham Corporation London in 1904 for 500-kW and 250-kW machines for installation in a substation at Millbank Dock.)

In 1905, the Company built and installed the first UK Electric Mine Winder for the Tarbrax Oil Company, Lanark. At the same time many complete electrification schemes were undertaken, including the Power Station at Durham Collieries, the complete Snowdon Hydro-Electric Scheme and many tramways including those in Athens, Shanghai, Sunderland, Llandudno, Colwyn Bay and Falkirk.

Financial Crisis

In 1908 the company was involved in the Portmadoc-Beddgelert narrow gauge (2ft) railway in Wales, the construction of which was abandoned due mainly to the high cost of cutting through dense rock. The Company had ten electric locomotives ready for this scheme, five locomotives from Ganz & Co, Budapest and five built at East Pilton to the same design. Mr Portheim was in Moscow where he nearly succeeded in obtaining a £1,000,000 contract for an electrification scheme there but had to withdraw due to the firm's commitments at home, coupled with the Portmadoc-Beddgelert fiasco (8).

The Company was clearly overstretched and a comprehensive reorganisation had to take place. The outcome of this was a more cautious consolidation policy being adopted under the following Chief Executives and Managers: **Lee Murray, SE Bestow, JH Bunting, CS Hunt, Paul La Cour, John Peebles, WH Morton, and GGL Preece** (9).

During the 1914-18 War the company was engaged in the making of munitions and war equipment and after the war reverted to its former peacetime business of the manufacturing of electrical equipment.

In 1918, a new workshop was built for the manufacture of heavy engineering products for steel works such as rolling mills, shears, crushers, and the like but after a few years a trade slump caused this work to be discontinued (10).

The Formation of the Transformer Department

In 1904, within the trading arrangement with Ganz & Co, Budapest, a few transformers were made to Ganz design but core difficulties caused this project to be dropped (11). However, in the early 1920s, the need to be able to undertake complete electrical contracts resulted in the Company deciding to set up a transformer factory on the East Pilton site. To oversee this venture **JW Rodger** was engaged in 1924 as Manager of the Transformer Department which went into production in 1925 (12). In 1926 **Percy Butler** was engaged as Senior Transformer Designer, subsequently to become Chief Designer and, in 1943, Manager of the Transformer and Rectifier Departments. Mr Butler became Chairman of the IEE Scottish Centre in 1951 (13).

The Formation of the Fabrication Department

With the growth of the transformer business and the rapid-development of welded structures, a start was made in 1931 to make transformer tanks and associated parts; for this purpose a small bay was added to the transformer shop. By 1933 the demands for fabricated components grew to the extent that a Fabrication Department was established to supply the needs of all departments on the East Pilton site. All fabrication work was then moved into the Heavy Engineering workshop adjacent to, but separate from, the Rotating Department.

Over the years extensions were added to this workshop as the quantities and size of fabrications increased (14).

The Formation of the Mercury-Arc Rectfier Department

The demand for the Peebles La Cour Motor Converter continued from its inception until, in the 1920s, the more efficient Mercury-Arc Rectifier began to take over the function of ac/dc conversion. To cope with this change the Company, in 1929, entered into an agreement with Messers Brown Boveri & Co Ltd Baden, Switzerland covering the sole manufacturing and selling rights to manufacture Steel Tank Mercury-Arc Rectifiers to their design for the UK market. This established a Rectifier Department which came under the management of the Transformer Department at East Pilton. In 1930, the first Steel Tank Rectifier, of 1500-kW capacity, was installed in the Dewar Place Substation for Edinburgh Corporation. Over the following years many such units were made with capacities up to 2500 kW and dc voltages up to 1500 volts.

In 1932 in order to extend the range for installations of lower capacity a licence was obtained from Société Anonyme Hewittic of Paris to supply Glass Bulb Rectifiers.

Many Mercury-Arc Rectifier installations were undertaken including four successive orders between 1932 and 1939 from the Southern Railway Company for complete substations where a total of 115 units of 2500-kW capacity, with remote supervisory control, were built for the London-Brighton and South Coast main line schemes. These Southern Railway contracts at the time of the 1930s depression sustained the company over a very difficult period.

Another installation of note, delayed due to the intervention of the 1939-45 war, was the electrification of the Manchester-Sheffield-Wath railway line. The line had an overhead dc voltage of 1500 volts which was supplied from eleven substations. A total of nineteen grid-controlled steel tank mercury-arc rectifiers were manufactured and the installation took place in the period 1947-54 (15).

During the 1939/45 war the factory was again engaged in the manufacture of war munitions and a great variety of war equipment. At the same time the factory continued to produce its normal products to meet the demands of key industries. When the war ended the factory returned to its pre-war role of the manufacture of electrical equipment.

The Post War Period.

The war ended with **JW Rodger** as Managing Director at the helm; he had been appointed in 1941. Then in 1952 **WB Laing** and **P Butler** joined the Board of Directors and became joint General Managers of the Company (16). WB Laing was the IEE representative on the Joint

Committee for National Certificates and Diplomas and he was nominated for the chairmanship of the IEE Scottish Centre but was unable to accept the honour because of pressure of business at Bruce Peebles. During the early part of this phase much development took place. The Company increased its range and size of motors and generators, particularly with the undertaking of many generators for the North of Scotland Hydro-Electric Scheme being established at that time. These machines ranged in sizes from 3 MW up to 21 MW totalling about 200 MW of machinery. Similar overseas orders for generators were also undertaken.

The Transformer Department was also undertaking work for the North of Scotland Hydro-Electric Board as well as for the other Electricity Boards in the UK. The transformer factory, erected in 1925 had, over the years, been expanded and upgraded by the addition of new bays and heavier cranes but the immediate need, just prior to 1953, was to cope with the higher voltage of the new 275-kV National Grid. This resulted in many alterations to the factory especially to provide the necessary test voltage clearances. The first two of these high voltage units were installed in 1953 at Clydesmill power station, the Scottish end of the 275-kV interconnector from south of the border (17).

After the death of P Butler in 1953 **RW Flux**, who joined the company in 1952, was appointed Manager of the Transformer Department. He was an active member of the IEE who became a member of the IEE Council in London. In 1954, **Duncan McDonald** joined the Company as Chief Transformer Designer and this brought about a big advance in the design and manufacture of transformers (18). The digital computer, then very much in its infancy, was used to the full in all aspects of design work, accompanied by much development work on transformer construction. One of the many major developments was the building of large transformer cores without bolts penetrating the active material - the 'boltless core'.

In 1959 Duncan McDonald was promoted to Chief Engineer of the Company and a year later he was invited to join the board of Directors. Following the death of JW Rodger in 1956, WB Laing was appointed Managing Director of the Company. Much development work continued in expanding the range and capacity of motors and generators. One major contract undertaken in the early 1960s was for two 60-MVA hydrogen cooled Synchronous Compensators for the CEGB West Weybridge site in Surrey.

The Merger with Belmos & Co Ltd

The merger with Belmos in 1961 brought many changes to the management and direction of the Company. The Belmos company's parent factory was at Bellshill, its main product being flameproof switchgear for the mining industry but it also owned a number of other manufacturing units in London, Dundee, Blantyre and Bothwell. When the merger took place the Belmos Chairman, **Thomas Coughtrie CBE, LLD** was appointed Chairman of the Board of Bruce Peebles & Co Ltd. A holding company was formed and named 'Bruce Peebles Industries Ltd' under which Bruce Peebles at East Pilton then operated and, in 1962, Duncan McDonald was appointed Managing Director, the year during which his pioneering work was recognised by an Honorary Fellowship bestowed by Heriot-Watt College.

The Distribution Transformer Agreement with Ferranti and English Electric

In 1962 a general contraction in the demand for distribution transformers saw Bruce Peebles entering into an agreement with Ferranti and English Electric to pool their respective resources and to form a new Company named 'Distribution Transformers Ltd' (DTL). A factory was set up to manufacture these transformers, (initially in sizes up to 1000 kVA) at Broxburn, West Lothian as a joint venture. This, for Bruce Peebles, released much needed space at the East Pilton transformer shop for the larger units then on order. In time, the Broxburn factory became wholly owned by Bruce Peebles when firstly English Electric was taken over by GEC, and later, when Ferranti relinquished its share of ownership.

The new High Bay extension to the Transformer Factory

In 1962 the company decided to build a large transformer extension to the factory on the north of the existing one at East Pilton to cope not only with the immediate and future National Grid voltages but for anticipated higher voltages for the export market.

This new extension covering 80,000 sq ft, with an initial cranage of 200 tons, went into production in 1964. (Later the cranage facility was augmented to 350 tons as the transformer shipping weights increased). This expansion of capacity

One of three single-phase "boltless" multi-core units to form an 800 MVA 23.5/432-kV Generator Transformer.

was accompanied by much development in the design and production of high voltage units for transmission and power station applications. One of the many major contracts undertaken in the 1980s in this new extension was for the eight converter transformers for the UK end of the 2000-MVA dc link between the UK and France. All eight units, each with a site weight of 500 tonnes, are situated at Sellindge in Kent.

The Merger with Reyrolle Parsons

The next merger took place in 1969 with Reyrolle Parsons, Newcastle. One of the immediate effects of this merger resulted in the Parsons Power Transformer work being transferred from Newcastle to the Bruce Peebles East Pilton site and the name of Bruce Peebles Ltd. became 'Parsons Peebles Ltd' operating under the control of the Reyrolle Parsons Group.

In 1974 Duncan McDonald, Managing Director of Parsons Peebles Ltd at East Pilton, reformed the site into two companies, viz, 'Power Transformers Ltd' and 'Motors & Generators Ltd' each headed by separate Managing Directors.

In 1975 the company was awarded the Queen's Award to Industry for Export Achievement (this honour was repeated in 1988 and 1991).

In 1976 Duncan McDonald became Chief Executive of the Reyrolle Parsons Group and was awarded a CBE for his services to export.

His interests were wide through his membership of several Councils and Boards including the Scottish Economic Council, the Engineering Industrial Council, the Overseas Projects Board, the Council of the IEE and committees of the Scottish Council Development and Industry. In addition he was Vice-President of the Engineering Employers Federation and Chairman of the Scottish Universities/Industry Liaison Committee.

Sir Duncan McDonald (1921-1997)

During this period, from 1976, a number of changes within the East Pilton factory took place, one of which was the transfer of dc motor and generator work to the Witton factory in Birmingham, this factory being part of the Group through an earlier acquisition by Parsons. This allowed the Motor & Generator Department at East Pilton to concentrate predominantly on the manufacture of large ac machines.

The Rectifier Department continued to supply ac/dc conversion units, but just as the motor converters were overtaken by mercury-arc rectifiers this, in its turn, was overtaken by solid state rectification and the Department incorporated these more efficient units into their products but on a much reduced scale.

The Merger with Clark Chapman

Duncan McDonald, as Chief Executive of the Reyrolle Parsons Group, played a leading role in this merger to form a new group called Northern Engineering Industries (NEI). On the group's formation in 1977 he became its first Managing Director. He was appointed Chief Executive in 1980, and then in 1983, Chairman of the NEI group which employed over 35,000 people and had a turnover of over £350 million; during Duncan McDonald's chairmanship this grew to almost £1 billion. In 1980 he was elected a Fellow of the Royal Academy of Engineering and in 1982 Heriot-Watt University awarded him an Honorary Doctorate of Science. For his long and devoted service Duncan McDonald was further rewarded with a knighthood in 1983 and the IEE made him an Honorary Fellow in 1984. This research engineer who became a world authority on the design of high-voltage power transformers and who reached the highest rank in industrial management retired in 1986 and died on 23rd February 1997 at the age of seventy-five (19).

The merger and the formation of NEI, in time, brought about a further series of changes to the East Pilton site which then operated within this much larger controlling group as 'Parsons Peebles, NEI Bruce Peebles Ltd' subsequently to be renamed 'NEI Peebles Ltd.'

In 1987, with much of the machining being undertaken by other parts of the group and elsewhere, the machine shop at East Pilton was shut down and the complete manufacturing unit of Motors and Generators moved out of the original (1903) building to continue manufacturing within the transformer factory buildings. This move was followed by the demolition of the 1903 building leaving the East Pilton site with a much more compact manufacturing unit employing a much reduced workforce to match the downturn of orders.

In 1988 the Fabrication Department phased out the making of large fabrications by having this work subcontracted to other parts of the Group and other companies.

The acquisition of Northern Engineering Industries Ltd by Rolls Royce

In 1989 Rolls Royce took over the whole of NEI Ltd which was then incorporated into the Rolls Royce Industrial Power Group. The East Pilton site retained the name NEI Peebles Ltd, until 1993 when it was renamed 'Peebles Electric Ltd'.

In 1991 the Peebles Distribution Transformers manufacturing unit at Broxburn was moved into the East Pilton site where it operated for seven years until 1998, when it ran into severe and difficult trading conditions and was closed down.

The acquisition of the Transformer Factory by the VA Tech Elin Group

In 1998 the Austrian Company, VA Tech Elin Group acquired all the Electrical Transmission and Distribution operating units, (T&D), from the Rolls Royce Industrial Power Group. This included the Peebles Power Transformers unit at East Pilton. Later, in May 1999, the Peebles Electric Machines Unit (Motors and Generators), was acquired by a new Scottish Company, Peebles Electrical Machines Limited, which has links with the firm Perry Engineering of Adelaide, South Australia.

The destruction of the Transformer Factory at East Pilton

In April 1999 a disastrous fire destroyed the Transformer Factory at East Pilton. The company immediately stated its intention to rebuild the factory, and spent the next four months searching for the best location to meet the necessary criterion to ensure a good future for the plant. In August 1999, VA Tech Peebles Tranformers announced that a decision had been made to rebuild the factory on an 8-acre site within the Port of Leith and aim to have it in production in the latter half of the year 2000 [20].

This short history is a brief account of the many phases of change that the firm has had to encounter throughout its 100 years of existence. It has battled through many vicissitudes, but it is remarkable that the name *Peebles* has survived to the present day. It is not, perhaps, so surprising that this is so, when one considers that the late **Sir Duncan McDonald (1921-1997)** was at the helm throughout much of the merger and take-over period. He had a great admiration for Peebles past achievements and frequently avowed his determination to maintain 'Peebles' in the company name.

It is also remarkable that, with the recent acquisition by VA Tech Elin Group, the name of the transformer factory retains the Peebles name and that the location of the new premises at Leith Docks is to be in the area where the original electrical manufacturing unit was established on the lst of January 1899 at Tay Works in Leith by **David Bruce Peebles**, 100 years ago.

References

1. Bruce Peebles Booklet No.104. *The Story of Bruce Peebles 1866-1954,* pages 9-10.
2. Copy of an Extract from *The Life and Letters of Sebastian Ziani de Ferranti,* The National Archives of Scotland. GD349/12/7.
3. *Bruce Peebles News*, Vol.2, No. l, page 6.
4. IEE Journal, September 1951. The National archives of Scotland.GD349/12/7
5. Bruce Peebles Booklet No.104. Page 12.
6. *Edinburgh Evening Dispatch*, 30th March 1903.
   The National Archives of Scotland. GD349/12/6.
7. Bruce Peebles News, Vol.6 No.l.Pages 3-4.
8. Ibid., Vol.2 Nol Page 8.
9. Ibid.,, Vol.6 No.1.Page 5 Insert.
10. Ibid.,, Vol.2 Nol.Page 8.
11. Ibid.,, Vol.2 Nol.Page 4 Insert.
12. Ibid.,, Vol.3 No4.Pages 11-12.
13. Ibid.,, Vol.3 No3.Page 1 Insert.
14. Bruce Peebles Booklet No.104. Page 43.
15. Ibid.,. Pages 39-40.
16. Bruce Peebles News. Vol.3 No4.Page 1 Insert.
17. Ibid., Vol.3 No4.Page 7.
18. D. McDonald. *Power Transformers for High Voltage Transmission*
19. *The Scotsman*, Obituary of Sir Duncan McDonald, 28th February 1997
20. *Edinburgh Evening News*, 20th August 1999.

Acknowledgements:
   Appreciation is expressed to colleagues and associates of Bruce Peebles for helpful discussions and comments which have made the compilation of this short history possible. Appreciation is also expressed to "The National Archives of Scotland" for access to material used in the compilation of this short history.

(iii) The Electronics and Software Industries of Scotland

by Professor Jeffrey H Collins BSc, MSc, DSc,

CEng, FIEE, FRSE, FREng, FInstP, FIEEE, HonDEng

Background

The Electronics Industry in Scotland is over fifty years old and is now often referred to as "Silicon Glen", as a counterpart of the illustrious "Silicon Valley" in California. The Scottish Industry combines an impressive array of indigenous and multinational companies, mainly having headquarters in the USA, Japan and Taiwan; and many entrepreneurial start-up companies.

Today Scotland produces 40% of European personal computers. There are some 400 electronics companies employing over 50,000 people and generating a revenue of £10 billion. These companies are diverse and range from Original Equipment Manufacturers (OEMs) of components and systems through to service sector companies engaging in contract manufacture, tooling design, materials and equipment supply. A key strength is the pervasiveness of microelectronics in the design and manufacture of silicon semiconductor "chips" and their subsequent utilisation in consumer and military products. The industry characteristic of the multinational companies located in Scotland is off-shore volume manufacture geared to the information and telecommunication sectors complemented by near market R&D carried out alongside their manufacturing areas. The Electronics Industry in Scotland has been complemented in recent years by the growth in infrastructure companies which are necessary to support the personal computer and semiconductor manufacturers.

The Software Industry in Scotland was born some thirty years ago. It has flourished considerably in the 1990s. The "Yellow Pages" for Edinburgh 1998/99 under "Computer Software" lists over 100 companies! The Scottish Software Federation, which was initiated in 1985, lists in its 1997 directory of member companies some 250 paying members. Amongst the current membership are large end-users including Banks, Insurance, Utility, Mechanical Engineering and Telecommunication Companies; and major Electronics Companies who have experienced a considerable growth over recent years in their software requirements for design, manufacturing and support information systems. Additionally, in recent years the Scottish Software Federation has seen a burgeoning in its membership from the smaller software supply companies dedicated to such diverse 'added value' applications as embedding software in electronic products, creating information system packages, data mining, Internet infrastructure and generating electronic games. These latter companies have a close affinity with the motion picture industry. Recently, and uniquely in the UK, a Masters degree in the Electronics Games area has been launched with great success by Abertay University. Employment in the Software Industry in Scotland is estimated to be several thousand. One company, Kingston-SCL Ltd, who major in billing and administration systems for the telecommunications industry are currently expanding to a workforce of 900. The top ten software supply companies have annual turnovers exceeding £7 million.

This plethora of Electronics and Software Companies has been excellently backed by both the Further and Higher Education Sectors in terms of providing the formal education of students necessary to inculcate the initial basic skills for these market-places. Through the auspices of their Industrial Liaison Offices (ILOs) the educational sectors have provided specific staff training to these industries, fostered joint research and development projects, and overseen the generation of intellectual property and the creation of spin-off companies. The ILOs' task has been difficult with the need to balance short-term returns with the long-term need to get new techniques into the market-place.

Scottish Enterprise (SE), and its forerunner the Scottish Development Agency (SDA), both funded by Government, played a major role in recent years in attracting multinational companies with the Scottish Office, through Locate in Scotland, nurturing the growth of start-up companies, and supporting and fostering academic-industry relationships. SDA and SE have effectively taken over the mantle of the largely privately sponsored, but highly influential, Scottish Council Development and Industry (SCDI). This latter organisation played the major role between the late 1940s and 1960s in attracting inward investment and furthering the industrial infrastructure in Scotland. Their Report, in 1961, by **Sir John Toothill** who established the Ferranti Edinburgh factory in the 1940s, on the Scottish Economy, was a benchmark at the time. The excellent work of the Scottish Council Development and Industry continues today.

The Electronics Industry
The make-up of the Electronics Industry in Scotland has changed considerably in recent years in keeping with the dynamics of product

supply and demand, company restructuring, and the economic fortunes of the market-places in the world. Large multinational companies like Timex, Honeywell, Burroughs which came to Scotland in the 1940s are no longer present. Philips have also left. However, their plant in Dunfermline is now occupied by the US company, Solectron, which currently employs over 1,000 people and provides integrated outsourcing solutions to the electronics industry. General Instruments and National Semiconductor, which came in the late 1960s with Motorola, to establish semiconductor manufacturing plants, are now under different ownership; as is the Digital Equipment Corporation (DEC). Since 1998 DEC has become part of Compaq, a major personal computer manufacturer, with a considerable manufacturing presence in the West of Scotland. DEC had already sold its semiconductor manufacturing plant, established in 1985 at South Queensferry, to Motorola in 1993. Hughes Aircraft Corporation which located in 1960 to the new town of Glenrothes to manufacture germanium diodes, continues to thrive as part of Raytheon. Surprisingly for a Japanese company, Mitsubishi have recently closed two manufacturing plants in the East of Scotland.

However, other multinational companies remain mainly under the same ownership and continue to grow strongly whilst gaining world-wide autonomy for their products. These include NCR who came to Dundee in 1946 and who today are a major world manufacturer of 'hole-in-the-wall' automatic teller machines; IBM who came to Greenock in 1951 and is now an autonomous division and a focus for the world-wide supply of its personal computers; Hewlett-Packard who came to South Queensferry in 1966 now have world-wide autonomy for the company's telecommunications measurement systems; and Burr Brown in Livingston. Motorola, who came in 1969 as a semiconductor manufacturer, have also set up a large factory at Bathgate for the supply of mobile phones using the latest printed circuit board technology. Motorola now has 6,500 employees in Scotland and is Scotland's biggest manufacturing employer. NEC who came in 1983 continue to expand their semiconductor manufacturing facilities in Livingston and now also manufacture Packard-Bell personal computers.

Turning to examples of the indigenous companies, Ferranti are now much smaller, being absorbed within the Marconi Group of GEC one of whose companies, Marconi Instruments, has been in Donibristle since the 1950s. The significant number of printed circuit board companies which set up in the Borders continues to wax and wane and regularly change ownership. This scenario with its downsides in terms of closures and changes of ownership is more than compensated for by the upsides of company expansions, amalgamations and entrepreneurial start-ups. It is generally acknowledged that the Scottish Electronics and Software Industries today are stronger than they have ever been.

Scotland has been blessed in building its electronics and software industrial infrastructure by people of great foresight and commitment. One such is **David Simpson**, a Fife man, whom the Hughes Aircraft Company appointed as its Managing Director when it came in September 1960 to set up its germanium diode manufacturing plant. David Simpson in an informal address in 1963 to the Bo'Ness Scout Group spelt out the need for such infrastructure suppliers with the words:

> *An electronics community can be compared to the atomic bomb in some ways, where a critical mass is needed before spontaneous fission can take place. So it is with us - the industry cannot operate in a vacuum, we need to exchange ideas, people and products with other firms in similar fields.*

David Simpson also started up Hewlett Packard's operations at South Queensferry in 1966 which later had other Scots as its Managing Director including **Peter Carmichael** and **Finlay MacKenzie**. Scotland was indeed fortunate that, on his retirement as President of the huge Gould Corporation in the USA in the late 1980s, David Simpson returned to Scotland. During the last ten years he has served as Chairman of over ten start-up electronics companies and also established, in 1997, the Elvingston Science Centre in East Lothian to incubate companies on the Estate where he now lives. David Simpson could, therefore, perhaps fairly claim to have founded 'Silicon Glen'.

Electronics and Software entrepreneurs have abounded in Scotland characterised by people who have been prepared to be risk-takers and lay their hard-earned personal money 'on the table' and compete with their innovative products on the international stage. However, it was not until 1981 that venture capitalists came into existence in Scotland starting with Advent Technology and their £10-million fund raised by Noble Grossart from UK Financial Institutions specifically to back start-ups and to ensure that they were both properly funded and managed. Even today financial backing for risk takers in "Silicon Glen" compares most unfavourably with "Silicon Valley", where failure is viewed positively! One of the first entrepreneurs was **Robert Pringle** who established Nuclear Enterprises, an electronics instrumentation company, in 1956. He was joined by his brother, **Derek**, from Ferranti in 1958, who later established SEEL in 1981, an information technology systems integration and service provider which still trades today.

Another Ferranti employee, **Robbie Maclean**, with **Mike Moran,** who came from the Decca company, established Microwave and Electronic Systems Ltd (MESL) in 1964. Although MESL was established in humble Nissen Hut premises in Newbridge, Midlothian, it set out with great ambitions. In the early days of MESL it even competed successfully in supplying the equivalent of Hewlett Packard's sophisticated microwave measurement systems. However, the big breakthrough came in 1969 when MESL was invited by the BBC to participate in its programme *How to make your first million.* During the programme Robbie Maclean explained, in lay language, microwave Doppler radar and, as an example, demonstrated a very cheap solid state form, running off a 12-volt supply, consuming 3 watts that would detect the movement of human intruders in a room. Today's police radar traps for speeding cars are based on the same Doppler principle. This BBC programme illustrated the power of the media in marketing new products; a role which now seems destined for the WEB!

By 1974, MESL had shipped over 50,000 units to the security industry for the protection of industrial premises. This success enabled MESL to invest in research towards a passive infra-red sensor for human body heat detection which highly advantageously had a power consumption of only 20 milliwatts - a world first. Today such sensors are endemic and sell to the consumer for outside intruder protection of houses with their halogen lamps for typically under £10. The first MESL passive infra-red sensor was introduced to the market in 1972 and again 50,000 units were rapidly sold. Upgrades in performance and styling rapidly followed and, in 1980, units were installed to protect the Burrell Collection in Glasgow. Over one million of these particular units were sold. The abundance of unique technology in MESL throughout their three plants, which included solid-state processors for high resolution radar, attracted Racal who purchased MESL in 1979. This led to further sustained growth, which still continues, and to the availability to other Racal companies of the technological talents of the MESL staff.

Just as Ferranti's and Hewlett Packard have provided 'apprenticeships' for their staff before some left to set up new companies the same can be said of MESL. Notable have been **Matt Snodgrass** at Diagnostic Instruments Ltd and **John Aitken** at Pentland Systems; the successful role **Jim Johnston**, the former Managing Director of MESL, has played as Chairman of several start-up companies; and **Mike Moran**, who was a cofounder of Advent Technology.

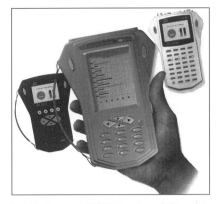

Portable Computer Di-225, *Courtesy of Diagnostic Instruments Ltd.*

Others who contributed to the culture of electronics entrepreneurship in Scotland in the 1970s and 1980s included **Hugh Smeaton** who left Hewlett Packard to build the world's first electronic-fund-transfer point of sale (EFTPOS) machines; and the Americans **Len Brownlow** who founded Rodime as a spin-off from Burroughs to manufacture computer hard discs, and **Dave Wood** who founded International Power Semiconductors. These companies except Rodime, which led in the 1990s to the formation of today's Calluna, are no longer operating. However, these entrepreneurs contributed much to imbuing others to be risk takers and through their influence on founding bodies like the Scottish Electronics Technology Group (SETG) in 1982 as a partnership between industrialists and academics under the sponsorship of the Scottish Development Agency, providing a proactive forum for the identification of infrastructure needs, the exchange of ideas, and the provision of help to those seeking to set up businesses. In late1984 SETG organised a Venture Capital Forum at the Gleneagles Hotel with the Scottish Council Development and Industry at which thirteen start-up companies presented their business plans to the Scottish financial community. Companies presenting included Cairntech in mobile communications, Flexible Technology in high-precision flexible and flexirigid circuits, Lamberton in heavy-duty industrial robots, and Russell ph in electrochemical sensors. Another SETG initiative was the setting up in 1985 of an Annual EFTPOS Conference for Bankers which still runs today! In recent years SETG type activities have strengthened greatly through its expansion, due to the efforts of **Professor Dave Mackay**, into the Scottish Electronics Forum, with its powerful membership of industry executives. Very recently, the Scottish Electronics Forum has amalgamated with the very important Scottish Supply Base Forum to form an integrated focus for the Scottish electronics industry. Scottish Enterprise launched the Birth Rate Initiative some two years ago and was backed by its network of thirteen Local Enterprise Companies which formed 'Technology Ventures' and the CONNECT network to commercialise Scotland's science and technology base. The latter resulted from a joint study undertaken by Scottish Enterprise and the Royal Society of Edinburgh. All these initiatives are professionally managed by full-time executives.

Today's strength of Scotland's microelectronics industry owes much to the foresight of **Professor WEJ (Ewart) Farvis** of the Department of Electronics and Electrical Engineering at the University of Edinburgh. As early as 1964, Ewart was running a Postgraduate Diploma Course, involving Visiting Lecturers from the industry, and hosting an IEE Symposium on *Microminiaturisation* in recognition of the start-up of microelectronics integrated circuit manufacturing in Scotland. In 1965 **Dave Packard** visited the Department and subsequently made the decision to start the Hewlett Packard plant at South Queensferry. Indeed the plant's first product was evolved by **Dr Roberts**, previously a staff member of Professor Farvis's Department

Professor Farvis then made the bold decision to dedicate the Department to microelectronics activities. In 1967 funding was obtained for a clean room and equipment for research and the retraining of industrial personnel into the new microelectronics fabrication technologies. These efforts have continued and flourished at Edinburgh ever since, in fact over thirty years! Today a new building, funded by the University of Edinburgh and Scottish Enterprise houses the latest research and industry contracts, and will serve as an incubator centre for new microelectronics start-up companies. These are under the direction of **Professor Tony Walton**. There are also significant, and complementary, microelectronics fabrication activities in the Department of Electrical Engineering at the University of Glasgow through a team led by **Professor Chris Wilkinson** and at the University of Dundee in the Advanced Materials Centre headed by **Professor Jim Cairns**.

Professor Chris Wlkinson

Jim has recently said: "Major electronics companies aim to produce semiconductor chips with line widths of less than 100 nanometers by the year 2005. Our research demonstrates that this may be achievable much sooner!".

In 1968 Ewart Farvis obtained Wolfson Foundation pump-priming funds to establish the Wolfson Microelectronics Liaison Unit, alongside the Department of Electrical Engineering, to foster and promote academic-industry interactions. Its mission was to improve the training of engineers in microelectronics, to introduce new microelectronics technology into industry and to exploit commercially the research ideas conceived in the university. Noteworthy in Wolfson's start-up was the appointment of two Visiting Industrial Professors and the appointments of full-time professional staff. An important focus rapidly emerged namely the development of the GAELIC software suite for the design of integrated circuits in conjunction with the Department of Computer Science. In 1985, at the wish of the staff, it was floated as a private company, Wolfson Microelectronics Ltd, under its Managing Director, **David Milne,** and its Technical Director is **Jim Reid**. The company thrives today as a world-wide supplier of mixed-signal semiconductor devices. It has established a peerless reputation for high performance audio and video products and general-purpose data converters. Its turnover last year was £14 million; its future looks very bright indeed.

David Milne

Professor Peter Denyer was one of the staff who served his 'apprenticeship' in integrated circuit design at the Wolfson Microelectronics Liaison Unit before joining the academic staff at Edinburgh and also working with the Advent Venture Capital Group. In the early 1990s, Peter with a colleague, **Dave Renshaw**, invented a light-sensitive silicon-imaging circuit which became the basis for low-cost highly integrated camera and vision systems for commercial applications leading, in 1997, to its microminiature digital colour camera. The inventors, and **Roy Warrender**, with financial assistance from the University of Edinburgh's Quantum Fund and the Scottish Development Agency formed the company, VLSI Vision Ltd, in 1990. After further financing from a US corporate investor and a private placing the company was listed on the London Stock Exchange in 1995

263

as the Vision Group. Recently Vision has been acquired by the European based ST Microelectronics Group. This now enables Vision to compete on the world stage by having sufficient resources, access to in-house "chip" manufacturing, and to undertake research work for the whole group. As Peter Denyer has observed - 'Look ahead, and plan how you are going to find the necessary finance'. Peter is now the Managing Director of the Vision and Imaging Business Unit of STM.

The links between academia and industry in the field of microelectronics continue to expand apace as a result of the academic strength in this area. A major recent inward investment was the arrival in Livingston of the California-based Cadence, a world leader in software suites for the design of complex silicon integrated circuits. Its vision in Project Alba is to realise systems on a single semiconductor chip through System Level Integration (SLI). Cadence aims to build up to 2,000 highly qualified staff and thereby become the focus from Scotland for a Virtual Component Exchange whereby global companies will wheel and deal on-line to find the components they need for their new products. To generate this number of staff, Cadence with Scottish Enterprise, obtained the commitment of four Scottish Universities (Edinburgh, Glasgow, Strathclyde and Heriot-Watt) to founding The Institute for System Level Integration at the Alba Centre. **Professor Steve Beaumont** of Glasgow University, was appointed as Director. Its mission is to carry out research, industrial training and education in System Level Integration in general, and System-on-Chip technology in particular. Quite naturally, the Institute's first initiative in October 1998 was to launch a modular MSc degree course in the well-equipped premises of the Alba Centre to help fulfil the huge staff needs. An Engineering Doctorate Programme in SLI is being launched in October 1999 having received funding from the UK Engineering and Physical Sciences Research Council (EPSRC).

Motorola's mobile phone manufacturing plant at Bathgate has recently announced a further expansion of 1000 Scottish jobs giving a total employment there of 3000 people. This expansion is designed to cope with the production of its V-series phone - the smallest mobile phone in the world. In addition its L-series mobile phone is be the only mobile phone that works across three continents. This plant has also been the spur to a collaboration started some three years ago between West Lothian College of Further Education and Napier University and supported by the Lothian and Edinburgh Enterprise of the Scottish Enterprise network on another campus in Livingston. The major aims of the Scottish Advanced Manufacturing Centre are to retrain and upgrade industry staff, particularly factory line workers, in advanced printed circuit-board manufacturing techniques and to undertake contract work for industry.

The strength of the Scottish Universities in knowledge based disciplines including computer science, artificial intelligence and microelectronics, and the significant presence of multinational semiconductor "chip" manufacturers were two inevitable driving factors in the Cadence decision to locate in Scotland. Even by 1984 Scotland, with 1.5% of Europe's population , produced 21% of the merchant integrated circuits made in Europe and some 80% of the UK output. There were then between 30,000 and 35,000 wafer starts per week and over 3,500 people were employed. This dominance in semiconductor manufacturing has continued with today some 20% of Europe's silicon being processed in Scotland. The world-wide semiconductor industry has experienced a 16% compound growth rate through the 1990s. It is predicted that in the millennium year, 2000, semiconductors will account for 25% of world-wide electronic equipment revenue. In turn the capital investment needed to sustain the semiconductor industry has grown almost exponentially as circuit feature sizes, now in submicrons, have decreased at almost the same rate; and as silicon wafers have steadily increased in size up to today's 12 inches! Investments just in upgrading production lines can now exceed several hundred million pounds per annum. A key staffing point is the growing need for software specialists in semiconductor research and development. As **Bertrand Cambou** of Motorola, Phoenix observed at a Royal Society of Edinburgh Seminar in 1997:

"Motorola's split between hardware and software engineers and technologists changed from 95:5 in 1990, to 50:50 in 1996!"

It is a great tribute to the multinational semiconductor manufacturers, Motorola and NEC, that they have sustained these ever-increasing levels of financial investment and shown continued faith in the competence of their Scottish workforce and managers. One person who deserves great credit for these successes which are so critical to the well-being of the Scottish economy is **George Bennett** of Motorola. George received his first degree from Heriot-Watt University and worked part-time alongside **Robbie Maclean** at Ferranti. He obtained his PhD at Glasgow University before co-founding a wafer polishing company, Logitech. George joined Motorola at East Kilbride in the1970s and steadily worked his way up to become General Manager and is now a

Vice-President of Motorola UK. Recently he has served as Chairman of the Scottish Electronics Forum and founded the National Microelectronics Centre for all UK-based 'chip' manufacturers, which is located on the Heriot-Watt Campus at Riccarton.

Today, new areas related to electronics also flourish in the Scottish Universities. One field which has seen extraordinary activity is optoelectronics. Typical has been an EPSRC funded joint research programme of five universities originally led by **Professor Des Smith** of Heriot-Watt University (who incidentally founded the thriving company, Edinburgh Instruments in the 1970s), who for many years has had the vision of this research leading to the building of an optical parallel processing computer. Both Strathclyde University and St Andrews have recently founded Photonics Institutes directed at novel lasers and their applications. Scottish Enterprise has also strongly backed optoelectronics. Since 1996 they have funded three Enterprise Fellowships, administered through The Royal Society of Edinburgh, to commercialise research in the discipline. One of these awards went to **Jeffrey Wright** at Napier University who is developing blue light emitting polymers which should be cheaper to produce than the liquid crystals currently used in flat screen displays. **Frank Placido** of the University of Paisley was named in 1999 as 'Scottish Innovator of the Year' in the *John Logie Baird Awards* for his development of optical filters which can reflect potentially blinding laser light while still allowing 90% transmission of ambient light. A striking example of commercialisation is that of the Department of Electronics and Electrical Engineering at the University of Glasgow which is internationally recognised for its pioneering research in opto-electronic integrated circuits. In 1999 an agreement was signed with Kymata, spun out of Southampton University, to manufacture new devices for high-bandwidth telecommunication systems at a new Livingston facility. In return for supplying the intellectual property, the University of Glasgow will receive an equity stake, royalties, access to Kymata's resources, and a commitment to joint research.

The Software Industry

The Scottish Software Industry in sharp contrast to the Scottish Electronics Industry is predominantly home-grown and is just over half its age! Today, the two Industries are inextricably linked: integrated circuit design being just one of many examples. One can argue that a major factor in the origins of the Scottish Software Industry is the role played by the Scottish Universities Computer Centres and the academic Departments of Computer Science in the days of IBM, DEC, ICL and Amdahl mainframe computers. Innovators in the 1960s included **Dennis Gillies** at the University of Glasgow and **"Tommy" Thomas** and **Sid Michaelson** at the University of Edinburgh.

T. Thomas   S Michaelson

Edinburgh established the Edinburgh Regional Computer Centre (ERCC) which serviced, through its full-time programmers, hardware and operational support staff, some twenty Scottish Universities and Research Institutes, Newcastle University and, in the late 1970s, even Scottish Schools. These were the pre-network times, the era of punch cards, and the use of computers solely for 'number crunching'! A key feature was the use of the in-house developed Edinburgh Multi-Access System, known as EMAS, which remarkably survived until 1985. In parallel to such as the ERCC, the Scottish Universities began to graduate software engineers for industry in significant numbers in the early 1970s just as the microprocessor with its diverse application potential appeared.

Today's Scottish Software Industry should also be indebted to the British Universities setting up JANET around 1980 through the Computer Board for Universities and Research Councils. This joint academic network, which used dedicated telephone lines, allowed E-mail type communication between academic staff, and even students, at Universities in the UK and the USA with additional access to supercomputer facilities and documents and research data in Libraries. The exposure which students in Scottish Universities obtained to JANET enabled the birth of local area networks in the 1980s and the INTERNET in the 1990s to be readily taken on board throughout Scotland. An optical fibre based SUPERJANET was implemented in the mid-1990s allowing remote teaching and also real-time demonstrations from theatres of surgical operations. Noteworthy is the considerable financial support and encouragement that the Scottish Higher Education Funding Council (SHEFC) has given both to this endeavour and to ensuring that Scotland has sufficient software graduates to satisfy the burgeoning needs of its Software Industry.

Another significant initiative, in what may be fairly termed the development by the Scottish Universities of the Scottish Software Industry's infrastructure, was the national Alvey Programme in Advanced Information Technology which took place between 1981 and 1986. Two key features were the requirement for academic-industry collaboration and the merging of projects of several cognate disciplines such as computer science, electrical engineering, linguistics, and artificial intelligence. This latter discipline had been pioneered in Scotland in the 1970s by **Donald Michie, Richard Gregory** and colleagues. However, it had been tragically stopped for a decade by a damning Report of the then Science Research Council. Fortunately Alvey revived the discipline of artificial intelligence to the later benefit of the software industry in Scotland and to the foundations of the Turing Institute by Donald Michie at the University of Strathclyde and the Artificial Intelligence Applications Institute by **Jim Howe** at the University of Edinburgh. In turn, companies have been set up including **Rob Milne's** Intelligent Applications Ltd and **Paul Wilk's** Artificial Intelligence Solutions Ltd.

Several of Scotland's software companies emerged in the early 1980s from the Scottish Universities. Examples are Edinburgh Portable Compilers Ltd (EPCL) which was spun out of ERCC by **Geoff Millwood** and **Peter Stevens** and grew to over 60 people. Lattice Logic Ltd, which provided software tools for the design of integrated circuits, was spun out of Edinburgh's Department of Computer Science by **John Gray**; as was Clan Systems, who make sophisticated computer printers, by **Hamish Dewar**.

John Gray went on to European Silicon Structures, which was backed by the Advent Technology Venture Capital Group, whilst Lattice Logic re-emerged as 3L with a number of its former employees and still trades today. Later John Gray founded Algotronix for the development of programmable "chips" which was purchased a few years ago by Xylinx from the USA who now have, in consequence, their research and development base in Edinburgh. John Gray could be fairly described as one of the first Scottish software entrepreneurs!

ICL, a mainframe computer manufacturer, located to Dalkeith in the 1970s to support their Scottish customers machines. However in 1983 they left. The upside was, this led to the spawning of several companies including Office Work Stations (OWL) founded by **Ian Ritchie,** recently the President of the British Computer Society. OWL was eventually sold and now undertakes research and development in interactive multimedia software for its parent company, Matsushita. Another was Spider Systems which was founded by **Peter Palmer, Martin Ritchie** and colleagues for network switching. Interestingly, both Spider Systems and SEEL took licences from ERCC to manufacture their X.25 switch. Spider Systems was purchased in 1997 by the Shiva Corporation of the USA but regrettably the Scottish facility has now been closed down. Three messages emerge from these experiences, namely that competing on the world stage in the computer and software demands relationships with multinational companies; that the Scottish Software Industry suffers, as does its Electronics counterpart, from the dynamics of change; and that 'trade sales' lead to the original entrepreneurs, like Ian Ritchie and Martin Ritchie, becoming 'business angels' playing a key role in funding new-start companies.

Another initiative of Scottish Enterprise, in conjunction with its Local Enterprise Companies, was to establish in the early 1990s Project SOFTNET, which is an infrastructure covering nine Software Incubation Centres. Seven of these are located in the Central Belt of Scotland. The other two are in Dundee and Aberdeen. Each contains a cluster of small software companies in buildings with centrally managed, yet low overhead facilities. These, in turn, provide the occupying companies with a profile and image greater than could be achieved individually. Three multinational companies have been closely associated with Project SOFTNET - Hewlett Packard at South Queensferry, NCR in Dundee and BAeSEMA in Glasgow. Hewlett Packard directly provided the building on its site at South Queensferry for its Software Partner Centre which had built up by 1993 to some fourteen companies, three of whom became suppliers to Hewlett Packard in the telecommunications field. One of the other companies was ASCADA Limited whose Chairman and Chief Executive is **Ron Dunn**, a former Managing Director of Ferranti in Edinburgh, and now also the chairman of the management committee for the Alba Centre. ASCADA provides systems software for the control and management of complex distribution networks for electricity, telecommunications, water, gas and transportation.

The ten largest software companies in Scotland in December 1998, according to the publication Software Echo, were in turn:- Kingston SCL; Graham Technology established in 1986 in Glasgow; Newell and Budge in Edinburgh; Weir Systems in Glasgow; SCROMAGG, a systems integrator headquartered in Motherwell, CRS Computers of Livingston; Real Time Engineering located in Glasgow and Aberdeen, who like many others are involved in Year 2000 auditing; Atlantech Technologies located in Glasgow, who provide network management solutions to the telecommunications industry; Concept Systems of Edinburgh, who specialise in integrated navigation systems and data processing systems for oil and gas exploration; and Zonal Retail and Data Systems.

With the demise of mainframes in the late-1980s, and the advent of distributed computing with workstations and personal computers, there still remained an ever increasing need for 'number crunchers' of extraordinary power for areas like weather forecasting, oil exploration, protein sequencing, and fundamental physics and astronomy calculations. For many years Scotland had been inconvenienced by having to use remote supercomputers at London and Manchester. Just like the 1960s, Edinburgh University became UK innovators this time through **Professor David Wallace** of its Physics Department by writing the software languages for the operating systems and application packages required for a brand new breed of high performance supercomputers. These were parallel computers which have the great advantage over mainframes of being scaleable through "nodes" to any size, and thus power. In 1990 the Edinburgh Parallel Computer Centre (EPCC) was formed with the mission of accelerating the effective exploitation of parallel computers through academia, industry and commerce. EPCC has been an enormous success and thrives today. By the end of 1994 it had over sixty full-time professional staff, thirty technology transfer partnerships with end-user companies in high 'added-value' niche markets, and over one hundred research projects carried out by some three hundred and fifty academic users throughout the UK. The virtues of EPCC can be summarised as: academics 'win' through exceptional facilities, end-users in industry and commerce 'win' by evaluating the technology at minimised cost, and vendors 'win' through the shop window created by EPCC. Again Scottish Enterprise played a critical role in supporting EPCC's bid to EPSRC (now part of Silicon Graphics) for the 256-node Cray T3D, which at the time was one of the ten most powerful computers in the world!

As might be expected from the above, the Scottish Universities have been very active in recent years in spawning new start software companies with the help of their Industrial Liaison Offices. One example is Quadstone which was founded in 1995 by four senior staff members of EPCC. Besides parallel computing, the founders brought with them the new tool of 'genetic algorithms' which had earlier been the basis of the physics PhD thesis of **Nick Radcliffe**. Quadstone's ambition is to become the world's leading supplier of large-scaleable behaviour modelling software. Quadstone has developed two products, Decisionhouse and Transactionhouse, which together help its clients undertake leading-edge analysis of their customer databases, known as 'data mining', and thereby assess their customer relationship management techniques and credit risk strategies. Major clients of Quadstone include Barclays Bank, the Liverpool Victoria Group in Insurance, J Sainsbury and the UK's mobile telecommunication companies. Currently Quadstone employs over seventy staff in Edinburgh, London and Boston. Their Managing Director is **Neil Heywood**, formerly the General Manager of EPCC. Neil has made the observation that: 'finding potential partners for Decisionhouse was easy. It was finding customers with the right background and commercial interests that proved hard'. Another quote from **Neil Heywood** is:

'software programming has no rules, only good practice. The latter I learnt by serving my apprenticeship under John Gray at Lattice Logic'!

The Future
Inventiveness and entrepreneurship in Scotland can be traced back to the times of **Lord Kelvin**, **Fleeming Jenkin**, who contributed to integrating the science of telegraphy, **Professor Archibald Barr** and **William Stroud**, who founded their famous optical company in 1888, **Alexander Graham Bell**, the television pioneers, **John Logie Baird** and **Alan Campbell Swinton** and the radar pioneer, **Sir Robert Watson-Watt**. It is interesting to note that Strathclyde University established *The John Logie Baird Institute of Vision Technology* on 10th November 1999.

Today's vibrant Scottish Electronics and Software Industries also have a great debt to many unsung heroes who have striven individually against considerable odds whilst never sacrificing their self belief in the cause they exposed of inventiveness and entrepreneurship. Several of these heroes have been identified in this Chapter. Credit is also due to the foresight and commitment of the *Scottish Council Development and Industry* and the Government sponsored *Scottish Enterprise* and its predecessor, the *Scottish Development Agency*, in bringing together industry with the educational sector. Thereby, Further and Higher Education in Scotland have played a fundamental role in continuously providing new manpower throughout industry and commerce, upgrading staff skills, technology transfer, and generating and researching ideas from which new companies have been spawned. Collaboration between the private sector, the public sector, and the educational system is at an all time high, and an opportunity exists for the IEE to play a larger role in this forum, now that its Scottish Engineering Centre is up and running in Glasgow. Indeed, perhaps Scotland can now claim for its Electronics and Software Industries an advance on **David Simpson's** profound words of 1963: 'a critical mass has been achieved and spontaneous fission is taking place.' However, one common theme, as John Gray observed, underlines the successful indigenous companies, namely that they have inevitably become a 'trade sale' to a multinational company. The formidable challenge thus remains: to build a Scottish company to a comparable scale of a multinational. Here the role of venture capitalists would seem paramount rather than to rely solely on government-led funding.

It is a pleasure to record that two of Scotland's Banks have taken a considerable interest in the affairs of the IEE. In 1989/90 the Bank of Scotland gave the Institution's Faraday Lecture emphasising the role and future of information technology in their business. Recently **Viscount Younger of Leckie**, Chairman of the Royal Bank of Scotland, addressed IEE Industrial Affiliates, members and engineering representatives at the Scottish Engineering Centre and observed that:

………the IEE has an important role to play in raising skills levels and should regard the new Scottish Parliament as a friend and partner……the Scottish Parliament's ability to influence policy makers in London and Brussels will depend on the quality of argument it deploys, and the Parliament will therefore benefit from good briefings and contact with bodies such as the IEE.

Thereby, the IEE has been challenged to find its 'niche' in order to contribute effectively in the new millennium to enhance the infrastructure with vibrant collaboration underpinning the Electronics and Software Industries in Scotland.

References

1. *Enquiry into the Scottish Economy 1960-1961*. John Toothill. Scottish Council (Development and Industry) 1961.
2. *Glenrothes Factory Open - Ceremony by Lord Polwarth*, The Scotsman, 1ˢᵗ September 1960.
3. *On the Crest of a Personal Wave: David Donald profiles David Simpson*. The Scottish Business Review, June 1967.
4. Industry Policy and the Scottish Economy. N Hood and S Young. Edinburgh University Press 1984.
5. *Silicon Glen - Myth or Reality?* by JH Collins. IEE Proc. Part F, 133. Feb 1986.
6. *Silicon Glen Reality or Illusion - A Global View of High Technology in Scotland* by Andrew Hargrave, Mainstream Publishing Co (Edinburgh) Ltd. 1985.
7. *Science and Technology Prosperity for Scotland - Commercialisation Enquiry*, Report of the Scottish Enterprise and the Royal Society of Edinburgh, 1996.

(iv) Electronic Equipment
for Civilian and Defence Purposes
by Alex M Hall BSc, PhD, CEng, FIEE

The recent history of electronics design and manufacture in Scotland started during the 1939-1945 War. This led to increased numbers of graduates, resulting in an increase in the numbers of members in the IEE in Scotland who were involved in electronics. At first, the equipments were for defence purposes but later diversification led to other non-defence designs. In this chapter the history of some of the companies involved will be discussed. A useful snapshot of Electronics Companies in Scotland in 1985 together with a brief history is given in ref. 1.

Early History

As far as the design and manufacture of light current devices was concerned, the manufacturing capability set up by **William Thomson, Lord Kelvin (1824-1907)** was much earlier. He has already been mentioned in the history of the IEE in Scotland (Chapter I), being Scotland's first IEE Chairman, but it must be remembered that in 1899 he was 75 years of age and all his great contributions were behind him. He had been a member of the Institution of Telegraph Engineers since 1871. It is interesting to note that as this is being written an argument ensues over whether he should be remembered as a Physicist or an Engineer. He was, of course, both. The argument was sparked off by a plaque erected by the Institute of Physics at Kelvin's house in the Professors' Court in Glasgow University where he lived from 1870-99. The Institute of Physics called him a Physicist and, as he held the post of Professor of Natural Philosophy, are justified in doing so. However, we, as engineers, know he was a leading light (no pun intended) of our society. We should recognise that the divisions between Physics, Applied Physics and Engineering, particularly Electrical Engineering, are tenuous. Kelvin's fame in the engineering of the Transatlantic cable is as great as his solutions to the theoretical aspects of telephone transmission lines.

So where does his engineering achievement stand? Before discussing the company manufacturing instruments which he founded, we should look at his contribution to electrical engineering. Kelvin claimed to be the first person to light his home entirely by electricity. In a letter he sent to **Mr (later Sir) William Preece (1834-1913)**, a pioneer of wireless telegraphy and telephony, dated 16th March 1886 Thomson says:

> In answer to yours of yesterday, I began electric lighting in my house in June 1881. By the end of the year I had 106 lights in my house, and soon afterwards I had 52 lights in my classroom, 12 in my Laboratory, and 10 were fitted in the Senate room of the University. My lamps are Swan 85v 16 candle. I made a Faure battery for myself from 120 cells arranged in three parallels and used it incessantly for about 18 months till I found it worked to death.
>
> Last year I got an improved Faure-Sellon-Volckman battery from the Electric Power Storage Co. By the accompanying copy of the letter I have sent to Mr Drake you will see how splendidly satisfactory this has been. I scarcely ever have the engine going except during the day to charge the battery. Without the engine I get from the battery ample current for 40 lights: when I want more than 40 lights I use the engine and battery together in the usual manner and then I have ample current for 70 to 80 lights
> (4 vol. 2).

Kelvin often claimed to have had the first house illuminated entirely by electricity in the planet. Although at Cragside in Northumberland, the home of **William George, Baron Armstrong FRS (1810-1900)**, he claimed it to be the first to be lit by hydro-electric power, in December 1880, six months earlier than Kelvin. However, only 45 lamps were involved which seems unlikely to completely replace existing lighting, especially as Cragside in Northumberland is a much larger house than Kelvin's. A claim has been made that electric lighting at the house of **Sir Joseph Swan (1828-1924)** in Gateshead predates both, but it is likely that again this was only partial lighting. As Kelvin publicly stated his claim, and both Armstrong and Swan were known to him, had it been untrue, they would have queried it. Presumably the significant word is 'entirely'. Of course, Cragside's claim to be the first to be lit by hydro-electric power is valid. That was a 'do it yourself' job, and predates the period of this history, but Armstrong's other interests led to the founding of the Elswick Engineering Works in Newcastle famous for its ordnance, especially the Armstrong gun.

The building of iron ships posed a problem with the correction of ship's magnetic compasses and by 1848, Kelvin (William Thomson as he then was) suggested a new solution to the problem resulting in a patent in 1876. This in turn led to practical designs of compass cards and binnacles to contain the permanent magnets for correction of the compass. In 1884 he provided the capital to set up 'a new factory sited in Cambridge St, Glasgow, employing some 200 hands and a staff of trained electrical engineers in the test department' (3 p.775). After 1900 the firm became a limited company, **Kelvin and James White Ltd**. In the thirty-three-year period from 1876 (the year of his first commercial patent) until his death in 1907 his firm supplied 10,000 compasses to the world's merchant and fighting ships.

By 1906 the 'dry card' compass was being replaced by the liquid compass but Kelvin White continued to make binnacles for the new type of compass. The company also made deep sea sounding apparatus to enable the outline of the sea bottom to be plotted, useful both in navigation, where the bottom had previously been plotted, and in cable laying. The firm's existence continued through various name changes and amalgamations. Kelvin and James White Ltd became **Kelvin Bottomley and Baird** which in 1947 amalgamated with the London firm of **Henry Hughes and Son** as **Marine Instruments.** When it was realised that two good names had sunk in oblivion the name was changed to **Kelvin Hughes**. The final demise took place in the mid 1960s when Smith Industries took over and closed the Glasgow plant.

A portable Laser Designator. Courtesy of Pilkington Optronics Ltd.

Another of the early manufacturers was **Barr and Stroud** in Glasgow. This company had a long pedigree of Scientific Equipment for the Services, starting with the optical rangefinder, patented in 1888, on which the firm was founded (2). In the ensuing years the firm branched out into the manufacture of submarine periscopes and electro-mechanical plotting tables to enable the prediction of aiming direction of a large warship's guns from range measurements. During the 1940s radar (pioneered by another Scot, Sir Robert A Watson-Watt (1892-1973)) was introduced to submarines and Barr and Stroud were involved in the design and manufacture of the microwave "plumbing" and the antenna for fitting to periscopes. The antenna had to withstand the pressure of the submarine at depth. Later, the company designed a range of electronic systems for aircraft, with the co-operation of **Ferranti Ltd** through the Scottish Office scheme mentioned later.

Although Barr and Stroud had only a limited contribution to the evolution of rangefinding from the prismatic rangefinder to radar, the next phase, an increase in frequency to the red wavelength laser rangefinding in the 1960s, brought it back into the firm's expertise. The design of laser rangefinder systems for tanks resulted in a design study which was finally produced in 1964. This led to a large increase in the number of electronics engineers employed by the company. These engineers, together with physicists and mechanical engineers were also involved in thermal imaging which had become an expertise developed by the company. In 1977 the company merged with the Pilkington Group in St Helen's, and continue to design and manufacture in Glasgow.

Developments after 1943

Ferranti Ltd set up a manufacturing base in Edinburgh in 1943, to manufacture aircraft gyro gunsights. However, they soon set up a research, development and manufacturing organisation producing radar systems and sophisticated gyros. By the 1950s they were the leading electronic company in Scotland and the Scottish Council invited them to encourage electronic design in Scotland, by assisting in the handling of Ministry of Defence contracts by firms with limited electronics expertise.

The author was one of many graduates given an opportunity to remain in Scotland because of this. The **Lithgow Group**, at that time, mainly known for shipbuilding, decided to take up this offer and use part of their wagon building plant - **Pickering's of Wishaw**. Until the accommodation was ready the design group were housed at Ferranti

Ltd, Crewe Toll. Eventually, we moved in to a cold and spartan building, with a couple of labourers to keep the place clean and make our tea ('billy cans' on a stove - a far cry from modern coffee machines, or the "tea lady" at Ferranti's). One of the Ferranti design staff came over and advised and monitored our design work. Ferranti's excellent facilities for testing (particularly environmental) were freely available to us and I certainly feel that as a team and as individuals we gained great strength from Ferranti. Many other firms presumably had similar experiences. In this particular case the Lithgow group decided to drop the electronic defence contracts and the team joined Barr and Stroud, strengthening the existing group there.

Ferranti continued with large defence contracts but also diversified into commercial areas such as computer aided design and manufacturing equipment and lasers, both high and low power. In 1978 they were taken over by GEC and continue with defence equipment designs.

During this period other English and American firms such as **GEC/ Marconi, STC, NCR, Burroughs** set up design and manufacturing units in Scotland.

Following the Ferranti initiative and various government initiatives to encourage foreign (mainly American and Japanese) companies to invest in Scotland, a number of firms such as **Honeywell, Hewlett Packard, Hughes Electronics, IBM, NEC, Motorola, DEC, Compaq**, set up factories, most of them using design staff, some using graduates in quality control procedures.

A few 'home grown' firms were set up, the more notable including **Nuclear Enterprises, Microwave and Electronic Systems (MESL), and Rodime.**

References

1. Hargrave, Andrew: *Silicon Glen, Reality or Illusion*, Mainstream Publishing, 1985: ISBN 0 906391 83 0 (cloth), 84 9 (paperback).
2. Moss, Michael and Russell, Iain, *Range and Vision*, Mainstream Publishing, 1988: ISBN 1 85158 128 6 (cloth)
3. Smith, W Crosbie and Wise, M Norton, *Energy and Empire, a Biographical study of Lord Kelvin, 1989*: ISBN 0 521 26173 2.
4. S P Thompson, *The Life of William Thomson, Baron Kelvin of Largs*, 2 Vol, London 1910.

(v) The Ferranti Contribution to Electronics in Scotland

by JB Smith MA, BSc, FIEE, CEng, FRSE

Ferranti - The Company

In 1943, midway through the Second World War, a new factory building appeared at Crewe Toll in north-west Edinburgh. It had been built by the Government, in accordance with a policy of dispersing military production, for the manufacture of gyro gunsights for fighter aircraft. The gyro gunsight was an ingeniously simple electro-mechanical computer which compensated for the relative speeds of the fighter and its target, enabling the fighter's guns to be optically aimed ahead of the target by the appropriate amount; its internal construction was not dissimilar to that of a domestic electricity meter. The name which appeared above the door of the new factory was FERRANTI, a company already in the business of manufacturing meters.

Sebastian Z de Ferranti (1864-1930)

The Ferranti company had been founded in the 1880s by the young **Dr Sebastian de Ferranti**, whose research into electrical transformers had demonstrated the feasibility of distributing electricity over significant distances in the form of alternating current. For financial reasons the company was established in Manchester and became a leader in transformer design and allied technology including switchgear and electricity meters.

The descendants of Sebastian Ferranti continued to hold a controlling interest in the company; his son Vincent was chairman and chief executive when the Edinburgh factory was opened. The Ferranti family still regarded the enterprise as a family business; they exercised a paternal attitude towards their employees and made themselves very accessible to their senior managers.

Staff working in Manchester in 1943 showed a marked disinclination to move to the new factory in Edinburgh and had to be given financial incentives with a guarantee that they would eventually return to Manchester. In the event, none of the twenty or so who agreed to be 'deported' to Edinburgh ever did apply to return to Lancashire. This intrepid band were led into the unknown by a young cost accountant, **John Norman Toothill** (later Sir John Toothill), who was appointed General Manager of the Edinburgh plant.

Science-Based Research for the Defence Industry

Three years later the war was over. It was assumed that production of gyro gunsights would come to an end. Ferranti had a factory in Edinburgh with nearly 1000 employees and no guaranteed future. The parent company made it plain that unless profitable work could be found for it, the factory would close. Toothill had other plans (although a Yorkshireman, he had enthusiastically embraced malt whisky and salmon fishing) and believed that there would continue to be a substantial defence industry based on new and developing technologies.

Sir John Toothill

Fortunately, the gyro gunsight (GGS) business did not immediately dry up; in addition to its generating servicing business, the removal of security restrictions meant that the GGS could be sold to minor air forces around the world at prices much more favourable than the Government had paid. Even so, the future of Ferranti Edinburgh hung in the balance for several years while various scenarios for ongoing business were considered.

Toothill, though not himself scientifically trained, believed fervently in the potential of science-based industry and he was a good judge of men. He set about recruiting young (and inexpensive) Scottish graduates to form the nucleus of a research team. Over the next few years this team obtained short-term development work from some of the

Government scientific establishments and explored various projects with either military or civil potential.

A demonstration in 1951 to the British Association for the Advancement of Science by **JB Smith** and **DM McCallum** on the potential of computers for solving logical problems (at a time when computers were regarded as merely 'number-crunchers') attracted some publicity. It became evident however that the securing of major defence contracts would be the most promising way forward. Toothill strengthened the management of the organisation by hiring a few experienced scientists from the Scientific Civil Service establishments at Farnborough (Royal Aircraft Establishment) and Malvern (Radar Research Establishment) and on this foundation, Ferranti Edinburgh set out to become a major player in the defence industry.

The Ferranti Philosophy

It was a time when military pundits were claiming that the era of the manned aircraft was at an end; unmanned guided missiles were to be the war engines of the future. The Ferranti team chose to dissent from this, believing the human brain to have capabilities not possessed by computers. Given the advantage of radar and similar aids, they claimed, a fighter pilot would still do better than an unmanned missile. However, weight carries a heavy penalty in fighter aircraft; radar equipments at that time were heavy and it appeared that a second man in the aircraft would be essential to operate such equipment. Ferranti took the bold line that it should be possible to design light-weight equipment which could be operated by the pilot himself. They were the only team in the UK who held this view; the Government thought this line unpromising and were unwilling to finance research into it. Ferranti did however manage to persuade FW Page, the chief designer of the English Electric aircraft division, to give them facilities to study whether the concept of a single-seat radar-equipped fighter could be applied to the *Lightning* aircraft, at that time under development. Ferranti built a prototype radar tailored to the *Lightning*; a key member of the team responsible for this development was **Donald Murdo McCallum**, later to succeed Toothill as General Manager of Ferranti Scotland. The resulting trials were brilliantly successful. Ferranti gained Government support and were on track to become a major defence contractor.

Ferranti Growth

The consequences of this triumph for Edinburgh and for Scotland were immense, albeit not fully appreciated at this crucial period of the early 1950s.

Hard on the heels of the *Lightning* contract came a contract for the radar and weapon aiming system of the naval *Buccaneer*. The design and manufacture of the equipment for these aircraft gave Ferranti a secure base from which to expand into related technologies. These included low-flying control systems, inertial navigation, moving map displays, optoelectronics; all of these to be applied to later generations of military aircraft, including the *Sea Harrier*, *Tornado* and the European Multi-Role Combat Aircraft, as well as the *Lynx* helicopter. Ferranti were able to liaise with aircraft companies around the world and to secure valuable export contracts. Simultaneously, with the aircraft systems, Ferranti were obtaining contracts for ground radar equipments and were also developing electronic valves and similar components. A significant fraction of Ferranti's research effort went into advanced manufacturing technology such as computer-controlled machine tools, computerised testing, improved assembly methods and the like. Advanced mechanical engineering design went hand in hand with the continually changing electronic technology.

Ferranti multi-mode radar, ECR 90 as fitted to the Eurofighter Typhoon aircraft.

Over the next ten years the group grew to over 5000 employees, drawing not only on the local schools and the Scottish universities but attracting graduates in various disciplines from as far afield as 'Oxbridge'. For specialist skills related to manufacture, Ferranti had from the outset operated their own school for the training of both apprentices and shop-floor assembly workers. Specialist skills on the design side were not forgotten; in 1954, assisted by the Scottish Council for Development and Industry, Ferranti moved into a new laboratory block at Crewe Toll so that staff from smaller firms could be taken on secondment. Ferranti engineers who designed pilot-operated equipment were required to take flying lessons (though not on jet fighters!) to familiarise themselves with the tasks of an aircraft pilot. For the airborne testing of equipment, a Ferranti Flying Unit was set up at

Edinburgh Airport; initially a *Dakota DC3* was set up as a flying laboratory so that equipments could be tested under in-flight conditions; this unit grew to a point at which several fighter aircraft fitted with sophisticated instrumentation were being flown by Ferranti pilots and observers carrying out trials. Quality assessment techniques, in line with those adopted by major US defence contractors, were developed to enable the company to tender for guaranteed reliability contracts.

As the Scottish Ferranti Group expanded, additional premises were set up in and around Edinburgh; by the end of the 1970s, in addition to three major sites in Edinburgh, the Group had plants in Dundee and Dalkeith, subsequently acquiring sites in Livingston, Bellshill, and Aberdeen.

Associated Growth of the Scottish Electronics Industry

The early success of Ferranti was of great value to the Scottish Council (Development and Industry), who were able to point out to multinational companies considering inward investment that Ferranti had been able to build up a competent labour force virtually from scratch. By 1951 five US companies (Timex, NCR, Honeywell, Burroughs, IBM) had opened branches in Scotland, and many others followed. Most of the incomers benefited greatly from Ferranti's training programmes. In 1985 an astute analyst was to write:

For over 30 years, multinational companies establishing themselves in Scotland have acquired many of their core engineers and managers from Ferranti. Tens of companies have started in the precision mechanical engineering and printed-circuit board fields as Ferranti subcontractors. A number of notable entrepreneurs of the Scottish electronics industry served their apprenticeships with Ferranti. (1 p.98)

Ferranti in the Community

Ferranti placed great store on participation in local activities, this attitude being strongly linked with Toothill's early recruitment of Scottish graduates, who in time became the senior management of the group.

Sir John Toothill himself was commissioned by the Scottish Council in 1961 to head a major enquiry into the Scottish economy (2), subsequently known as the *Toothill Report*. Other Ferranti managers including **DM McCallum, J Drury, KR Brown, C Allen, JB Smith, WDH Gregson** inter alia made notable public contributions by serving on the governing bodies of various institutions e.g. University Courts, the Royal Society of Edinburgh, the Scottish Council (Development and Industry), The Institution of Electrical Engineers (IEE) and The Institution of Mechanical Engineers (IMechE) Committees and Council, the Edinburgh Chamber of Commerce, the Scottish Electrical Training Scheme and several others, less obviously relevant e.g. Church of Scotland, Edinburgh International Festival, Livingston Development Corporation and the like. **JB Smith**, in his capacity as Chairman of the Electronics and Control Section of IEE Scottish Centre, organised and carried through successfully the first microelectronics conference in Scotland, held in Edinburgh University in April 1964.

Ferranti in Crisis

The parent Ferranti company suffered severe financial difficulties during the high inflation of the 1970s when a downturn in UK demand for distribution power transformers led them to concentrate on export business with consequent pressure on cash flow. In 1974 the Government was compelled to safeguard its defence contracts by taking an equity holding in Ferranti and requiring the company to appoint a new chief executive, **John Derek Alun-Jones**, a director of Burmah Oil, in his early forties. The immediate impact of these changes on the Scottish Group was minimal and indeed the financial strength of the Scottish operation was a vital factor in the recovery of the parent company.

The Government's holding in the company came to an end in 1978 when Ferranti became a listed company on the London Stock Exchange. This opened the way for Alun-Jones to press forward with his vision of building Ferranti into a world leader in electronics through a policy of expansion of the company by mergers and acquisitions.

Ferranti Scotland in the World

The selection of **Donald McCallum** as General Manager of the Ferranti Scottish Group when Toothill stepped down from the post in 1968 proved to have been a wise one. In addition to being a brilliant engineer, McCallum had superb judgement, and he inherited from Toothill a fine management team, mostly engineers and (though with notable exceptions) mostly Scots. By the mid-1980s the

Sir Donald McCallum (1922-)

Scottish Group of Ferranti under his leadership was stable, profitable and still cautiously expanding. In addition to maintaining their ongoing high profile in defence, they had established subsidiary companies in the USA (California, Ohio and Massachusetts), Germany, France, Switzerland and England, exploiting fallout expertise in computer graphics, computerised inspection, inertial navigation, electro-optics, fluid flow measurement and the provision of services to the oil industry.

By the time McCallum (by then Sir Donald) retired from the post of General Manager in 1985, the Scottish group had played its part nobly in bringing Ferranti on to the world scene.

The Ferranti Formula

The phenomenal success of Ferranti in Scotland, as measured by technical brilliance, financial return, exceptional growth rate and international reputation, deserves to be analysed. Credit has to be given in the first instance to the visionary entrepreneurship of John Toothill and to the support given to him by the Ferranti family who controlled the parent company. John Toothill believed fervently that science-based research was the key to successful business and from the outset insisted that the Edinburgh branch would do its own research and would not be simply a manufacturing arm of a company with its research department in England.

The bright young engineers and scientists recruited by Toothill matured into project and departmental managers; Sebastian de Ferranti, the founder of the company, had been a brilliant engineer and his son and grandsons were not afraid to give managerial responsibility to scientists and engineers. Heads of design departments were given substantial freedom to develop their sector of the business in the way they thought most desirable. Some of the young men who joined straight from military service at the end of the war found this freedom astonishing, but soon grew to enjoy it, and stayed with Ferranti for the whole of their career. Every encouragement was given to the scientific staff to keep abreast of developing technology, of which there was a great deal as electronics moved from valves to transistors to integrated circuits and new areas of the frequency spectrum opened up. Liaison with the Scottish universities and technical colleges was strong, fostered by the fact that Edinburgh is a small city; the Scottish Centres of the engineering Institutions played their part in this cross-fertilisation.

The Ferranti fashion of treating the firm as a family business also created a friendly atmosphere; the dozen or so senior managers met daily for lunch and the General Manager carved the joint. Employees at all levels were on Christian name terms. To the outside world Ferranti may have seemed a slightly eccentric organisation; what other company chairman would, like Sebastian Ferranti, have thought of organising an "Inventors' Dinner" in Manchester so that he could meet all those of his staff who had filed patent applications for the company? Ferranti in Scotland were a happy band; their biggest fear was that their company might be swallowed up by the cash-rich GEC, their greatest UK rival. This was to prove only too prophetic at the end of the day.

Conclusion

The Ferranti name is no longer seen over factories in Scotland or anywhere else, the company having been destroyed as a corporate entity by a financial disaster in 1989 arising from a misjudged merger with US-based International Signal on a basis which proved to be fraudulent. However, the name is still remembered with affection - everyone in Edinburgh knew someone who worked for the company.

The technical legacy of Ferranti Scotland lives on within the firms which absorbed its expertise and continued its business. Because Ferranti once came and flourished there, Scotland is the richer.

References

1. Collins, J.H. *Silicon Glen - Myth or Reality ?*
   Chairman's Address, IEE Electronics Division, 1985
                          IEE Paper 4165F.
2. Toothill, J.N. *Enquiry into the Scottish Economy, 1960-61.*
   Scottish Council (Development & Industry), 1961

The Authors

Fred Breingan CEng, MIEE was born and brought up in Glasgow. After leaving secondary school, he embarked on a Hankey Engineering Cadetship course, with study at both Stow College of Engineering and the then Royal Technical college, now the University of Strathclyde, Glasgow. On course completion, he was drafted into the Royal Navy, where he served as an electrical officer both on ships and at naval airstations. On demobilisation in 1948, he joined the transmission division of the  British Electricity Authority in Scotland where he worked for many years as a field engineer. He then transferred to management and finally served as the SSEB Transmission Operations and Maintenance Engineer until his retirement in 1987. His interests include music, gardening and hillwalking.

Professor Jeffrey Collins BSc, MSc, DSc, CEng, FIEE, FRSE, FREng, FInstP, FIEEE, HonDEng was a senior academic at the Universities of Glasgow, Edinburgh (as Head of the Department of Electrical Engineering, where he is now Professor Emeritus), Napier, in the USA at Stanford and as a tenured full Professor of Electrical Engineering at The University of Texas at Arlington.

His technical expertise lies in the fields of solid-state electronics, computer-integrated manufacturing and information systems. He has published over 190 papers and articles in scientific journals and trade magazines. He was a co-recipient in 1979 of the Hewlett-Packard Europhysics Prize.

His working life has been dedicated to furthering relationships between education and industry on both sides of the Atlantic. He was a cofounder and Research, Quality Assurance and Technical Director of MESL (now Racal-MESL). He has held Directorships in seven other

UK high technology companies including Filtronics and the venture capital company, Advent Technology; as well as the Riverbend Bank in Fort Worth, Texas.

His chairmanships include the Information Technology Committee, the Wolfson Microelectronics Institute and the Edinburgh Parallel Computing Centre at the University of Edinburgh. He was the founding Director of the Automation and Robotics Research Institute at The University of Texas at Arlington, Chairman of the Scottish Electronics Manufacturing Centre at Napier University and the Senior Technical Specialist for Lothian Regional Council.

His UK committee service includes: Council Member for the Royal Academy of Engineering, the Ministry of Defence, the Department of Education and Science, the Department of Trade and Industry, the Science Research Council, and the Higher Education Funding Councils. In 1985-1986 he was the Chairman of the Electronics Division of the IEE and delivered the paper *Silicon Glen, Myth or Reality?* as his address to the Division .

RD Cowan CEng, MIEE was educated at Renfrew High School and took his technical qualifications by evening study at Paisley Technical College. He spent the early part of his working life in the Shipyards of Clydeside (1935-1947). In 1947 he was appointed a Junior Mains Engineer with Kirkcudbright County Council Electricity Department and started work there on 1st January 1948 - 3 months before the Electricity Supply Industry in the UK was taken into public ownership. He held various posts in the District and Area Headquarters of the Dumfries and  Galloway Areas and Districts of the South of Scotland Electricity Board. He retired as District Engineer for Dumfries and Galloway in 1986. After his retiral he wrote a book on the History of Electricity Supply in Dumfries and Galloway. The title *Sticks and Strings* should not be taken as a reflection on the condition of the overhead system (which could match any elsewhere) but was a tribute to the Engineers and Linesmen who designed and built the lines.

Jack Davidson CEng, FIEE, LInstMC served three years of his engineering apprenticeship with Robert Kilpatrick & Co Ltd, Dundee on general electrical contracting and two years on works maintenance. This was followed by four years of test gear development for dry battery manufacture and work on electro-chemical processes with Burndept (Vidor) Ltd., Dundee. He returned to electrical contracting for four years as the north-east Scotland supervising engineer with James Scott & Co, (EE) Ltd, Perth. He was appointed principal assistant with Ian Hunter & Partners, Consulting Engineers, Edinburgh. He was a construction engineer for eight years with the United Kingdom Atomic Energy Authority at Dounreay and at Winfrith Heath for a further two years. For the next twenty years he was the electrical engineer for Glenrothes New Town. Since his retirement, in 1985, he has been associated with the Electrical Contractors'  Association of Scotland (SELECT) in a technical and training capacity and as a member of several committees and working groups of the Institution of Electrical Engineers, The British Standards Institution, the Health and Safety Executive and the Institute of Petroleum.

He joined the Institution of Electrical Engineers as a Student member in 1945 and was elected a Fellow in 1985. He is a past chairman of IEE Scotland North, Scottish Power Section and the Scottish Centre of the Institution. He has been a membership interviewer for the Institution for the past twenty years as well as a member of Panel B of the Wiring Regulations Committee since its formation. He has been the Institution's Scottish representative for the recording and preservation of historic electrical equipment since 1985.

Douglas S. Deans BSc, CEng, MIEE, DipEE

After finishing his studies at Paisley College of Technology and completing his training with the Scottish Electrical Training Scheme Douglas took up his first post with James Kilpatrick & Son in Paisley where he worked for several years as a contracts engineer. However following his wish to be more involved in the design of electrical installations he took up the post of Assistant Building Services Engineer with one of the Scottish New Towns, Cumbernauld Development Corporation. By his early thirties he had been promoted to Senior Principal Engineer responsible for the design of building services for the full range of domestic, commercial and industrial buildings designed by the Corporation. He worked there for nearly 25 years before taking early retirement when the Scottish New Towns were wound up.

Just before his retirement he studied with the Open University and obtained a BSc. mainly in mathematical subjects.

Retirement has brought him the time to enjoy his many hobbies and interests including ham radio, meteorology and weather satellite reception, and gardening to mention but a few.

JH Dripps BSc, PhD, MIPEM graduated from Queen's University, Belfast with an Honours degree in Electronic and Electrical Engineering in 1970. He then worked for 2 years in Shorts (Aircraft & Missiles) in analogue and digital design of factory production line test equipment. After this he returned to university to complete his PhD in digital data transmission by short wave radio. This was sponsored by the Admiralty (ASWE, Portsmouth). In 1977 he joined Ferranti airborne radar group as a senior R&D engineer working on digital signal processing. In 1980 he became a lecturer at Edinburgh University where he is now a senior lecturer teaching communications and analogue circuit design. He also acts as tutor on 4th year digital communications and systems courses. His research interests are signal processing, transducers and analogue circuit design. He has over 50 publications and is co-author on a book on signal processing.

Robin M Dunbar BSc, MSc, PhD, CEng, FIEE

Robin M Dunbar attended the Royal High School in Edinburgh and

University of Edinburgh where he gained his BSc in Electrical Engineering, (1959), DiplElectronics, (1960), and MSc, (1963). For studies in subsea electromagnetic wave communications he received his PhD from Heriot-Watt University, Edinburgh, in 1986. He worked as a radar research engineer for Ferranti Ltd in Edinburgh until he joined Heriot-Watt University in 1964, developing teaching and research in Electromagnetics, Communications, and Electromagnetic Compatibility. His main research activities since 1969 have been in the area of subsea vehicles, communications, navigation, sensors and imaging and he was Technical Manager for an EC-MAST-II hydroacoustic communications project over 1992-1996. Currently his research activities encompass hydroacoustic model validation, subsea laser communications, and marine electromagnetics, and he has authored over 50 papers. He is a Chartered Engineer and a Fellow of the Institution of Electrical Engineers.

Professor WEJ (Ewart) Farvis CBE, FRSE, CEng, Hon FIEE,

born in 1911, was schooled in Bristol where he took his BSc(Eng) following an engineering apprenticeship in electrical power and machines. He arrived in Scotland in 1936 to take up an Assistant Lectureship in mathematics and electrical engineering at Dundee Institute of Art and Technology. In 1937 he was appointed Assistant Lecturer at University College Swansea and in 1940 he was appointed a Senior Scientific Officer at the Air Ministry Research Establishment at Malvern where his interests expanded to encompass electronics and microwave engineering. In 1945 he was given the rank of Squadron Leader as a member of the SIGESO mission to German research institutes. After the war he resumed his pre-war lectureship at University College Swansea to introduce a new honours course in electronics and communications.

In 1947 he took the London University External BSc degree in Physics. In 1948 his new interests persuaded him to apply for the Edinburgh University Lectureship in which he initiated a research programme in electronics, developed the post-war electrical engineering courses and laboratories and a new Post-Graduate Diploma Course in Electronics and Radio. In 1960 he was appointed the first Professor of Electrical Engineering and Head of Department of Edinburgh University which post he held until his retirement in 1977.

His appointments and honours included:

Advisory Director of the Scottish Electrical Training Scheme (SETS), 1957-61.

Chairman SE Scotland sub-centre IEE, 1961.

Chairman IEE Joint Professional Group J5 (Education and Training, 1966.

Member of Council IEE 1972-78.

Member of Council of the Science Research Council (later Science and Engineering Research Council), 1976-1980.

Elected Emeritus Professor 1977.

Consultant Electrical Engineer 1977-1985.

Elected Fellow of the Royal Society of Edinburgh, 1958.

Awarded Officer of the Order of the British Empire (OBE), 1972.

Awarded Commander of the Order of the British Empire (CBE), 1978.

Awarded Honorary Fellowship of IEE, 1987.

Douglas S Gordon, BSc, PhD, CEng, FIEE, FIOA was educated at George Watson's College, Edinburgh and Edinburgh University. After training periods at British Thomson-Houston and Metropolitan Vickers Electrical Company, he was employed in the Research Department of the latter firm on decimetric and centimetric measurements and applications. He joined the staff of the Electrical Engineering Department at Glasgow University in 1946 and among  other commitments he engaged in research and consultancy in the broad field of mechanical vibration and acoustics.

He was elected a member of committee of the Scottish Students' Section of the IEE in 1939 and has been involved in a wide range of IEE activities in Scotland and in London having served on membership, examinations, scholarships, education and training, and exemptions committees, qualifications and professional services boards; Chairman, South-West Scotland Sub-Centre 1965/66, Chairman, Scottish Centre 1971/72, Council Member 1975-78 and Scottish Convener for membership interviews from 1984 to l996. His educational activities included being a member of the Scottish Joint Committee for National Certificates and Diplomas for many years, an assessor, examiner and moderator in other fields of higher education such as Scotvec, CEI and EC examinations. He was awarded a certificate in 1998 by the Engineering Council for "outstanding service to the engineering profession".

Dr James S Grant, BSc, FREng, HonDTech, FIEE graduated from the Royal College of Science and Technology (now Strathclyde University) in 1959 with a BSc(Hon) in Electrical Engineering. He joined the Generator Division of GEC Witton, Birmingham, holding various design and production posts before becoming Chief of Test and Inspection until taking up an appointment in 1972 with the SSEB, at Cathcart House, as Electrical Rotating Plant Engineer. In 1978 he was appointed Principal Engineer in charge of the Electrical and Electronic  Group at the SSEB's Research and Development Centre at East Kilbride. He was appointed Technical Services Manager in 1980. During 1987 he started a 12-month secondment to the post of Manager, Shop Automation Project, and was instrumental in the introduction of computerised cash collection and appliance sales into the SSEB's seventy-three high street shops.

In 1989, in preparation for privatisation of the Electricity Supply Industry, he was appointed Chief Engineer of the newly-formed Nuclear Division of SSEB responsible for the creation of an Engineering Department with the necessary capability to ensure the continued safe operation of the nuclear plants. In 1990 he was appointed Director of Engineering of Scottish Nuclear Ltd and appointed to the Board as Technical Director in 1995. He retired from Scottish Nuclear in 1997.

He became a Member of the IEE and a Fellow in 1983. In 1994 he was elected a Fellow of the Royal Academy of Engineering and in

1999 was awarded the degree of Honorary Doctor of Technology by The Robert Gordon University.

Dr Alexander McConnell Hall BSc(Hons), PhD, CEng, FIEE, born on 7th February 1927, was educated at Queen's Park School, Glasgow, the Royal Technical College and Glasgow University where he graduated BSc(Hons) in Electrical Engineering in 1946. His degree course was compressed during the 1939-45 war and he had to take his third year during the summer of 1945. In the 'sandwich' arrangement between the first and second years he obtained industrial experience at Metropolitan Vickers at  Trafford Park, Manchester. He received two years of post-graduate training at Pye Radio in Cambridge after which he became a member of staff at the Royal Technical College, Glasgow to complete his Doctorate of Philosophy researching ferromagnetic materials at microwave frequencies. In 1953 he was appointed to the staff of RY Pickering, Wishaw (part of the Lithgow Group) and in 1955 he joined Barr & Stroud Ltd, Glasgow remaining there until his retiral in 1988 as Manager, Electronics Development. He joined the IEE as a Student Member in 1946 and was elected a Fellow of the Institution in 1969.

John T. Henderson BSc, DipRTC, CEng, FIEE was born in Glasgow in 1925 and educated at Rutherglen Academy. He studied Electrical Engineering at the Royal Technical College, Glasgow and was awarded a Diploma of the Royal Technical College and a BSc of Glasgow University in 1946. He served as a Lieutenant in REME 1946-8 and returned to college for postgraduate honours in 1949.

After a two year apprenticeship with Metropolitan Vickers in Manchester he joined the Erection Department of Metropolitan Vickers in Glasgow. From 1953-6 he was the electrical engineer with John Dalglish and Sons and in 1956 joined the Technical Department of Scottish Cables

Limited becoming Director and Chief Engineer in 1970 till 1977. He served as Marketing Manager (Far East and Pacific) with BICC Supertension Cables from 1977 till 1987

He was a member of the Executive Committee of the Scottish Electrical Training Scheme (SETS) from its formation and was a Director from 1977 till 1987 and Chief Executive 1987-8.

He served on various IEE committees being Chairman of the South West Scotland Subcentre in 1969-70, Chairman of the Power Section Scotland 1973-4 and Chairman of the Scottish Centre 1974-5. He was also a member of various IEE Committees in London and a member of the Scottish Branch, CEI 1976-7.

He is married, has three children and five grandchildren and enjoys golf, swimming and gardening.

David C King BSc, DipER,CEng, FIEE was born in 1939 in Edinburgh. He was educated at Craigentinny Primary School, Broughton High School and Edinburgh University graduating with a first class honours degree in Electrical Engineering in 1960 and with a postgraduate Diploma in Radio & Electronics in 1961. He joined the Scottish Electrical Training Scheme (SETS) in 1958 and completed his vocational training with the South of Scotland Electricity Board and Bruce Peebles Ltd and graduate training

with the North of Scotland Hydro-Electric Board, Belmos and Harland Drives before joining Bruce Peebles as a control systems engineer in 1962. In 1966 he took up a lecturing post in the Electrical Engineering Department at Heriot-Watt University. For the next twenty years at Heriot-Watt he lectured on topics such as digital electronics, computer hardware and microprocessors applications and was involved in the early underwater research. He was made a senior lecturer in 1979 and during his tenure at Heriot-Watt he was elected to membership of both the Senate and the Court of the university. In 1987 he was awarded the Wang Chair in Information Management and appointed Associate Head of the Department of Engineering at Glasgow College. From 1993 to 1994 he was Head of the Department of Engineering at Glasgow Caledonian University. He retired from his full time post in September 1994 and worked as a part time Professor in the Department of

Engineering until 1998. In his forty or so years of IEE membership he has served on a number of committees being a past-chairman of the IEE Scotland-Electronics and Control Section and the IEE Scotland-Science, Education and Management Section and he is currently a member of the IEE's Education Committee.

EurIng. John Lough. BSc(Eng), CEng, FIEE is a Chartered Engineer who is registered to practice as an Electrical Engineer throughout the European Community He retired from British Telecom in 1991 as District Manager for the Highlands and Islands of Scotland. Subsequent consultancy work has seen him with the Highlands and Islands Development Board and Highlands and Islands Enterprise using telematics technology to regenerate rural areas; with University of Manchester Institute of Science & Technology chairing teleworking and video-conferencing forums; with the European Commission evaluating projects; and as Chairman of the User Group European ISDN User Forum, and Managing Director of the new EIUF Ltd., promoting awareness of advanced telematics throughout Europe, with, in the last two years, special emphasis on the development of ISDN in Central & Eastern European Countries. A Fellow of the Institution of Electrical Engineers, he is a past Chairman for the North of Scotland, and currently an International Membership Assessor. He is, during 1999, Senior Vice Chairman of IEE Scotland

Iain Alexander McKenzie BSc, CEng, MIEE graduated in 1960 and

worked on design, construction and commissioning of Sizewell 'A' Power Station, several South of Scotland Electricity Board 400-kV and 275-kV transmission substations, the 230-kV transmission system in Nova Scotia, Canada and several petrochemical projects, including a polypropylene plant in Canada and Sullom Voe Oil terminal in the Shetland Isles. He was a Forward Planning Engineer involved in the investigations of future Scottish generation requirements and consequent transmission network reinforcement. Since 1980 he has worked with the South of Scotland Electricity Board (now ScottishPower) as a control development engineer. He heads the Control Development section whose task is to determine and deliver the real time information requirements for the grid control function.

Stanley Watt Milne MBE, CEng, MIEE was the Works Director,

Power Transformers of Bruce Peebles & Co Ltd in Edinburgh. A Dundonian by birth, he was educated at the Morgan Academy and after his apprenticeship with Lowdon Brothers, Engineers of Dundee he attended Dundee Technical College gaining a student apprenticeship with Bruce Peebles in Edinburgh.

His military service commenced in July 1939 a few months before the outbreak of World War II. He served initially with the 1st Army Militia and then with the 73rd HAA Artillery Regiment until his demobilisation in March 1946. He returned to Bruce Peebles to complete his student apprenticeship after which he joined the Transformer Test Department, initially to set up and operate the Impulse Testing of transformers. He served Bruce Peebles in various capacities for thirty-seven years, his last twenty-two years being spent in Works and Power Transformer Production management.

He was elected to corporate membership of the IEE in 1951 and is a Chartered Engineer. He was appointed Works Director, Power

Transformers of Bruce Peebles in 1974 and awarded the MBE for his services to industry in 1981, two years before his retirement in 1983.

Alan Smith BA, CEng, FIEE was educated in Aberdeen and entered the Royal Air Force in 1947. He completed a three-year course in Radio Engineering at No.1 Radio School, RAF Cranwell in 1950. He served on a number of maintenance units and radar stations in the UK and overseas.

He joined BBC Northern Ireland as a television engineer in 1960 and transferred to BBC Scotland in 1968 as a communications supervisor. After a period as Communications Manager, Scotland, he became Broadcast Systems Manager, Scotland until his retiral from the BBC in 1990.

James B Smith GM, MA, BSc, FRSE, FIEE, CEng was an undergraduate at Edinburgh University at the outbreak of the 1939 war. He immediately volunteered to be commissioned in the Corps of Royal Engineers and served in North Africa, Sicily, Italy, France and Germany, rising to the rank of Captain and being awarded the George Medal and mentioned in despatches.

After the war he returned to his University course and graduated MA and BSc, also becoming involved in work which the University had placed with Ferranti. This led to his being offered a post in Ferranti in 1947 as Senior Research Engineer. He remained with Ferranti for nearly 40 years, becoming Group Quality Manager in 1960 when the application of mathematics to reliability assessment occupied him for several years. In 1966, despite having no formal accountancy qualification, he became Group Financial Controller, a post subsequently designated as Assistant General Manager. He served as a director of over a dozen Ferranti subsidiary companies until his retirement in 1985.

In addition to being a Fellow of the Institution of Electrical Engineers, he is also a Fellow of the Royal Society of Edinburgh and an Honorary Fellow of the University of Edinburgh.

David Tedford OBE, OM(Poland), FRSE, CEng, FIEE

After wide experience in industry and academia, David Tedford was appointed in 1972 to the Chair of Electrical Engineering at the University of Strathclyde where, with extensive research in insulating systems and dielectric materials, he has contributed substantially to the establishment and development of one of the largest and most successful university electrical power engineering research groups in the UK. Among a wide range of external activity, he was a member and chairman of two IEE professinal committees, deputy chairman of the Science, Education and Technology  Divisional Board of the IEE and a member of its Council from 1992-95. He was much involved with the Electricity Council (Research Committee), CIGRE (National Executive) and the Royal Society of Edinburgh (Vice President) and was extremely active as a technical advisor overseas (eg planning of the new Hong Kong University of Science and Technology). He was awarded the IEE Achievement Medal (Power) in 1996.

Additionally, from 1982-92 at Strathclyde, Professor Tedford undertook various roles as Pro-Vice-Chancellor, and was much involved in the formulation of the University's computer and IT strategy and of specific plans with industry relating to Associate Company Schemes (DTI Award) and direct collaborative ventures, these in addition to a wide range of management and administrative responsibilities including overseas policy. In 1993, he was appointed Scientific Advisor to the Scottish Office Industry Department and later to the new post of Chief Scientific Advisor to the Secretary of State for Scotland, dealing with policy, longer term strategy and other general issues concerning science, engineering and technology in Scotland and their commercial exploitation/industrial application.

In 'retirement' he continues to be involved in his research, is presently Chairman of the Court of the University of Abertay, Dundee, is a non-executive director of two companies, a member of two Science Centre Trusts and chairman of two 'technology education' working groups, as well as casual consultancy.

JD Wightman BSc, CEng, FIEE was born in Edinburgh and educated at George Heriot's School. He studied electrical engineering at Heriot-Watt College, Edinburgh and graduated with an Associateship of the college in 1948. He gained his practical experience with Bruce Peebles, Edinburgh, and was directed to the Royal Aircraft Establishment, Farnborough in 1943.

In 1948 he joined the Technical Department of Scottish Cables Ltd and in 1950 the Technical Services Department of the Clyde Navigation Trust.

In 1953 he joined the National Coal Board, Central West Area, Glasgow before taking up the post of Divisional Electrical Engineer Reconstruction at Headquarters in Edinburgh in 1957 for all new sinkings and colliery reconstructions throughout the seven areas of the Scottish coalfield. In 1967 the Divisional Board disbanded with the formation of the North and South Areas and he became the Electrical Engineer for the North Area, Alloa.

In 1973 the two areas merged and he was made Electrical Engineer for the Scottish Area, Edinburgh until 1985.

He was a member of various IEE committees being Chairman of the South East Scotland Subcentre in 1971-72 and Chairman of the Power Section Scotland, 1979-80.

He is married, has two sons and five grandchildren and enjoys golf and photography.

Index

Harland Engineering Co Ltd, 76
Harwell, 139
Hastie, JS, 30
Hately, MC, 31
Hayward, Prof. G, 108
Haywood, Neil, 271
Heartland FM, 219
Heath, Prof. Fred, 63,97
Heaviside Layer, 208
Heaviside, Oliver, 208
Helszajn, Prof. J, 97
Henderson, HG, 31,33
Henderson, John, 20,30
Henderson, JT, 30,294
Henniker, HV, 31
Henry Hughes & Son, 276
Heriot-Watt College, 16,42,47, 49, 54,60
Heriot-Watt University, 60,63-5,70-1,97-100,112,253,266
Herrick, JF, 129
Hertz, Heinrich, 205
Hewitt, Prof. J, 87
Hewlett-Packard,57,96,100,258-262,269,278
'Hi-Fi', 210
Highlands & Islands, The University of, 203
Hinton, Sir Christopher, 138
Hird, WB, 30
HMSO Report, Post-War Building Studies, No11/944, 187
Holmes, JH, 129
Holmes, Robin, 113,115,119
Holograph Television, 221
Honeywell Controls Ltd, 76,258, 278,283
Honorary Secretaries-IEE Scotland, 31
Howard, BV, 30,66
Howe, J, 268
Howe, Prof. GWO, 16,29,30,39,40
Hughes Aircraft Corp., 258-9
Hughes Electronics, 278
Hunt, Prof. 101
Hunter, J, 184
Hunterian Museum, 129
Hunterston A, 140,141,160,162
Hunterston B, 141,142,163
Hutcheson, A, 18
Hutchison, James MS, 124
Hywell-Jones, E, 30

IATROS Ltd, 104
IBM, 100,258,278,283
IEE, 10,11,54,56,72,74,173,177,206,224,252,253,272
- Accreditation, 72
- Examinations, Parts I,II&III, 56
- SARTOR 97, 72,73
IEE Scotland, 7,15,79,204,274
- Dundee Sub Committee, 17
- Electronics, Computing & Control Section, 25
- Glasgow Section, 48
- Honorary Secretaries, 31
- Junior Section, 19
- Manufacturing Section, 26
- Power Section, 22,23
- Radio & Measurements Section, 21
- Roll of Chairmen, 30-1
- Scottish Centre Benevolent Cup, 17
- South East Sub Centre,20
- South West Retired Members' Section, 27
IEE Wiring Regulations, 173,177, 181,186
Image Analysis Centre, 99
Independent Television, 217
India Rubber Gutta-Percha & Telegraph Co Ltd, 169
Installation Engineering, A Century of, 173
Institution of Civil Engineers (ICE), 54
Institution of Electronic & Radio Engineers (IERE), 23,25-6,32,207
Institution of Manufacturing Engineers (IMfgE), 26,33,34
Institution of Mechanical Engineers (IMechE), 24,34
Institution of Production Engineers (IProdE), 33-4
Intelligent Motion Control Group, 81
International Computers Ltd, 267,269
International Electrotechnical Commission, 188
International Geophysical Year, 43
International Society of Electricians, 185
Inverkip Power Station, 134
'Inverness' Endoscope, 129
Ironside, Dr C, 93